ESSENTIAL MECHANICS

Owen Elbourn

CollinsEducational

An imprint of HarperCollins*Publishers*

Published by
CollinsEducational Ltd
77–85 Fulham Palace Road
Hammersmith
London
W6 8JB

First published in 1993

British Library Cataloguing-in-Publication Data

A catalogue is available on request from the British Library.

ISBN 0–00–3276317

Cover design by Ridgeway Associates

Typeset by Dorchester Typesetting Group Ltd and printed in
Great Britain at the University Press, Cambridge

Foreword

Every book in the Essential Series is designed carefully to put you in control of your own learning.

When you use this book, you will not only cover the core elements of your course but you will also benefit from the author's use of modern teaching and learning techniques, with the result that you will make the best possible use of your time.

This book has:

- an introductory section at the beginning of each chapter, which focuses your attention on its contents and which tells you exactly what you will have learned by the end of the chapter.
- periodic summaries and reviews which regularly remind you of the content you are covering and so reinforce your learning.
- notes in the margin of the text, where the author takes the role of a tutor: picking out key facts, highlighting and explaining difficult concepts and guiding you to a better understanding of the main text
- a guide to making notes as you work through the book.

Learning is not easy: nobody learns without effort. However, if you use this book effectively you will not only succeed in your course and in your exam but you will also enjoy the experience of learning.

Also in the HarperCollins Essential Series

Essential Psychology
G C Davenport

Essential Government and Politics
Jim Cordell

Essential Marketing
Tony Proctor

Essential Accountancy and Finance
Bijon Kar

Essential Practical Psychology
Keith Maglennon

Series Editor: Roger Gomm

Introduction

When you have worked through this book you will be ready to tackle advanced level papers in mechanics in a single-subject examination.

How to use this book

The book has been written with the aim of your working through every example included in it, provided the topic covered is in the syllabus of your particular examination. The recommended order of working is set out in the plan on page viii. Each of the questions is provided with a full solution and after you have done a question you should work through the solution in the book even if you know yours is correct. Most of the teaching in the book is done through the solutions so do follow them closely. When working, always concentrate on the principles being used and why they are being applied. Mechanics solutions are often easy to follow once you have got going. The hard part is getting your ideas together and deciding where to start.

▶ Do you have a copy of the syllabus for the examination you are going to attempt? If not, get one soon and check it against the plan on page viii.

Note making

There is not much point in keeping your solutions, correct or not, because the solutions are provided in the book. It is essential, though, that you make notes. After you have tried a question and seen its solution, make notes on the aspects of the question that are pertinent to you. It is most useful to make notes about why, even though you understand the solution, you failed to make a start, etc. Your note book is quite personal: a relevant note for you may be quite unnecessary for someone else, and vice versa. You are strongly recommended to make the notes as suggested: having to write down why you failed really does bring understanding!

▶ Note making

If this book is your own you may prefer to use the margin provided to build up your notes and make the text book into your personal note book as well.

A few principles, many applications

As you proceed with this course you will realize that Mechanics is really the application of a few principles to different mechanical situations. In themselves, these principles are not difficult to understand. As you become aware of this, concentrate on understanding the principles and the applications. You are not interested in remembering formulae parrot fashion, substituting numbers and hence meaningless number crunching. You are interested in being able to appraise the mechanics of a situation, decide which principles are relevant and make appropriate deductions. There are some formulae which you will need to remember but only when you understand them and can derive them for yourself.

Appraise the mechanics of a situation, decide which are relevant, make appropriate deductions.

The structure of the book

Chapter 1 is a long chapter covering nearly all the principles you need. The questions in Chapter 1 are straightforward and are designed so you will understand, use and then remember the different principles illustrated. The work of this chapter is consolidated in worksheets 1–6.

Chapters 2–11 are each devoted to a different type of problem: the application of the principles you have learnt in Chapter 1 to harder problems. Worksheets 7–16 consolidate your work and they should be done completely. After that you will be ready to work through past papers.

It is recommended that you work through the book in the order presented, but after worksheets 1–6 you **could** go directly to any of the other chapters. The order is one which I have found to work best with students, in terms of the increasing difficulty of some of the topics. Each chapter begins with a list of the mechanics you should remember and a list of the pure mathematics you will need for the chapter. Hence there is a good degree of flexibility about the book.

Have you got copies of past examination papers for your syllabus? You will need them to practise what you have learnt. If not, try to get hold of some as soon as possible. You can buy them from the Examination Board, but most college libraries keep past papers.

Using your time

You will fail if you attend just one lesson a week and expect to get by with doing one hour on your own. If you are attempting applied mathematics then, together with the pure mathematics course which forms the full examination, you must expect to spend **at least one hour per day**, increasing as the examination draws near. In the earlier part of the course it is quite common to spend more of the time on pure mathematics with the balance changing as the course progresses. If you have fixed time, allocated equally to pure and to applied mathematics, you cannot do much about this. One hour per day is a good guide, two hours is much better, on the basis of a little and often.

Mathematics is a subject which does not lend itself to last minute revision before an examination. It demands a conscientious, understanding effort from the start. If you do this and give it the time it needs you won't go far wrong.

You should aim to finish your course, pure mathematics and mechanics – as far as the books are concerned – by February of the year you take the examination (my students used to aim for November the year before). In the remaining time you will need to work through every past examination paper you can get hold of.

Mathematics is not a question-spotting subject – i.e. one where you attempt to spot the forthcoming questions: it is one where the whole syllabus is examined every year. Your first attempts at papers may take days! You have to get that down to three hours. The only way is to do all the papers available: it does work.

▶ The **activities** in each chapter step you through the principles of mechanics and their application. The **worksheets** test you on what you have learnt and help you consolidate your learning.

▶ Equipment
The material needs of a mathematics student are simple – a pen, a pencil, a pile of scrap paper, a notebook and a basic scientific calculator. The calculator need not be elaborate (mine cost £7.00), so long as it has trigonometric functions, ln, log, e^x, 10^x, x^y, $\sqrt{}$, x^2 and M functions it will be fine. You will also need a rectangular block of wood, about 4 cm × 2 cm, a screw-in eyelet, 75 cm of string and some elastic bands.

▶ When you are studying, the time you spend will only bring reward if you are alert and ready for work. If you are feeling tired and jaded, go and lie down, have a nap and come back later. If you don't you will only be going through the motions.

▶ Revision from Day 1

▶ Working on past papers

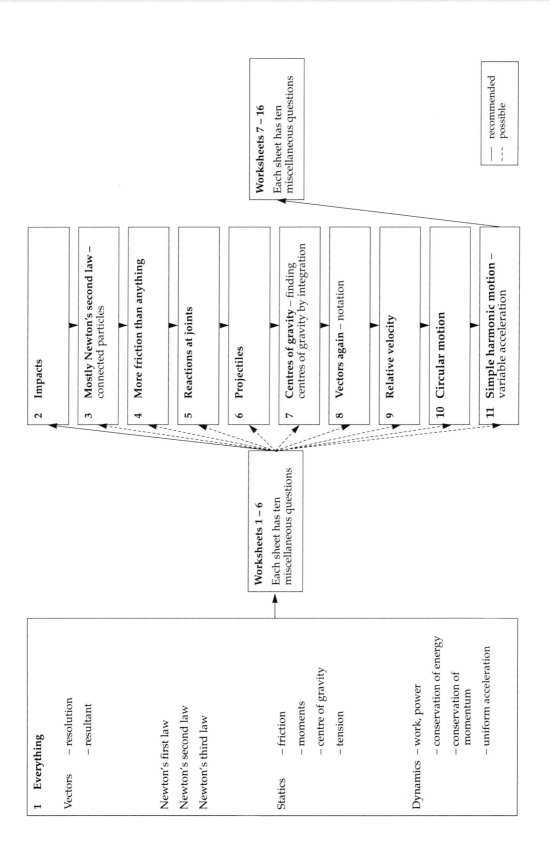

1 **Everything**

Vectors   – resolution
           – resultant

Newton's first law
Newton's second law
Newton's third law

Statics – friction
        – moments
        – centre of gravity
        – tension

Dynamics – work, power
          – conservation of energy
          – conservation of momentum
          – uniform acceleration

Worksheets 1 – 6
Each sheet has ten miscellaneous questions

2 **Impacts**

3 **Mostly Newton's second law** – connected particles

4 **More friction than anything**

5 **Reactions at joints**

6 **Projectiles**

7 **Centres of gravity** – finding centres of gravity by integration

8 **Vectors again** – notation

9 **Relative velocity**

10 **Circular motion**

11 **Simple harmonic motion** – variable acceleration

Worksheets 7 – 16
Each sheet has ten miscellaneous questions

—— recommended
- - - possible

Contents

What is Mechanics?

Chapter outline

When you have worked through this chapter you will have learnt about:

▎ vectors, resolution and resultants

▎ Newton's first, second and third laws of motion

▎ statics: friction, moments, centre of mass, tension

▎ dynamics: work, power, conservation of energy, conservation of momentum, uniform acceleration.

What is mechanics? One answer, from thousands of possibles, is 'A study of why things are as they are'.

You have put this book on the table in front of you. Why does it stay there? Why does the table stay where it is? Soon you will turn the page; what mechanics are involved in doing this? You may pick up a pencil to make a note; why does it not slip through your fingers? What are the mechanics of walking, cycling, flying a kite, driving a car, drinking a cup of tea and so on?

It is said that an apple falling from a tree hit Isaac Newton on the head. He wondered why the apple fell down; why did it not either stay where it was or even go up? From this simple beginning he evolved various principles of mechanics around which we base our studies.

► Isaac Newton – an important person in your studies. Read up about him.

In this course we shall study enough mechanics theory for you to analyse many of the actions just listed and hence many other situations.

It will help you very much if you constantly observe everything around you and ponder the mechanics involved. Ask yourself questions and see if you can answer them. Develop the frame of mind where you query, rather than just accept, what you see. Better still, if you can, discuss things with fellow students: some good arguments will follow.

As we consider why things happen we realize we are studying forces, velocities, accelerations, masses, distances and time, and we begin the course by having an overall look at these things.

Mechanics has many sections to it: statics, dynamics, hydrodynamics and so on. Our work will be confined to two of these sections: statics and dynamics.

► Statics

► Dynamics

> **Statics** is the study of mechanics of things which are stationary.
> **Dynamics** is the study of mechanics of things which are moving.

► The 'Get the block' symbol

Get the block!

It will be helpful if you get for yourself a rectangular block of wood about 5 cm by 4 cm by 2 cm (the measurements are not important but it helps if they are different from each other). Screw a small eyelet – the type used for fitting curtain wire – in the end. Find the weight of your block of wood, in grams. You will also need a piece of string, about 75 cm long, and a few new elastic bands. When the 'Get the block' symbol appears you will know what is meant.

AN INTRODUCTORY LOOK AT SOME OF THE BASICS

► Here we are studying statics.

► More on mass and weight later

► **Drawing diagrams**
A technique used throughout the book: broken/full continuous/broken lines; exploded diagrams

Why does a book stay where it is on the table? Put your block on the table. Why does it not fall to the floor? We have a force acting downwards because of its mass (this force is its weight), and this is opposed by a force acting upwards from the table. This can be shown on a diagram. We are interested only in what is happening to the block and hence the block is drawn with solid lines and the table with broken lines. Arrowed heavy lines are used to indicate forces, velocities, etc. Many diagrams are drawn slightly exploded so that what is happening to each part of the system can clearly be seen.

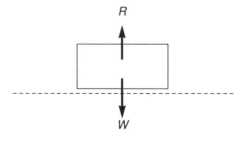

R = force exerted by table

W = weight, force due to mass of block

Increase the mass by balancing a book on top of the block. Now what have you got?

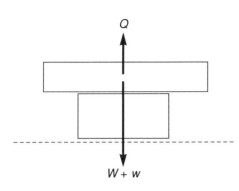

Q = force exerted by table on block plus book

$W + w$ = weight of block plus book

Remove the book and attach the string to the block.

Keeping the string parallel to the table, pull on it very gently

so that the block does not move. What have you got now?

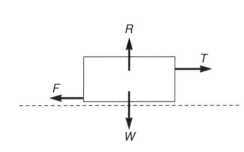

R, W as in first diagram

T = pull by string; equal to the tension in the string

► More on tension shortly

F = force which stops the block from moving; exerted by the table; known as force of friction

► Force of friction

► More on friction later in this chapter

Whilst pulling on the block with your right hand press down on it with your left hand. What do you notice now about the force that is needed from your right hand to make the block move?

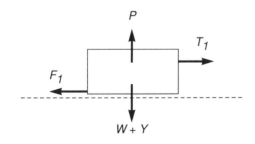

Y = force from hand

$\left.\begin{array}{l} T_1 = \text{pull by string} \\ F_1 = \text{force of friction} \end{array}\right\}$ both larger than before

By now, hopefully, you are making some sense of the diagrams.

Now let your block hang by the piece of string.

► Forces **on** and forces **by**

► Pay great attention to the use of 'on' and 'by' when talking about forces.

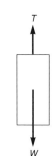

T = force exerted **on** the block **by** the string

What happens if T is greater than W?   Block rises.

What happens if T is less than W?   Block falls.

If the block is stationary what about T and W?

Equal in size and opposite in direction: they cancel each other.

Equilibrium

► Equilibrium defined

In all these situations where the block is still – 'at rest' is the expression often used – the block is said to be **in equilibrium**.

► Equilibrium is a word which we shall use often and sometimes it will be abbreviated to eqm.

Equilibrium is achieved by forces of equal size opposing each other on a body which is at rest, as in all the cases considered so far.

Returning to the block on the table:

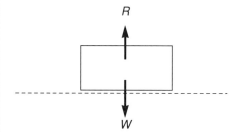

W, the weight of the block, is present wherever the block is.

R only comes into existence when the block is put on the table. It is the force exerted by the table on the block.

The force R is a reaction by the table to the force W, and this leads us to an important law in mechanics.

► Newton's third law of motion, NL3
► NL1 and NL2 follow soon.

Newton's Third Law of Motion
To every action there is an equal and opposite reaction. This is Newton's third law and it will be referred to as NL3.

► Solutions on page 5

 Activity 1.1

Copy the diagrams and draw in the forces needed for equilibrium, writing down any equations you can. Do all parts of the activity before looking at the solutions.

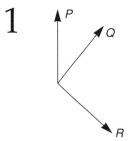

2
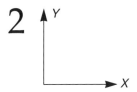

3   The diagram shows a plank resting on two supports.

4   The plank is now stood on its end, vertically. Draw the force diagram.

Resolving and combining forces

Now that we have gained some idea of what equilibrium is, it is time to consider some way of handling, in a mathematical sense, the forces we are talking about.

   Consider question 2 in Activity 1.1. The answer given is correct but cumbersome.

Get the block. Put it on the table and push it with your left hand across you to the right.

   Now repeat with your right hand, pushing directly away from you. Now push with both hands at the same time – where does your block go? Somewhere towards the top right-hand corner of the desk. You have now got the situation as described in question 2.

   Can you make the block do the same movement using one hand only?

   Yes.

▶ Resolving and combining forces
▶ Components and resultants

(GTB)

▶ Establishing a feel for the idea of two forces being replaced by one

Solutions to Activity 1.1

1
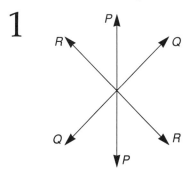

2

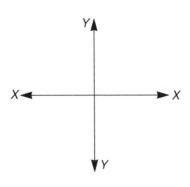

3

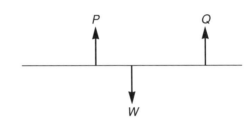

$P + Q = W$

Because in equilibrium and forces up = forces down.

► When you have finished these few questions remember the simple basic principles involved: you will be using them throughout the course.

4

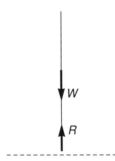

This means that the system

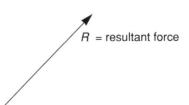

► Resultant

has become

and all that is needed to restore
equilibrium is a single force.

► Equilibrant

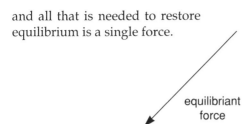

equilibriant
force

Vary your experiment a little by making the left-hand force big
compared with the right-hand force, and vice versa. If you have
access to a laboratory you may be able to rig up an experiment
where you can actually measure the two forces, left hand, Y, and
right hand, X, and the equibrant force needed for equilibrium. You
would find if you then drew a scale diagram for X and Y like this:

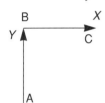

X and Y are the sides AB, AC of a right-
angled triangle ABC.

Then the hypotenuse AC represents the
force R.

Hence we have two results:

► Two significant results

(i)

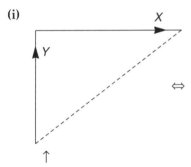

► Resultant

$\Leftrightarrow$

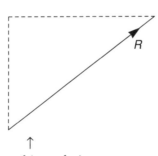

This can be replaced by   this, and vice versa.

(ii)

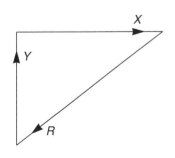

When the force needed for
equilibrium is added the triangle is closed, i.e. complete.
This is your first meeting
with the polygon of forces.

If a body is in equilibrium
and the forces on it are
drawn to scale they form a
closed polygon. The converse
is also true: if the polygon
is closed the body is in
equilibrium.

► Triangle of forces

► Polygon of forces

Resolution of forces

From your trigonometry you have

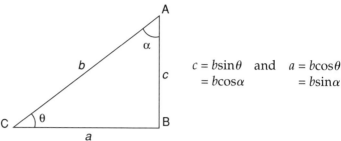

$c = b\sin\theta$ and $a = b\cos\theta$
  $= b\cos\alpha$ $= b\sin\alpha$

Simple but most important!
It applies to our force R: study and digest carefully.

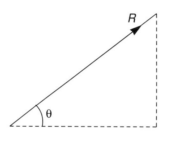 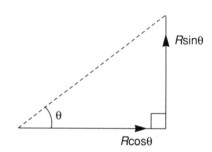

We can replace (i) with (ii) or (ii) with (i).
When we go from (i) to (ii) we are resolving the force R into components with directions which are at right angles to each other. When we go from (ii) to (i) we are combining forces to find their resultant.

Let us look at question 1 from Activity 1.1. Put in some values and realize the power of resolving and combining.

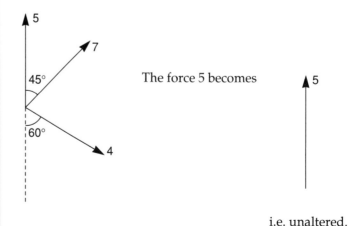

The force 5 becomes

i.e. unaltered.

The force 7 becomes

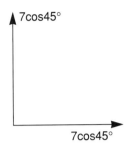

The force 4 becomes

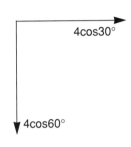

Study these carefully and note particularly, using the 4 force as an example:

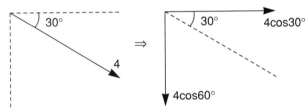

In the case of each component we follow the role for resolving.

Rule for resolving
Component is found as force × cosine of angle gone through to change from old direction to new.

▶ Rule for resolving – learn thoroughly!

Now what do we gain by this resolving?

Well . . .

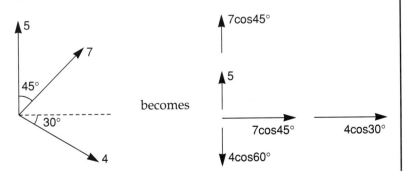

where forces are all in components acting up or across the page, i.e. in two directions which are perpendicular to each other.

This is equivalent to

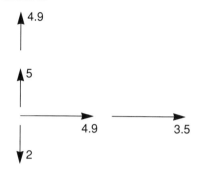

Calculator used to evaluate each component.

► All these steps may seem to make for a long solution but you are learning a sequence of simple steps which you will use often.

This simplifies to

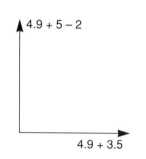

Components are added in each direction.

i.e.

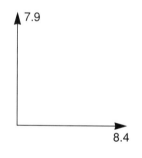

These are the components of the resultant force, *R*.

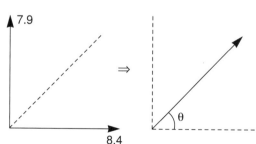

Final stage

where $R^2 = 7.9^2 + 8.4^2 \implies R = 11.5$

and $\theta = \tan^{-1}\left(\dfrac{7.9}{8.4}\right) = 43.2°$

To sum up

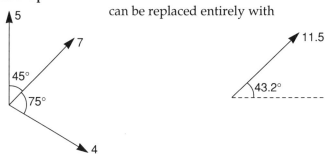

can be replaced entirely with

Review: Finding the resultant by resolving

Look back and consider the example we have just done. It may seem messy and long winded but it is in fact quite a straightforward routine.

1	Resolve forces into components	it is only after this is done that they may be added.
2	Add the components	to get the two components of the resultant.
3	Work out the magnitude and the direction of the resultant.	by Pythagoras using tangent.

► Summary of finding resultant by resolving

Resultant – the single force which is equivalent to a system of forces.

► Resultant defined

Equilibrant – the single force which would make the effect, or resultant, of a system of forces zero. The equilibrant is equal in size but opposite in direction to the resultant.

► Equilibrant defined

Finding the resultant by drawing

There is another way of finding the resultant – by drawing. This will explain itself as we follow the diagrams.

5 ▲   Draw one force, scale 1 cm = 2 units of force.

Add on a second force.

► Scale vector diagram – graphical solution

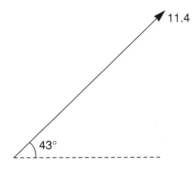

Add on the third.

► Does the order in which you draw the forces matter? Find out for yourself.

The gap between the beginning and the end represents the resultant.

Direction

This is not the first time we have mentioned direction and it must be obvious by now that direction is a factor equally as important as size.

► Vectors defined

Vectors

Force is a quantity in which both size and direction matter, or count, and as such it is a member of the family of **vector quantities** or simply **vectors**.

► Scalars defined

Scalars

Quantities where direction does not matter, i.e. they have size only, are members of the family known as **scalar quantities**, or **scalars**. Time is an example of a scalar: it can be measured for size but it has no direction.

All quantities are either scalar or vector; try sorting some out.

The way in which we have been treating forces can be applied to all vectors so techniques learned here will be repeated in future areas of our work.

Activity 1.2

▶ Solutions on page 16

1   A plan view (looking down from above) of a maypole looks like

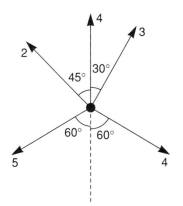

▶ Maypole – a pole around which people dance holding coloured ribbons which are attached to the top of the pole.

where the numbers and arrows indicate the different forces pulling on the pole.

Is there a resultant pull on the pole?

If so, **(a)** what size and direction has it?

(b) what is the size and direction of the equilibrant needed for there to be no pull?

2   The diagram shows a 10 kg mass hanging by two strings from a fixed ceiling.

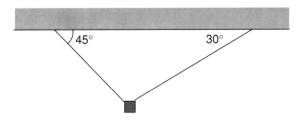

Find the tension in each string.

In this simply worded question three important new points are raised and we had better clear them up before we continue. They are **tension**, **mass and weight** and **acceleration due to gravity**.

Tension
The tension in a string pulled taut between two points is constant throughout its length and it is equal to the force exerted by the string on the points it is attached to.

▶ Tension

It is easy to visualize a chain under tension: the first link pulls on the second, and the second pulls on the first with equal and opposite force (NL3). Similarly with the second and third links, and so on all along the chain to the last link. The equal and opposite forces are the tension.

A string can be seen in the same way, the links being replaced with molecules of string. If no external forces act along the surface of the string then the tension, the force exerted by one particle on the next, is the same throughout the length of string.

► Force exerted by tension

The end of the string or chain is attached to something, e.g. a hook, on which it exerts a force equal to the tension.

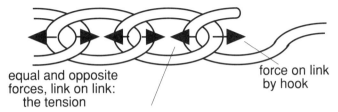

► Marking tension on diagrams

equal and opposite forces, link on link: the tension

force on link by hook

force by link on hook, and when you are drawing your diagrams, this is the force you are showing. Because it is at the end, draw your arrows as near as is practicable to the end of the string.

The diagram shows a bulb, weight W, hanging from the ceiling.

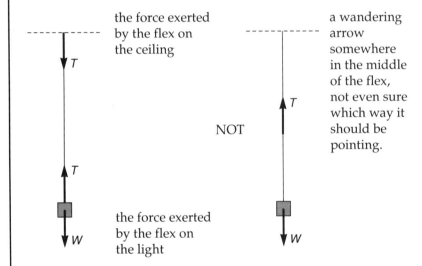

the force exerted by the flex on the ceiling

a wandering arrow somewhere in the middle of the flex, not even sure which way it should be pointing.

NOT

the force exerted by the flex on the light

Mass and weight

> **Mass**
> Mass is a measure of the amount of matter in a body, e.g. a bag of sugar has a mass of 2 kg on Earth, on the Moon, in space, anywhere. Mass is not a force.

► Mass

► Weight

> **Weight**
> Weight is the force exerted on a body by our planet Earth.

It was Newton who theorized that all masses affect each other (something like the pull of a magnet). The force of attraction between the Earth and any body is the **weight** of the body. When you pick up the bag of sugar you feel a force downwards on your hand: that is the force due to the Earth, the body's weight. The weight of a body is different on the Earth from what it is on the Moon and different again from what it is in space. The weight varies slightly over the surface of the Earth. Why?

The formula which works out the force of attraction is

$$F = \frac{GM_1M_2}{d^2} \text{ where}$$
G is a constant
M_1 = mass of one body
M_2 = the mass of the other body
d = distance between their centres of gravity

► Law of attraction – you should be aware of this although it is not an essential of the examinable course.

► More about centre of gravity later in this chapter

Here on Earth we have the practical application of this formula, and
   G is still a constant
   M_1 = mass of the Earth, a constant
   d = radius of the Earth
assuming the centre of gravity of the Earth is at its centre.
   So $\dfrac{GM_1}{d^2}$ is a constant which is always represented by g.

Hence the force exerted on the body is mg and g is the **acceleration due to gravity**, 9.81 m s^{-2}.

Acceleration due to gravity

There are three important things to note about acceleration.
1   We have said that d is constant but this is not exactly true. It varies because the Earth is not a sphere: d is less at the poles than on the equator and hence a body has greater weight at the poles. Also if you go up a big mountain d increases and hence a body weights less on the top of a mountain.
2   Newton's third law of motion applies and all bodies exert forces on the Earth equal and opposite to their weight.
3   The law of attraction applies between all bodies: there is a force across a desk between the pencil on one side and the ruler on the other. This force is so small compared with their weights that it has no effect. If the pencil and the ruler were in a space where there were no other forces at all then, because of the force of attraction, they would move towards each other and collide.

► Acceleration due to gravity $g = 9.81$ m s^{-2}
► **NB** Weight variation of the surface of the Earth because it is not a perfect sphere.

The weight of a body is given by mg
Hence, at the end of this lot, what really matters is that the weight of a body is given by mg. The 2 kg mass of sugar has a weight of 2g newtons, i.e. a 2 kg mass has weight of $2 \times 9.81 = 19.62$. Kilograms (kg) are not units of force. Weight is a force therefore you cannot have a weight measured in kg. This idea conflicts with our shopping experience: we have to remember that we buy 5 kg mass of potatoes, not 5 kg weight of potatoes.

► The important bit: the bit you must remember in all this: weight = mg

Solutions to Activity 1.2

1

▸ Resolving in action

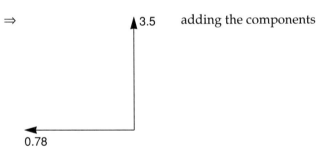

Resolving all forces into components which are in two directions at right angles to each other

⇒   ▲3.5   adding the components

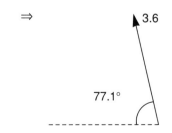

0.78

⇒   ▲3.6   using Pythagoras to find
                         $3.6 = \sqrt{3.5^2 + 0.8^2}$ and arctan to
                         find

▸ arctan and tan⁻¹ both mean the
same thing – arctanx = the angle
of which the tan is *x*.

77.1° $77.1° \left(\tan^{-1} \dfrac{3.5}{0.8} \right)$

2

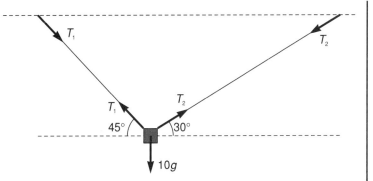

We have two unknowns, T_1 and T_2, and hence from algebraic considerations we are going to have to find two equations. Resolving vertically and horizontally gives

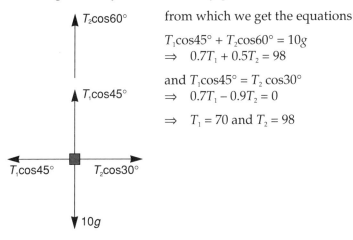

► The 1 and the 2 in T_1 and T_2 are only suffixes used to show that the tensions are different. They are not factors in any calculation.

from which we get the equations

$T_1\cos45° + T_2\cos60° = 10g$
$\Rightarrow \quad 0.7T_1 + 0.5T_2 = 98$

and $T_1\cos45° = T_2 \cos30°$
$\Rightarrow \quad 0.7T_1 - 0.9T_2 = 0$

$\Rightarrow \quad T_1 = 70$ and $T_2 = 98$

► A typical technique – forming two simultaneous equations

ACT **Activity 1.3**

► Solutions on page 19

1

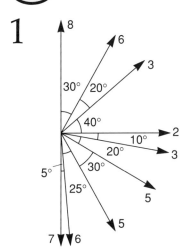

From my study window I can see a telephone pole which serves nine houses. The diagram shows the plan view and the horizontal pull exerted by each wire. Ignore the units.

Find the resultant pull exerted on the pole by the wires.

2

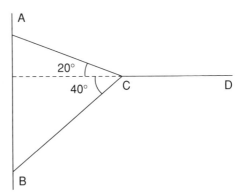

► **Smooth** surfaces do not exert any forces parallel to themselves.

► Meaning of 'smooth'

► The use of the word smooth is important in mechanics: it means that the force of friction is zero.

The diagram shows a mass of 50 kg held in equilibrium on a smooth slope by a rope AB. Find the tension in the rope and the force exerted on the mass by the slope.

3

A pole of a ridge tent is vertical and is held by two guy ropes fastened horizontally to a straight wall. The diagram shows the wall AB, the ropes AC and BC, and the tent ridge CD.

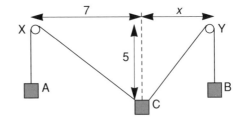

The tensions in the ropes are 59 N in AC and 70 N in BC. Find the pull of the ridge on the tent pole.

4

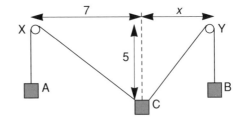

The diagram shows a mass C supported in equilibrium by two strings attached to masses A, 6 kg, and B, 7 kg. The strings pass over smooth pegs at X and Y. Lengths are as shown. Find x and the mass of C.

5

A rectangular uniform mirror, mass 8 kg, hangs on the wall and is supported by two chains. The chains, of the same length as the top edge of the mirror, are fastened to the same point on the wall and to the top corners of the mirror. The top edge of the mirror is horizontal. Find the tensions in the chains.

6 A man can either push or pull a wheelbarrow with the same force. Explain, in terms of the forces acting, why it is better to pull when he comes to a kerb.

► Something we always do – but why?

7 A kite is flying and it is stationary. The forces on it are a vertical lift, a horizontal force due to the wind and the force exerted by the string. What is the direction of the resultant of the horizontal wind force and the lift? If these forces are 20 N and 35 N respectively find the pull on the girl's hand and the angle the string makes with the ground (assumed level).

8 A paper boy carries his bag resting against his right hip with the strap over his left shoulder. The strap makes an angle of 30° with the vertical, the mass of the bag and papers is 20 kg and he is wearing a smooth anorak. What is the force exerted on his hip by the bag?

Solutions to Activity 1.3

1

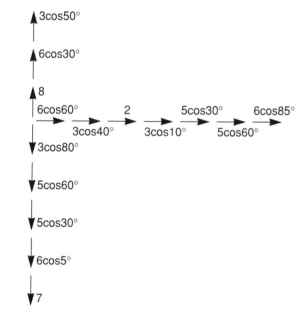

3cos50°

6cos30°

8

6cos60°   2   5cos30°   6cos85°

3cos40°   3cos10°   5cos60°

3cos80°

5cos60°

5cos30°

6cos5°

7

► No more as complicated as this one, but this example shows the power of this method by tackling such a complex problem.

which simplifies to

17.6

θ

5.2

from which the resultant pull $\sqrt{17.6^2 + 5.2^2} = 18.4$ acting in direction $\theta = 73.5°$, θ as shown on diagram.

2

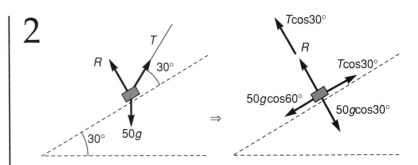

► Importance of good diagrams

In all these questions, persevere with every detail of the diagrams until you fully understand them. Correct diagrams are often the hardest and most essential part of the solution. It is in forming diagrams that you are
(a) interpreting the information given in the question
(b) forming the important deductions on which you are going to base your solution.

For this solution, considering what is happening:

parallel to the plane gives: $T\cos30° = 50\cos60°$
$\Rightarrow T = 282.9$ N

and perpendicular to the plane: $T\cos60° + R = 50g\cos30°$
$\Rightarrow R = 282.8$ N

► Not always just one method

Further notes on this solution
In the first instance we resolved parallel and perpendicular to the plane. We could have resolved horizontally and vertically to get

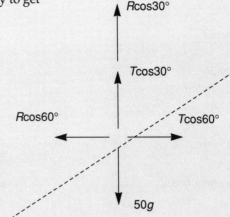

Our equations would then be:
$R\cos60° = T\cos60° \Rightarrow R = T$
and $R\cos30° + T\cos30° = 50g \Rightarrow R = 282.9$ N, $T = 282.9$ N

In this case, there is nothing to choose between the methods, but often there is because the algebra can be much easier by using one method rather than the other.

► Part of your studies will be learning to make the right choice.

3

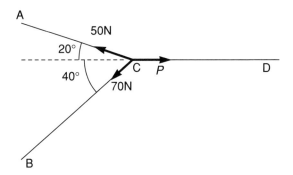

The ridge exerts a force P in the direction shown. (Could it be the opposite way?)

Resolving forces along the line CD:

$50\cos20° + 70\cos40° = P \implies P = 100.6$ N

4

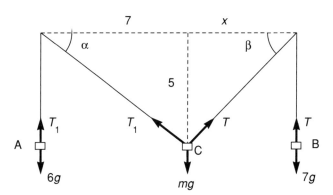

Smooth surfaces, therefore there is no force along the surface of the string and hence the tension is the same throughout each string.

    We can consider each of the masses A, B and C separately because each is in equilibrium in its own right.

Vertically for A: $T_1 = 6g$

Vertically for B: $T = 7g$

Horizontally for C:

$T_1\cos\alpha = T\cos\beta$

$\therefore\; 6g \times \dfrac{7}{\sqrt{74}} = 7g \times \dfrac{x}{\sqrt{5^2 + x^2}}$

because $\cos\alpha = \dfrac{7}{\sqrt{74}}$ and $\cos\beta = \dfrac{x}{\sqrt{5^2 + x^2}}$

$\implies\; 6\sqrt{5^2 + x^2} = \sqrt{74} \times x \implies x = 4.9$

Vertically for C: $T_1\sin\alpha + T\sin\beta = mg$

$\therefore\; 6g \times \dfrac{7}{\sqrt{74}} + 7g \times \dfrac{5}{\sqrt{49.01}} = mg$

$\implies\; m = 8.5$ kg

► Smooth surfaces and strings

► Use of sines: remember, if $x + y = 90°$ then $\sin x = \cos y$
This is the first time we have used sines when resolving: sometimes it is more convenient.

► Meaning of 'uniform'

Uniform – means the mass is evenly distributed through-out and then the centre of mass is at the geometric mid-point of the body: rod, beam, circular disc, etc. Centres of mass of other shapes will be dealt with as necessary throughout the book.

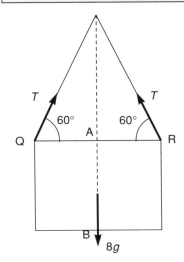

A symmetrical arrangement – the weight of the mirror is acting along the line AB and triangle PQR is equilateral.

Resolving vertically:
$2T\cos30° = 8g$
$\Rightarrow \quad T = 45.3\text{ N}$

6

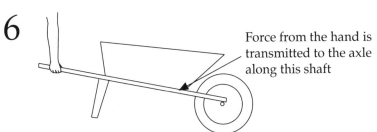

Force from the hand is transmitted to the axle along this shaft

► Remember this, next time you take a wheelbarrow up a kerb.

Diagrams show forces acting on the axle of the wheel. When pushing:

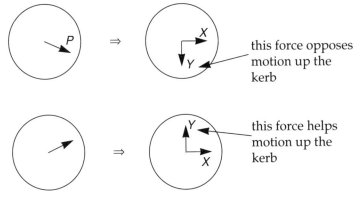

this force opposes motion up the kerb

this force helps motion up the kerb

7

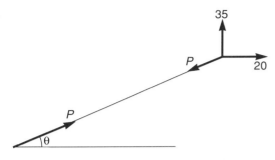

= tension in string

= force on hand

$P = \sqrt{35^2 + 20^2} = 40.3$ N

$\tan \theta = \dfrac{35}{20} = 1.75 \quad \Rightarrow \quad \theta = 60.3°$

Resultant of 35 and 20 is along the line of the string.

The force P at the kite is the equilibrant for the kite

▶ All this for a stationary kite – imagine the forces when the kite is diving and soaring!

8

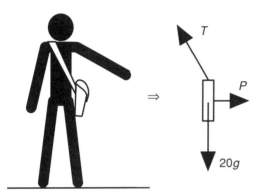

Smooth anorak ∴ no vertical force on bag due to anorak.

The force P shown is the force by hip on bag because we are showing forces on the bag, not the hip.

Force on hip by bag is P in opposite direction.

Resolving vertically: $T\cos60° = 20g \quad \Rightarrow \quad T = 226.3$ N

Resolving horizontally: $P = T\cos60° \quad \Rightarrow \quad P = 113.2$ N

▶ By now you will have realized that mechanics situations are happening all around you – you only have to look.

▶ two stages necessary,
$20g \quad \Rightarrow \quad T$ and then $T \quad \Rightarrow \quad P$.

 Activity 1.4

In this exercise you are given diagrams which you have to copy and insert the forces as requested. Do not write any equations at this stage.

▶ Solutions on page 26

1

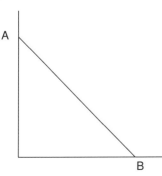

A uniform beam AB, weight W, is hinged to the wall at A and resting on the smooth floor at B.

   Draw the forces acting on the beam.

2

AB represents a spoon, with its centre of gravity at its midpoint of length, resting in a bowl which is hemispherical except for the flat base. Show the forces acting on the spoon if the bowl is assumed smooth.

3

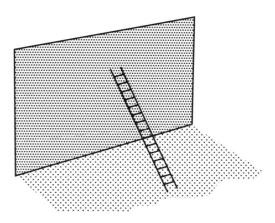

The drawing shows a ladder resting against a smooth wall. Draw a mechanics diagram and show the forces acting on the ladder.

Would equilibrium be possible if the ground were smooth?

4

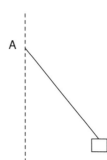

A block is fastened to a piece of string, the other end of which is fastened to a point A. The block is pulled horizontally until the string is at an angle of 45°. Show the forces acting on the block given that it has weight W.

5

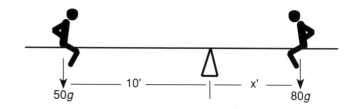

The diagram shows a see-saw with a man balancing his daughter. Their weights are W and w respectively. Show the forces acting on the see-saw. Ignore the weight of the see-saw.

6 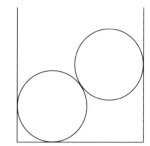 Two smooth identical spheres of weight *W* are inside a cylindrical tin as shown. The tin has no bottom. Show the forces acting on both spheres.

7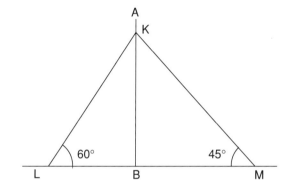

AB is a pole resting on the ground and it is held in a vertical position by two guy ropes KL and KM. Show the forces acting on the pole. The pole has weight *W*.

8 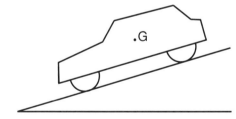 A car is parked on a slope. Its centre of gravity is at G. Show the forces acting on the car.

9 A bird is flying horizontally at constant speed. Show the forces acting on it.

10 A smooth string passes over a fixed smooth pulley and it has masses of 4 kg and 8 kg at its ends. Show the forces acting on the masses and on the pulley (the pulley has negligible mass).

Solutions to Activity 1.4

1

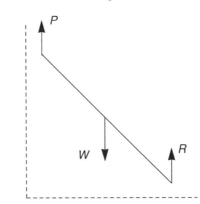

P can only act vertically because there are no other horizontal forces on beam.

W, the weight, acts through the midpoint of beam.

▶ ⊥ means 'is perpendicular to'

R is ⊥ floor because the floor is smooth and hence can only exert force ⊥ itself.

▶ Forces where a rod meets an edge

2

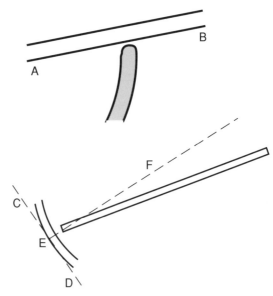

P ⊥ rod because rod and bowl are smooth – see note below.

Q passes through the centre of the circle because it is ⊥ tangent – see note below.

Because the surfaces are smooth there is no force // AB – the rim of the bowl is curved. Hence the only forces can be ⊥ AB, i.e. ⊥ rod, giving *P* as above.

▶ Forces where rod meets a curved surface

Smooth bowl therefore no forces along surface, i.e. in direction CD, the tangent. Only force is ⊥ CD which is along the radius EF. Hence force *Q* as above.

3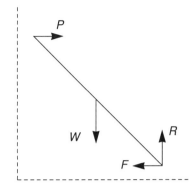

$P \perp$ wall therefore wall is smooth.

The force exerted by ground resolves into components F and N.

If the ground is smooth $F = 0$ and then, resolving horizontally $\Rightarrow$ $P = 0$, i.e. the wall is not there, and we have got something on a par with the Indian rope trick.

4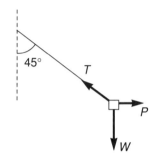

T is the force on the block exerted by the string and it is the tension in the string.

P = horizontal pull.

5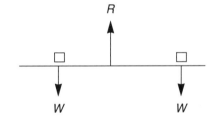

R is the force exerted upwards by the pivot on the see-saw.

► **NB:** Notice where the arrows indicating where the forces very clearly begin: on the see-saw.

6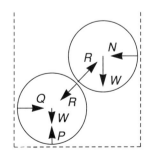

P, Q, R, N are all $\perp$ surfaces at points of contact.

N, Q are forces exerted by the cylinder on the spheres.

R is the force exerted by one sphere on the other.

► Curved surfaces in contact

► Notice the value of exploded diagrams on this page.

7

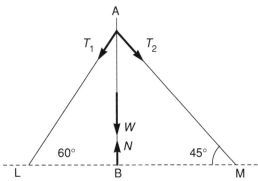

T_1, T_2 are forces due to guy rope tensions.

N is the force exerted by the ground (assumed smooth).

▶ In mathematics normal means perpendicular, not vertical, and it certainly does *not* mean OK or usual.

8

F_1, F_2 are forces of friction.

R_1, R_2 are normal reactions.

9

F is the force driving forward.

R is the resistance due to air.

L is the lift due to air.

W is the weight of the bird.

10

Tension is the same throughout the string because it is smooth and the pulley is frictionless, therefore there are equal upward forces due to the string on the two masses.

R is the force exerted by the support on the axle of the pulley. Why is R vertical?

(Refer to second part of question 3.)

(ACT) Activity 1.5

Now that you have got the diagrams for Activity 1.4 sorted out, go through all the questions again writing down any equations you can. Put your own angles on the diagrams where necessary.

► Solutions on this page

Solutions to Activity 1.5

1 System is in equilibrium, therefore $P + R = W$

2 System is in equilibrium, therefore
resolving horizontally for rod $\Rightarrow$ $Q\cos(\alpha + \beta) = P\sin\alpha$
resolving horizontally for rod $\Rightarrow$ $Q\sin(\alpha + \beta) = P\cos\alpha = W$

3 System is in equilibrium, therefore
resolving horizontally for ladder $\Rightarrow$ $P = F$
and resolving vertically for ladder $\Rightarrow$ $N = W$

4 System is in equilibrium, therefore
resolving vertically for block $\Rightarrow$ $T\cos45° = W$
and resolving horizontally for block $\Rightarrow$ $T\sin45° = P$

5 System is in equilibrium, therefore
resolving vertically for see-saw $\Rightarrow$ $R = W + w$

6 System is in equilibrium, therefore
resolving vertically for see-saw $\Rightarrow$ $P = W + W = 2W$
and resolving horizontally for whole $\Rightarrow$ $Q = N$

7 System is in equilibrium, therefore
resolving vertically for pole $\Rightarrow$ $T_1\cos60° = T_2\cos45°$
and resolving vertically for pole
$\Rightarrow$ $T_1\cos30° + T_2\cos45° + W = N$

8 System is in equilibrium, therefore resolving $\perp$ slope
$\Rightarrow$ $R_1 + R = W\cos\alpha$
and resolving // slope $\Rightarrow$ $F_1 + F = W\sin\alpha$

9

Newton's First Law of Motion
A body stays in a state of rest or uniform motion unless acted on by external forces.
Here we have uniform motion so the net force acting is zero. Hence resolving vertically $\Rightarrow$ $L = Wg$
and resolving horizontally $\Rightarrow$ $F = R$

► Newton's first law of motion NL1

► Newton's second law of motion
NL2

> **Newton's Second Law of Motion**
> **Force applied is equal to mass multiplied by acceleration.**
> This is well remembered as $P = ma$, where P is the force, m the mass and a the acceleration.
> There will be more on the background to this law shortly; however you will use it countless times in your work and in a practical sense all you need to remember is
> $P = ma$.

In this case:

horizontally: total forces forward: $F - R$
            mass W
            acceleration 0 because it is
                               moving at
                               constant velocity

therefore $F - R = W \times 0 \ \Rightarrow \ F = R$

vertically: total forces upwards $L - Wg$
          mass W
          acceleration (and velocity) 0

► Hence, by considering two apparently different approaches we have the same results and we are, in fact, showing how the laws used complement each other.

therefore $L - Wg = W \times 0 \ \Rightarrow \ L = Wg$

10 Pulley is in equilibrium therefore resolving vertically for pulley $\Rightarrow \ R = 2T$

Masses not in equilibrium.

If 8 mass goes down with acceleration a

NL2 $\Rightarrow$ $8g - T = 8a$
and for 4 mass $T - 4g = 4a$

force mass acceleration.

► Friction – where would we be without it? Because of it engines, hinges, knees, roads wear out. Without it cars would not go, or stop. We couldn't walk, walls couldn't be built. Half the time we are trying to remove it and the other half we are trying to increase it.

Friction

There has been a very brief reference to friction (page 3) and now it is time we looked at it in a bit more detail. There has also been much reference to smooth surfaces; how about when they are not smooth?

Get the block.

Pull it across your desk by its string. Mentally note the pull needed.

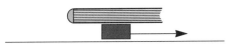

Now balance a heavy book on the block and pull again. What about the pulling force compared with no book on the block? Stronger.

► Analysis of a very simple situation

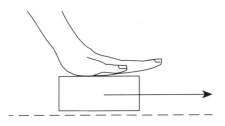

Repeat the exercise whilst pressing down on the block with your other hand. What about the pulling force now? Greater still. Press down harder. The pulling force? Stronger still.

►

Why does it get harder to pull the block? Let's look at the force diagram.

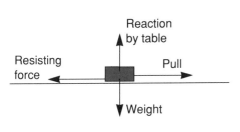

The diagram shows the forces acting on the block. The resisting force is the force opposing your pulling force.

This resisting force is the **force of friction** exerted by the desk surface on the under-surface of the block.

► Force of friction

Is the friction force acting when you are not pulling the string? No. It comes into existence only when the string is pulled. This is another application of Newton's third law, with the reasoning just as on page 4 in the case of the reaction to the weight. Friction is a force which opposes the motion of one surface over another. When the surfaces are not trying to move relative to each other the force does not exist.

► NL3

Is the force of friction limitless?

You have already answered this question.

As the weight on the block was increased so the pull required to move it had to be increased, i.e. the force of friction opposing movement was greater. But, in every case, the block *did* move, showing that there is a limit to the force available.

Now let's have a look at the maximum force of friction.

► Maximum friction

Put the block on the desk with a heavy weight on it.

Take the string and pull it very gently; now slowly increase your pull until the block moves.

Sketch a graph with F as ordinate, P as abscissae to show what you have done.

► abscissa – horizontal (x) axis
ordinate – vertical (y) axis

You should get:

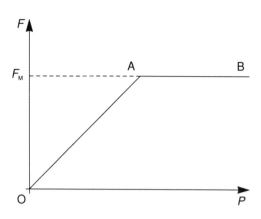

For OA: $F = P$ and we have equilibrium.

For AB: F has reached its maximum value F_M.

P is greater than F_M therefore no equilibrium.

► A little laboratory work

If you have access to apparatus you could try finding different values of F_M for different weights on the block. (A spring balance can be used to measure the weights and the corresponding pulls on the string.)

Draw a graph of F_M against W and you should get a straight line:

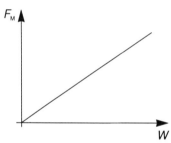

$F_M = aW$ where a is a constant, the gradient of the line.

Now $W = R$ R is the reaction of the desk on the block

and $a = \mu$ μ is a Greek letter pronounced 'mu'.

therefore $F_M = \mu R$

Now it follows that so long as $F \leq F_M$ we have equilibrium and hence the condition of equilibrium, in algebraic form, is

$F \leq \mu R$

► Coefficient of friction
F $\leq \mu R$

where the constant μ is called the **coefficient of friction**. It has a constant value for any two surfaces.

► An important result
F $\leq \mu R$

The result $F \leq \mu R$ is an important one and you will meet it often.

EXAMPLE
Try this question yourself before you read the solution.
    A piece of wood of mass 100 g rests on a board which is horizontal. A force of 0.4 N parallel to the board will just move the block.

(a)   Find the coefficient of friction between the piece of wood and the board.
One end of the board is now lifted until the board is inclined to the horizontal at 30°.

(b)   Find the forces parallel to the plane which will **(i)** just prevent the wood slipping down the plane and **(ii)** just pull the wood up the board. ($g = 10$ m s^{-2})

Solution
(a)

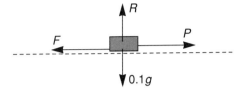

Just moves
when $P = F_M$

But $F_M = \mu R$
and $R = 0.1g$
$= 1\,\text{N}$

$$\Rightarrow \quad \mu = \frac{F_M}{R} = \frac{0.4}{1}$$

NB μ does not have any units $\left(\dfrac{F}{R} \quad \Rightarrow \quad \dfrac{\text{MLT}^{-2}}{\text{MLT}^{-2}} \quad \Rightarrow \quad \text{no units} \right)$

▶ The value of exploded diagrams again!

(b)

(i)

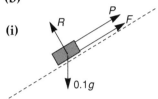

(ii)

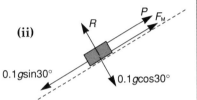

(i) Wood is about to slip down the plane therefore F
acts in the direction shown (opposing motion).
Resolving $\perp$ plane: $R = 0.1g\cos30°$
Resolving $//$ plane: $P + F = 0.1g\sin30°$
and because about to move: $F = \mu R$
therefore $P = 0.4 \times 0.1F\cos30° = 0.1g\sin30°$
therefore $P = \dfrac{1}{2} - 0.4\cos30° = 0.15\,\text{N}$

(ii) When the wood is about to move up the plane F
acts as shown.

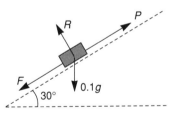

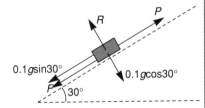

We have:
$$\begin{aligned}
P &= F + 0.1g\sin30° \\
&= \mu \times 0.1g\cos30° + 0.1g\sin30° \\
&= 0.04g\cos30° + 0.1g\sin30° \\
&= 0.86\,\text{N}
\end{aligned}$$

▶ Now cover this page and try to
answer the question – concentrate
on the principles involved, don't
learn this lot parrot-fashion.

► Solutions on this page

 *Activity 1.6*

1

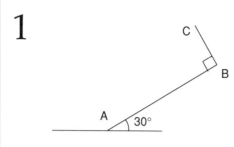

The diagram represents a board AB resting on a horizontal surface at A and supported at 30° to the horizontal by a string BC, where ∠ ABC = 90°. The board is uniform and has mass 5 kg. The tension in the string is measured to be 35 N.

Draw a force diagram showing the direction of the frictional force and the normal reaction acting on the board at A. Find the magnitude of both these forces. (g = 10 m s^{-2})

2 Consider, with diagrams, the forces of friction acting on your feet when you take a step.

► You need the weight of your block for this one.

3 Grip your block between finger and thumb and squeeze just sufficiently to lift the block. Assuming μ = 0.3 find the horizontal force exerted by your thumb on the block.

Solutions to Activity 1.6

1

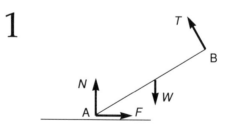

The diagram shows the directions of forces. Why is 'F' shown acting to the right?

Two reasons:

● Common sense – but beware because 'common sense' can be quite misleading.

● Logic – the better reason. The only other horizontal force acting is a component of T, which is to the left: hence F is to right for equilibrium.

Resolving horizontally: $F = T\cos 60° \Rightarrow F = 35 \times \dfrac{1}{2} = 17.5$ N

Resolving vertically: $N = W - T\cos 30°$

$$\Rightarrow \quad N = 5g - \frac{35\sqrt{3}}{2} = 19.7 \text{ N}$$

2 Back foot

$\Rightarrow$ tending to slip backwards ($\leftarrow$)

$\therefore$ friction acts forwards ($\rightarrow$)

► Some of the forces involved when walking

Front foot – two possibilities:

(a) If it hits the floor going forwards

then tendency is to slip forwards and friction acts backwards. $\Rightarrow$

(b) If it hits the floor going backwards friction acts forwards.

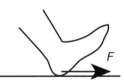

In both cases, once the foot is on the ground, the rear leg pushes and the front leg pulls the body forward. The front foot is then trying to slip back and is prevented by a frictional force acting forwards.

► Where would we be without friction?

3

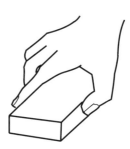

How is this diagram converted into a force diagram?

▶ Quite amazing what goes on when you pick up a box of matches!

Stage 1

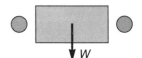

▶ A good example of this situation, put to practical use, is the clamp device used by builders to lift packs of paving slabs.

Stage 2   Put in the weight, *W*.

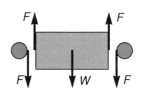

Stage 3   Friction on the block must be ↑ for equilibrium since the only other vertical force on the block is *W*, ↓.

Stage 4   *R* – normal reactions
Why are they all equal?
The force you are being asked to find.

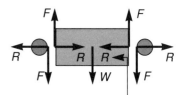

Resolving vertically for the block: $2F = W$

Block about to slip $\therefore \quad F = \mu R$

$$\therefore \quad R = \frac{F}{\mu} = \frac{W}{2\mu} = \frac{W}{0.6}$$

Substitute your own value of *W* remembering that it must be in kg to get an answer for *R* in newtons.

If you resolve horizontally for the block you can easily see why the normal reactions are equal.

▶ Limiting equilibrium
▶ Limiting friction

In this question there is reference to the block being 'about to slip'. When something is on the point of slipping, than it is said to be in **limiting equilibrium**. The force of friction is at its maximum or **limiting value** for the normal reaction existing in that situation.

In this case the only way we could increase the force of friction would be to increase the normal reaction, i.e. squeeze the block harder.

Newton's Second Law of Motion NL2

► NL2

► Force and movement

This law concerns the connection between force and movement. When a force is applied a consequence very often is movement of some sort. Most people would not have much trouble in pushing a bicycle but few people would be able to push a bus (there are some strong people around who can). Most can, just about, push a car. The force needed to push a car is much greater than to push the bike but the resulting speed is much less for the car. Why? Because the car is heavier then the bike.

So when a force is applied the size of the speed resulting also depends on the mass of the object being moved. These three quantities, F (force), m (mass) and v (velocity) are summed up in Newton's second law which states:

> The force is proportional to the rate of change of momentum.

It seems as though we cannot talk about one thing without further complicating the job by introducing something else, in this case **momentum**. Momentum is another often used quantity and it is defined quite simply as:

> momentum = mass × velocity = mv

► Momentum defined

There will be more on momentum in Chapter 2 but now we shall return to what we were doing.

In symbols the law becomes

$F \propto \dfrac{\mathrm{d}}{\mathrm{d}t} (mv)$ If you haven't done calculus leave this bit – you can come back to it later.

$k\dfrac{\mathrm{d}}{\mathrm{d}t} (mv)$

$= km\dfrac{\mathrm{d}v}{\mathrm{d}t}$ because in all our work the mass is constant

$= kma$

$\therefore \quad F = kma$

Now a force of 1 newton produces an acceleration of 1 m s^{-2} on a mass of 1 kg and if we substitute these values in $F = kma$ we get $k = 1$, and hence

$F = ma$ – the well known form, the bit you must remember.

It is important to remember that $F = ma$ is only valid if F is in newtons, m in kg and a in m s^{-2}. For any other units the constant k will not have the value 1.

► $F = ma$ is probably the equation you will use most frequently in dynamics.

► Units – velocity and acceleration

Units – velocity and acceleration

Velocity is a measure of the rate at which distance is changing with respect to time. Hence:

$$\text{velocity} = \frac{\text{change in distance}}{\text{time}}$$

$$= \frac{\text{metres}}{\text{seconds}} = \frac{\text{m}}{\text{s}} = \text{m s}^{-1}, \text{ metres per second}$$

Acceleration is a measure of the rate of which velocity is changing having regard to time. Hence:

$$\text{acceleration} = \frac{\text{change in velocity}}{\text{time}}$$

$$= \frac{\text{metres per second}}{\text{seconds}}$$

$$= \frac{\text{m s}^{-1}}{\text{s}} = \text{m s}^{-2}, \text{ metres per second squared}$$

Uniform acceleration

► We can visualize distance and velocity, we can feel force; but acceleration remains the complete abstract. Attempting to visualize it leads to many mistakes. Often quoted and just as often misunderstood. Be warned!

The last question in Activity 1.5 was different from all the others in that it was the only one where the system was not in equilibrium We applied NL2 and got the equations:

$$8g - T = 8a$$
$$T - 4g = 4a$$

Solving these gives us $T = \frac{16g}{3}$ and $a = \frac{g}{3}$

i.e. both the tension and the acceleration are constant. We shall now go on to develop the idea of constant acceleration, often referred to as **uniform acceleration**.

When something is moving with uniform acceleration there are three quantities which change, or vary. They are distance s, velocity, u, and time t. Now we can only handle any two of these at once and hence we are going to develop three equations, one for each pair of variables. Firstly for u and t:

► Velocity-time equation

The velocity-time equation

Acceleration is the rate of change of velocity.

$$a = \frac{\mathrm{d}u}{\mathrm{d}t}$$

Integrating: $at + c = u$

If, when the body sets off it has velocity u, i.e. $v = u$ when $t = 0$

then $u = c$

and we have $v = u + at$ the v, t equation

The distance-time equation

► Distance-time equation

Now $v = \dfrac{ds}{dt}$ so the v, t equation can be written

$$\frac{ds}{dt} = u + at$$

Integrating: $s = ut + \frac{1}{2}at^2 + c$

If, after no time, the body has not gone anywhere, i.e. $s = 0$ when $t = 0$, we get

$s = ut + \frac{1}{2}at^2$ the s, t equation

Time for some algebra now, as we eliminate t from the v, t and the s, t equations.

Distance-velocity equation

► Distance-velocity equation

Substituting for t from the v, t equation into the s, t equation, we get:

$$s = \frac{u(v-u)}{a} + \frac{1}{2}a\frac{(v-u)^2}{a^2}$$

$$= \frac{uv - u^2}{a} + \frac{v^2 - 2uv - u^2}{2a}$$

$$= \frac{v^2 - u^2}{2a}$$

Rearranging, we get
$$v^2 = u^2 + 2as \qquad \text{the } s, v \text{ equation}$$

Summary

If your problem involves v and s use

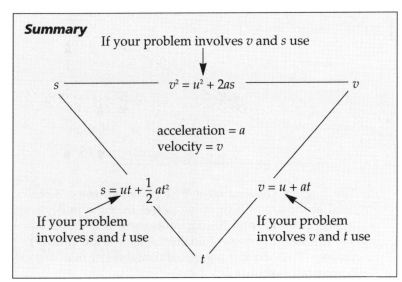

► The *s, v, t* triangle – you will use this often.

► Solutions on page 41

(ACT) *Activity 1.7*

In which we mix up the things we have done so far.

1 A particle has a velocity of 25 m s⁻¹ after it has been going for 3 seconds with an acceleration of 5 m s⁻². What velocity had it to start with?

2 A missile sets off with a velocity of 8 m s⁻¹ and an acceleration of –2 m s⁻². How far does it go in the third second?

3 A clockwork car has deceleration of 10 m s⁻². If it sets off with a velocity of 13 m s⁻¹ how far has it gone when its velocity is 5 m s⁻¹?

4 A boy of mass 70 kg does a skid stop (wheels locked) on his bike. Assuming uniform retardation from 12 km h⁻¹ to rest of 4 metres find the force of friction between the wheels and the road. (Ignore the mass of the bike.)

5 Two masses of 4 kg and 3 kg are connected by a smooth string and they hang over a fixed, smooth, light pulley. (As in Activity 1.3/1.4, question 10).

Find the acceleration of the masses and the tension in the string. If the heavier mass falls for 2 seconds from rest before it hits a fixed table find:

(a) its velocity when it hits the table

(b) how far it was above the table to start with

► Units of momentum defined at the end of the solution to this problem

(c) the momentum destroyed at the impact, if it does not rebound

(d) the upward force exerted by the support on the axle of the pulley.

► Solutions on page 47

(ACT) *Activity 1.8*

1

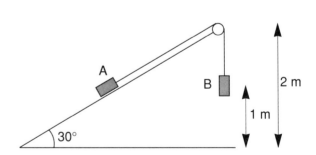

The diagram shows a smooth slope with a smooth pulley fixed at the top of it. A string passes over the pulley with masses A, 10 kg, and B, 4 kg, at its ends. A is on the slope and B is hanging freely. Initially the masses are at rest. The pulley is 2 m above the horizontal, and B is 1 m above the horizontal, as shown.

Does B rise or fall? With what acceleration?

Find how long it takes to reach either the horizontal or the pulley.

What is the momentum destroyed when a raindrop of mass 0.5 g hits the ground after falling 1000 m? ($g = 9.8$ m s^{-2}) It is estimated that rain is falling at the rate of 800 drops per m^2 per second. What is the momentum destroyed over a village of area 9 km^2 in 10 minutes?

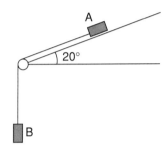

A is a mass of 8 kg and B is a 4 kg mass. The slope is rough, the string is smooth and it does not touch the slope.

The system is in limiting equilibrium, i.e. the force of friction acting on A has its maximum value. What is the force of friction acting on A?

The mass of B is now increased to 10 kg. With what velocity does A reach the bottom of the slope if it has 2 m to go to reach it? Remember the force of friction on A takes the value you have already found.

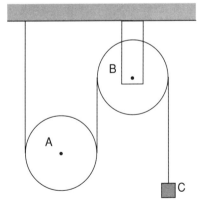

B is a smooth pulley which is fixed.

A is a smooth free pulley of mass m.

C is a block of mass M.

(a) If C moves down 2 m how far up will A go?

(b) Since A and C cover their respective distances in the same time how would you expect their speeds to compare?

(c) And their accelerations?

Check your answers at this stage.

(d) If the system is in equilibrium find M in terms of m.

(e) If $M = 2m$ find the acceleration of A.

▶ Uniform acceleration shown graphically – very useful

5

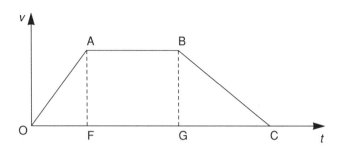

A body travels in three stages which are represented on the graph by the sections from O to A, A to B and B to C.

(a) Describe the motion.

(b) What does the slope of OA represent?

(c) What does the area ABCO represent?

(d) What does the slope of BC represent?

(e) Give the values of **(b)**, **(c)** and **(d)** in terms of the lengths on the diagram.

6 A mass of 1 kg and a mass of 100 kg fall simultaneously from the same height. When they hit the ground

(a) do they have the same velocity?

(b) do they arrive at the same time?

▶ Don't confine your answer to 'yes' or 'no' – give reasons!

(c) do they have the same momentum?

7 Find the acceleration (assumed uniform) of a body which sets off from rest and arrives at a point 100 m from its starting point, with a velocity of 80 m s^{-1}. From your answer, suggest what the 'body' might be.

8 Refer to question 1 of Activity 1.3, on page 18.
If the forces had instead been acting on a body of mass 20 kg resting on a smooth horizontal surface what would be its acceleration? Assume the forces are in newtons.
If the surface were changed to a rough one what force of friction would be needed for equilibrium to be maintained?

9

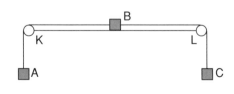

KL is a smooth horizontal table. A has mass 4 kg, B has mass 5 kg, C has mass 6 kg. Find the acceleration of B.
How far, and in which direction, must the table be tilted for B to be in equilibrium?

10 A rifle is fired horizontally, at shoulder height, on level ground. At the same instant a nut falls off the rifle. Ignoring air resistance, which reaches the ground first, the bullet or the nut?

11 A particle of weight W is in limiting equilibrium on a rough sloping plane. The plane is inclined at α to the horizontal and the coefficient of friction is μ. Show that $\mu = \tan \alpha$.

Solutions to Activity 1.7

1 The problem involves v and t, hence use $v = u + at$.

$\therefore \quad 25 = u + 5 \times 3 \quad \Rightarrow \quad u = 10 \text{ m s}^{-1}$

2 The problem involves s and t, hence use s $= ut + \frac{1}{2}at^2$.

The 'third' second is from the end of the 'second' second to the end of the 'third' second.

After 3 s: $s = 8 \times 3 + \dfrac{1}{2} \times -2 \times 3^2 = 24 - 9 = 15$ m

▶ Difference between 3 s and third second

After 2 s: $s = 8 \times 2 + \dfrac{1}{2} \times -2 \times 2^2 = 16 - 4 = 12$ m

Therefore distance travelled in 3rd second $= 15 - 12 = 3$ m

▶ Remember that the 't' in these equations is the time from the start: it is important that you sort out the difference between 3 seconds and 3rd second.

3 The problem involves s and u, hence use $v^2 = u^2 + 2as$.

$5^2 = 13^2 + 10 \times 5 \quad \Rightarrow \quad s = 7.2$ m

4 Frictional force of the road on the wheels is the force which stops the bike.

NL2: $F = ma$ m is known; what about a?

v, S known $\therefore \quad v^2 = u^2 + 2as \quad \Rightarrow \quad$ finding a

$\qquad\qquad 0 = 12^2 + 2a \times 4$ – mistake here ; easily done!

Units are wrong because u is in km h^{-1}.

$u = 12 \times \dfrac{1000}{60 \times 60} \text{ m s}^{-1} = \dfrac{10}{3} \text{ m s}^{-1}$

$\therefore \quad 0 = \left(\dfrac{10}{3}\right)^2 + 2a \times 4 \quad \Rightarrow \quad a = -\dfrac{100}{72} \text{ m s}^{-2}$

$\Rightarrow \quad F = 70 \times \dfrac{100}{72} = 97.2$ N

5

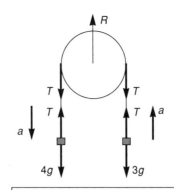

Applying NL2 for $4g$ mass
$$\Rightarrow \quad 4g - t = 4a$$

Applying NL2 for $3g$ mass
$$\Rightarrow \quad T - 3g = 3a$$

► Important technique defined

In forming these equations notice particularly the way in which different parts of the system can be considered in isolation.

When we say 'NL2 for $4g$ mass' we are concentrating solely on that mass and what is happening to it.

The only part of the main diagram that we are looking at is

     and hence the equation.

► Force diagrams and other quantities

Another important point to stress is that the main diagram is a force diagram and only forces appear on it. Notice that the acceleration, a, is indicated at the side and it does not appear as an arrow on a mass or the string. So

► Good practice on diagrams

     good, as above.

or 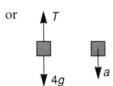   good, showing a force diagram and a separate acceleration diagram.

     not good. Neither a force diagram nor an acceleration diagram. This practice would lead to confusion in the more complex problems to come.

There is a technique where people use single headed and double headed arrows for forces and accelerations but students often find this confusing. Develop good practice from the start as indicated above.

Now to return to the problem.

Solving the equations we get: $a = \frac{g}{7}$ m s^{-2}

$$\text{and } T = \frac{24g}{7} \text{ N}$$

(a)   The problem involves, u and t hence use $v = u + at$.

$v = 0 + \frac{g}{7} \times 2$ 'from rest' $\Rightarrow$ $u = 0$

$\therefore$ $v = \frac{2g}{7}$ m s^{-1} after 2 s

(b)   The problem involves s and t, hence use $s = ut + \frac{1}{2}at^2$.

$s = 0 + \dfrac{1}{2} \times \dfrac{g}{7} \times 2^2 = 2.8$ m

(c)   Momentum $= mv$

At impact $mv = 4 \times \dfrac{2g}{7} = 11.2$ Ns

▶ Note on units at end of this solution

(d)   The pulley is in equilibrium hence

resolving vertically for the pulley $\Rightarrow$ $R = 2T$

$\therefore R = \dfrac{48g}{7} = 67.2$ N

In this last part you may well think that $R = 7g$ because the pulley is supporting a total weight of $4g + 3g = 7g$. However such thinking would be totally and utterly wrong: the masses are not in equilibrium and hence the solution we have.

▶ Common sense leading to error!!

An introduction to the theory of units

In mechanics we have three basic units and all other quantities or units can be expressed in terms of these three – a bit like all colours being a combination of the three primary colours, red, yellow and blue.

The three basic units are mass, M, length, L, and time, T.

▶ Units:

$\text{Velocity} = \dfrac{\text{distance}}{\text{time}} = \dfrac{L}{T} = LT^{-1}$

▶ velocity

$\text{Acceleration} = \dfrac{\text{velocity}}{\text{time}} = \dfrac{LT^{-1}}{T} = LT^{-2}$

▶ acceleration

$\text{Force} = \text{mass} \times \text{acceleration} = M \times LT^{-2} = MLT^{-2}$

▶ force

– and as already defined our basic unit here is the newton.

$\text{Momentum} = \text{mass} \times \text{velocity} = M \times LT^{-1} = MLT^{-1}$

▶ momentum

now $MLT^{-1} = MLT^{-1} \times \dfrac{T}{T} = MLT^{-2} \times T.$

▶ The use of units in this way is important in science and it is used to unravel many problems. For those studying chemistry there is a close connection with forming chemical equations. You will do very little more on the theory of units in your mechanics course.

Since MLT^{-2} is in newtons, and T is in seconds momentum has units called **newton seconds**, Ns.

Velocity and speed

Consider the following situation.

You are caught up in a slow-moving traffic jam. A ladybird starts to walk across the dashboard from left to right. It maintains a straight path directly from left to right on the dashboard and it always walks at the same speed. A diagram of the path of the ladybird, relative to the road, looks like this.

► A high-powered ladybird!

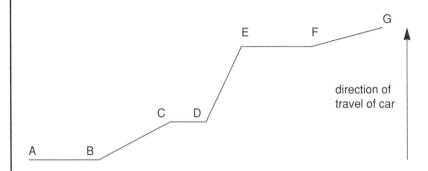

What meaning can you attach to the diagram? When is the car not moving? When does the car have a speed (a) half (b) twice that of the ladybird relative to the dashboard?

AB, CD and EF represent the times when the car is stationary.

BC is when the speed of the car is half that of the ladybird and in DE the car's speed is twice that of the ladybird.

Consider DE in more detail.

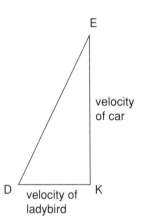

DK and KE represent the velocities of the ladybird and the car respectively. DE represents the final velocity of the ladybird.

Velocities are vector quantities and are treated in just the same way as other vector quantities you have met.

There is no link between the two velocities shown in the diagram except that the magnitude of KE is twice that of DK (this has already been referred to) and these magnitudes are the **speeds**.

Speed is a scalar quantity, i.e. direction is not considered when speed is used.

Now think about this.

A motorist drives along a level perfectly straight road at a constant 30 mph. What about his velocity?

► Velocity considered – constant and varying

It is constant because neither speed nor direction is changing.

He then slows down to 20 mph. What is the velocity?

Velocity changes because of change in speed.

The road then becomes a winding one but the motorist maintains a constant 20 mph. What happens to the velocity?

His velocity varies because the car keeps changing direction.

Now everybody knows what acceleration is! Change in speed: it describes going faster, or slower – but are you sure?

A child is going round at constant speed on a roundabout. Is she accelerating?

Acceleration is actually change in velocity and is itself a vector quantity. Although she is moving at constant speed the child's direction is changing all the time; therefore her velocity is changing and hence she is accelerating.

► **Remember:** with velocity, if either speed or direction (or both) changes then acceleration occurs.

There will be much more on this later.

Solutions to Activity 1.8

 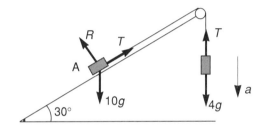

Let the system have acceleration a as shown.

Forces and masses are known, acceleration is wanted. Hence

NL2 for A: $T - 10g\cos60° = 10a$

NL2 for B: $4g - T = 4a$

Eliminating T $\Rightarrow$ $4g - 10g \times \dfrac{1}{2} = 14a$ $\Rightarrow$ $a = -\dfrac{g}{14}$

This negative result simply means that our original guess of acceleration being downwards on B was wrong and in fact B accelerates upwards.

Using the s, t equation $\Rightarrow$ $s = ut + \dfrac{1}{2}at^2$

$$\Rightarrow 1 = \frac{1}{2} \times \frac{g}{14}t^2$$

$$\Rightarrow t = \sqrt{\frac{28}{g}} = 1.7 \text{ s}$$

2   Momentum = mu

It is necessary to find u.

Using the s, u equation $\Rightarrow$ $v^2 = u^2 + 2as$

$\therefore$ $v^2 = 2 \times g \times 1000$ $\Rightarrow$ $u = 140 \text{ m s}^{-1}$

Momentum of drop $= \dfrac{0.5}{1000} \times 140$ divide by 1000 because m must be in kg

$$= 0.07 \text{ Ns}$$

Momentum destroyed in 10 minutes over an area of 9 km² at 800 drops per m² is $0.07 \times 800 \times 9 \times 1000 \times 1000 \times 60 \times 10$

$\underbrace{\qquad\qquad}_{\text{area in m}^2} \underbrace{\qquad}_{\text{time in s}}$

$= 3.36 \times 10^{10}$ Ns, using standard form.

▶ It is sometimes necessary to make assumptions!

Assumptions made:
- Falls from rest – reasonable
- No air resistance – an important assumption necessary at this level of mechanics but cannot be ignored in reality
- Water does not rebound on impact – debatable.

3

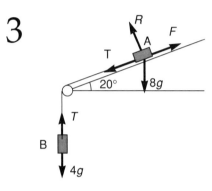

F is force of friction

In equilibrium, therefore

resolving // plane for A:
$F = T + 8g\sin20°$

and resolving vertically for
B: $T = 4g$

∴ $F = 4g + 8g\sin20°$

∴ $F = 6.7g$

Let B have acceleration a downwards.

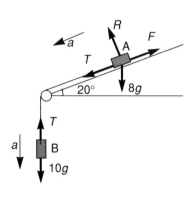

NL2 for A:

$T + 8g\sin20° - F = 8a$

NL2 for B: $10g - T = 10a$

Add to eliminate T

$\Rightarrow$ $10g + 8g\sin20° - F = 18a$

$\Rightarrow$ $a = \dfrac{1}{18}(10g + 8g\sin20° - 4g - 8g\sin20°)$

$= \dfrac{6g}{18}$

$= \dfrac{g}{3}$ m s⁻¹

Using the s, u equation $v^2 = u^2 + 2as$

$\Rightarrow$ $v = \sqrt{2 \times \dfrac{g}{3} \times 2}$

$= 3.6$ m s⁻¹

4 **(a)** If QC increases by 2 m, then PSR decreases by 2 m, i.e. PS and SR decrease by 1 m each.

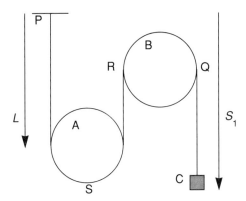

▶ You will meet this working on mechanical advantage and velocity ratio in physics.

∴ A rises 1 m.

(b) If s_1 increases by 2 m and l decreases by 1 m in the same time then the speed of C is twice that of A.

(c) The speed of C is twice that of A.

▶ Connected velocities and accelerations

i.e. $\dfrac{ds}{dt} = -2\dfrac{dl}{dt}$

Differentiating: $\Rightarrow$ $\dfrac{d^2s}{dt^2} = -2\dfrac{d^2l}{dt^2}$ $\Rightarrow$ if $\dfrac{d^2s}{dt^2} = a$

$\dfrac{d^2l}{dt^2} = -\dfrac{a}{2}$

i.e. if C accelerates down with value a then A accelerates up with value $\dfrac{a}{2}$.

(d)

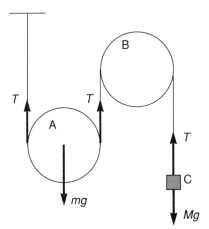

System is in equilibrium, therefore

resolving vertically for C: $\Rightarrow$ $T = Mg$

and resolving vertically for A: $\Rightarrow$ $2T = mg$

Eliminating T: $\Rightarrow$ $2Mg = mg$

∴ $M = \dfrac{m}{2}$

(e)

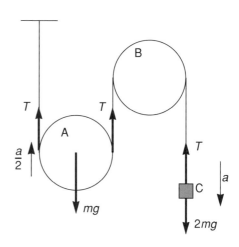

$$\text{NL2 for C:} \quad \Rightarrow \quad 2mg - T = 2ma$$

$$\text{NL2 for A:} \quad \Rightarrow \quad 2T - mg = m\frac{a}{2}$$

$$\text{Eliminating } T: \quad \Rightarrow \quad 3mg = 9m\frac{a}{2}$$

$$\Rightarrow \quad \frac{a}{2} = \frac{g}{3}$$

$$\therefore \quad \text{acceleration of A is } \frac{1}{3}g \text{ m s}^{-2} \text{ upwards.}$$

5

► The velocity-time graph analysed

(a) The body sets off from rest and accelerates uniformly to A; it then travels at constant velocity to B; finally it decelerates uniformly to rest at C.

(b) Slope of OA $= \dfrac{\text{change in velocity}}{\text{change in time}} = \text{acceleration}$

(c) Area = velocity × time = distance travelled at constant velocity

► A popular topic – the *v-t* graph illustrates well the useful properties of graphs.

(d) Slope of BC = deceleration from B to C

(e) Acceleration O to A $= \dfrac{\text{AF}}{\text{FO}}$

Distance travelled $= \dfrac{1}{2} \times \text{OF} \times \text{FA} + \text{FA} \times \text{FG} + \dfrac{1}{2} \times \text{GC} \times \text{BG}$

Deceleration B to C $= \dfrac{\text{BG}}{\text{GC}}$

6 Both masses have the same acceleration, g, and fall from the same height, h.

(a) For either or both:
$$v^2 = u^2 + 2as \quad \Rightarrow \quad v^2 = 2gh \quad \Rightarrow \quad v = \sqrt{2gh}$$

(b) For either or both:
$$s = ut + \frac{1}{2}at^2 \quad \Rightarrow \quad h = \frac{1}{2}gt^2 \quad \Rightarrow \quad t = \sqrt{\frac{2h}{g}}$$

(c) Momentum of 1 kg mass $= 1 \times \sqrt{2gh} = \sqrt{2gh}$ Ns

Momentum of 100 kg mass $= 100 \times \sqrt{2gh} = 100\sqrt{2gh}$ Ns

7   The problem involves s and u, hence use $v^2 = u^2 + 2as$.

$\Rightarrow \quad 80^2 = 2 \times a \times 100 \quad \Rightarrow \quad a = 32 \text{ m s}^{-2}$

$a = 32 \text{ m s}^{-2} \quad \Rightarrow \quad u = 32 \times 6 = 192 \text{ m s}^{-1}$ after 6 seconds.

$192 \text{ m s}^{-1} = 691.2 \text{ km h}^{-1} = 432 \text{ mph}$

Hence the 'body' is possibly a Tornado jet fighter or bomber.

8

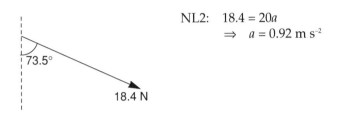

NL2: $18.4 = 20a$
   $\Rightarrow \quad a = 0.92 \text{ m s}^{-2}$

Force of friction for equilibrium is

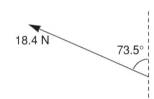

9

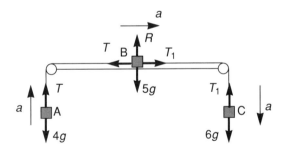

Using NL2:

for A: $T - 4g = 4a$ **(1)**

for B: $T_1 - T = 5a$ **(2)**

for C: $6g - T_1 = 6a$ **(3)**

Substituting for T and T_1 from **(1)** and **(3)** in **(2)**

$6g - 6a - 4g - 4a = 5a \quad \Rightarrow \quad a = \dfrac{2g}{15} \text{ m s}^{-2}$

► Systematic setting out, leads to . . .

► . . . effective solution!

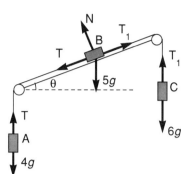

The diagram shows the table tilted to angle θ. The whole system is in equilibrium.

$\therefore$ resolving vertically for
A: $T = 4g$

and resolving vertically for
C: $T_1 = 6g$

Resolving // slope for B: $T_1 = T + 5g\sin\theta$

$$\Rightarrow \quad 6g = 4g + 5g\sin\theta$$
$$\Rightarrow \quad \sin\theta = \frac{2}{5} = 0.4$$
$$\theta = \sin^{-1}0.4 = 23.6°$$

10

The velocity diagrams at the beginning for

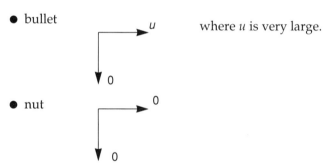

- bullet   where u is very large.

- nut

In this problem the important fact is that both bullet and nut have initial vertical velocity of zero.

Since they both fall the same vertical distance with the same acceleration, g, they reach the ground at the same time (refer to question 6) – hard to believe, but true!

► Consider then the speed of the bullet when you consider the horizontal distance covered before it hits the ground.

11

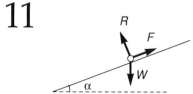

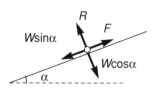

Resolving // plane: $F = \sin\alpha$

Resolving $\perp$ plane: $R = W\cos\alpha$

For equilibrium: $F \leq \mu R$

$$\Rightarrow \frac{F}{R} \leq \mu$$

$$\therefore \quad \frac{W\sin\alpha}{W\cos\alpha} \leq \mu \quad \Rightarrow \quad \tan\alpha \leq \mu$$

In this case equilibrium is limiting therefore $\mu = \tan\alpha$.

'Show that' questions occur frequently in mechanics. Quantities are usually given in algebraic form and you are given the end result. The problem lies in finding all the work, reasoning, etc. which is necessary to get from the given information to the end result.

▶ Show that . . .

Energy

Get the block.

Hold the free end of the string in one hand and the block in the other, keeping the string taut and horizontal.

Let go of the block.

What happens? It falls.

Why? Attraction of masses, weight, not supported.

What shape is its path? Circular.

Now hold the string and let the block hang, at rest.

Now let go of the string.

What happens? It falls.

Why? – and so on.

What is its acceleration? g (= 9.81 m s^{-2})

Which equations apply to this motion? Uniform acceleration.

And the s, v equation? $v^2 = u^2 + 2gh$

If it starts from rest $u = 0$ and $v^2 = 2gh$

$$\Rightarrow \frac{v^2}{2} = gh$$

If the block has mass m we write

$$\frac{mv^2}{2} = mgh$$

and this is the essential part of one of the most used principles in your work.

▶ We are here looking at energy in terms of mechanics.
There are other forms apart from the kinetic and potential energy we confine our attention to.

LHS $\frac{1}{2}mv^2$ This quantity is the **kinetic** energy of the block. It is the energy the block has because of the fact that it is moving; hence the word 'kinetic'.

▶ Kinetic energy

RHS mgh This quantity is the **potential** energy of the block. It is the energy the block has by virtue of its state or position; it is in a state where it is capable of doing work (more of this shortly) and hence the use of the word 'potential'.

▶ Potential energy

▶ Conservation of energy

As our block falls it gains speed and loses height: it gains kinetic energy and loses potential energy. The greater the gain in kinetic energy, the greater the loss in potential. This leads to the law that the total amount of energy that the block has remains constant but it does change from kinetic to potential and vice versa. This is quite true – with one important proviso: no external forces must act on the block in its direction of travel.

It is assumed in our work that resistance due to air does not exist (not true, ask any parachutist) but a denser medium (oil, syrup, even water) does offer resistance and hence an external force opposing the motion. When a space rocket takes off, or when a car sets off up a hill, they gain in both kinetic and potential energy which is obtained from the energy produced by the engine. In this case the energy of the car is not constant; it is being given more and more energy from the engine.

▶ Applying the principle of conservation of energy

When we are applying the principle of conservation of energy we may write down one of two considerations:

● total energy at position one = total energy at position two

● energy lost in one form going from position one to position two = energy gained in other forms going from position one to position two.

▶ Some of the larger pleasure grounds offer study packs on the mechanics of their various rides.
   If you get the chance get one of these packs and study it at the pleasure ground in a practical manner.

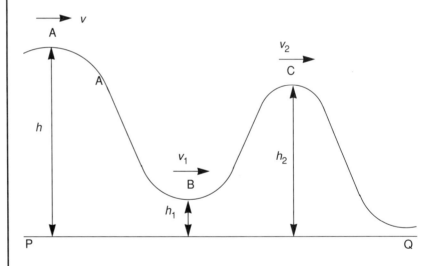

The diagram shows part of a roller coaster ride and we shall consider the energy of the car at A, B and C.

We neglect the forces of resistance in this case.

At A: total energy $= \dfrac{1}{2}mv^2 + mgh$

At B: total energy $= \dfrac{1}{2}mv_1^2 + mgh_1$

At C: total energy $= \dfrac{1}{2}mv_2^2 + mgh_2$

The principle of conservation of energy states

energy at A	=	energy at B	=	energy at C
$\frac{1}{2}mv^2 + mgh$	=	$\frac{1}{2}mv_1^2 + mgh_1$	=	$\frac{1}{2}mv_2^2 + mgh_2$

Considering the section from A to B, and rearranging

$$\frac{1}{2}mv_1^2 - \frac{1}{2}mv^2 = mgh - mgh_1$$

i.e. kinetic energy gained = potential energy lost   **(1)**

and for B to C, and rearranging

$$\frac{1}{2}mv_1^2 - \frac{1}{2}mv_1^2 = mgh_2 - mgh_1$$

i.e. kinetic energy lost = potential energy gained   **(2)**

The statements **(1)** and **(2)** summarize the simplest and most practical way of using the principle of conservation of energy.

Quoting the total energy at each point of a motion, as we did at A, B and C, is a little more cumbersome and it invariably necessitates an arbitrary line, PQ, called the **level of zero potential energy**.

> **Units of energy**
>
> Kinetic: $\frac{1}{2}mv^2 \Rightarrow MLT^{-1}LT^{-1} = ML^2T^{-2}$
>
> Potential: $mgh \Rightarrow MLT^{-2}L = ML^2T^{-2}$
>
> and 1 kg m² s⁻² is defined as 1 **joule.**

► Research J.P. Joule 1818–1889

Use of principle of conservation of energy
After you have used the principle of conservation of energy a few times you will find it not very difficult to apply: the more difficult part is deciding when it can and cannot be used.

In the next exercise you have to decide whether or not, in principle, the principle of conservation of energy could be used.

 Activity 1.9

► Solutions on page 56

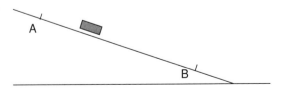

Your block is on a sloping plane. It slides down the plane. Consider the motion between A and B.

2 Consider the motion of your block hanging on the end of its string and set swinging side to side (a simple pendulum).

3 Consider the motion of a ball bearing dropped in a tall cylindrical jar containing syrup.

4 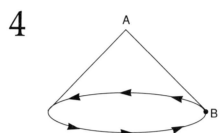 Hold the free end of the string attached to your block at A and set the block moving in a horizontal circle at constant speed *d*. Consider the motion.

5 Again hold the free end of the string stationary and get the block moving in vertical circles. Consider the motion now.

6 An aeroplane does a vertical circle, loops the loop, at constant speed. Consider its motion.

Solutions to Activity 1.9

1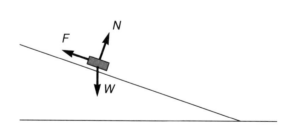

The force diagram is as shown.
The force *F* acts along the direction of travel; it is an external force therefore the principle of conservation of energy does not apply.

You should rightly query the fact that a component of *W* acts along the line of travel. However, the weight of a body is considered in the energy i.e. *mgh* and in our work weight is not an external force.

If the plane is smooth $F = 0$.

N is ⊥ direction of travel.

Hence the principle of conservation of energy does apply.

Chapter 1   What is Mechanics?   57

2

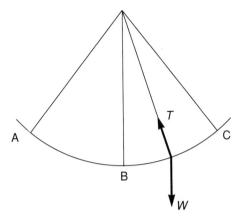

The block swings from A through B to C. At A and C it is stationary.

At B it is going at its fastest.

The forces acting are shown.

T acts $\perp$ motion.

► The simple pendulum

There are no external forces in the direction of travel therefore the principle of conservation of energy applies.

3

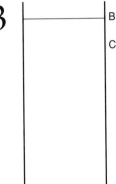

A description of the motion would be: the ball is dropped from A, falls freely to B where it hits the syrup, slows down to some point C (fairly near the surface), falls at constant speed to the bottom D.

From A to B air resistance is neglected and the principle of conservation of energy applies.

From B to C to D there is a considerable resistive force and the principle of conservation of energy does not apply.

► Compare this with the fall of a parachutist.

4

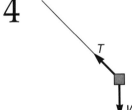

T is $\perp$ direction of travel.

No other external forces, therefore the principle of conservation of energy applies.
    But it is of no value in this case therefore both kinetic and potential energy remain constant and no useful equation can be formed.

► Compare this with a child on a roundabout.

5

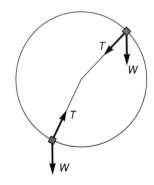

The diagram shows the block in two different positions, emphasizing that the only external force, T, is always $\perp$ motion.
    The principle of conservation of energy applies.

► A simple point but remember it!

6 Extra force is needed in the direction of travel to maintain speed. Kinetic energy remains constant but potential energy increases, therefore the principle of conservation of energy does not apply.

Work

Let us consider the cases when the principle of conservation of energy did not apply in Activity 1.9. Why did it not apply? Energy was spent overcoming resisting forces (questions 1 and 3) or energy increased by assisting forces (question 6). When energy is spent by a body the body has **done work on** something else (e.g. overcoming a resistance). When the energy of a body increases work has been **done on it** (a bicycle setting off).

It follows that work done is equal to energy change:

work done ⇔ energy change

Consider an archer firing an arrow.

 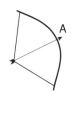 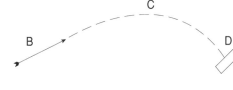

Starting point	Ready to fire	Path of arrow
Bow relaxed	Bow under tension	Bow releases energy to arrow (bow works on arrow) and arrow has kinetic energy at B equal to potential energy of bow at A.
	Work has been done on bow by archer.	
	Bow has gained energy: this is potential energy and there will be more of this later.	At C, some kinetic energy is lost but potential energy is gained.
		At D, potential energy is lost but kinetic energy is regained.
		The arrow works against resistance of target and all energy is lost.

Two definitions now follow:

Work done by a constant force:
$W = Fx$ Units: $F = MLT^{-2}$ $x = L$
$\therefore\ Fx = ML^2T^{-2}$ as on page 55
i.e. joules.

▶ Joules

The rate at which a force works is called the **power**.

Power

$P = \dfrac{d}{dt}(Fx) = F\dfrac{dx}{dt}$ remembering that F is constant

i.e. $P = Fv$ Units: $F = MLT^{-2}$ $u = LT^{-1}$

$\therefore$ $Fu = ML^2T^{-3}$

and the units of power are **watts**.

▶ Watts = joules per second
▶ Research James Watt 1736–1819

(ACT) Activity 1.10

▶ Solutions on page 60

1 What was the energy in a catapult if it fired a stone of mass 100 g vertically to a height of 30 m? How much work was done by the boy in pulling the elastic?

2

A girl freewheels on her bicycle up a slope to a standstill at D.

	A	B	C	D
Velocities	u	v_B	v_C	0
Distances		$2x$	x	x

Write down your application of the principle of conservation of energy at the points A, B, C and D.

3 A cricket ball is hit at a speed of 40 m s^{-1}. It rises to a height of 40 m and is finally caught by a fielder 50 m from the bat. How much work is done on the ball by the fielder in catching it? (Or should it be work done by the ball on the fielder?)

4 A cat of mass 4 kg jumps to a height of 1.5 m. Making the jump takes the cat 0.2 seconds before it leaves the ground. What is the average power developed by the cat as it jumps?

5 A pile of four baker's trays are stacked as in **(a)** (overleaf). They are then rearranged to form a pile as in **(b)**, with A going to the bottom, B second one up and so on. How much work has been done?

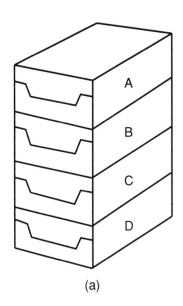 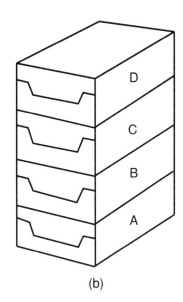

(a)   (b)

Solutions to Activity 1.10

▶ When elastic is stretched it has potential energy – more later.

1 The cycle of energy change is:

(a) the boy does work on elastic, i.e. he gives it energy

(b) the elastic contracts and gives kinetic energy to the stone

(c) the kinetic energy is converted into potential energy as the stone reaches its greatest height

(d) the potential energy changes back into kinetic energy as the stone falls

(e) the kinetic energy is converted into other forms of energy on impact with the ground (heat, sound, etc.) which are outside the scope of our work.

Potential energy gained $= \dfrac{100 \times 9.8 \times 30}{1000} = 29.4$ joules

$\therefore$ energy in catapult was 29.4 joules

and work done by boy was 29.4 joules.

2

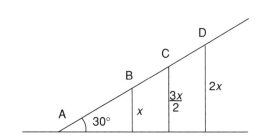

$$\begin{array}{ccccccc}
\text{Energy} = & \text{energy} & = & \text{energy} & & = & \text{energy} \\
\text{at A} & \text{at B} & & \text{at C} & & & \text{at D} \\
\frac{1}{2}mu^2 & = \frac{1}{2}mv_{\text{B}}^2 + mgx & = & \frac{1}{2}mv_{\text{C}}^2 + mg\frac{3}{2}x & & = & mg2x
\end{array}$$

3 Initial kinetic energy of ball = 136 joules (assuming catch on level with bat).

Ball is then brought to a standstill, i.e. it loses its energy.

It works against the resistance offered by the fielder's hands therefore the ball does 136 joules of work on the fielder.

4 At the end of the jump:

the cat has potential energy = $4 \times g \times \frac{3}{2} = 6g$ joules of KE

power = work done per second (rate of working)

$$= \frac{6g}{0.2}$$

$$= 30g \text{ watts}$$

► KE = kinetic energy

5 In moving, the trays A and B lost PE whilst C and D gained PE.

A lost as much PE as D gained.

B lost as much PE as C gained.

∴   net gain in energy of pile is zero.

∴   no work done.

► PE = potential energy

A simpler view
The centre of gravity of the whole stack is at the same height in both **(a)** and **(b)** therefore no work is done.
Now try and tell the breadman he hasn't done any work!

► Centre of mass, centre of gravity follows immediately.

Centre of mass, centre of gravity

At the end of the last activity we had a question in which we mentioned **centre of gravity**. It is now time to look at this in a little more detail.

Get the block.

Fix your ruler with an edge uppermost (trap it between two heavy books).

Balance the block across the ruler.

► Centre of gravity

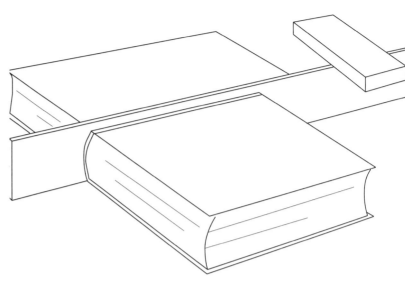

Why does it take so long to do this?
Why does the block keep falling off?

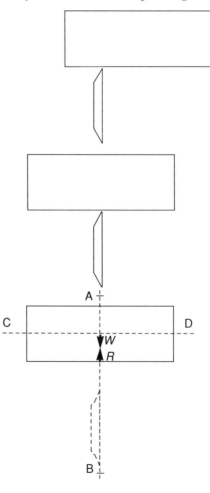

It falls off, because there is more of the block on the right-hand side than the left-hand side.

Now it balances. Why? There is the same amount of block on both sides.

If we draw the forces, we get this diagram where
W is the weight of the block
R is the reaction on the block by the ruler.

Since we have equilibrium: $R = W$
Where have we put the force, W?
It is shown opposing and in line with R – it has to be for equilibrium. Therefore the weight of the block acts along the line AB.

By a similar exercise (balancing the block on its end) you can see that the force *W* also acts along the line CD.

Hence the weight acts at the point where the lines meet.

This point is the **centre of mass** or **centre of gravity** of the block. For much of our work we consider the block to be replaced by a particle of the same mass as the block, situated at the centre of mass of the block.

Lay your ruler flat on the desk perpendicular to one edge. Side it slowly towards the edge:

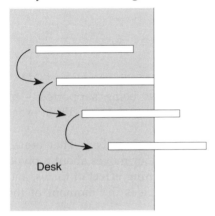

– falls off! Why?
Explain in terms of forces acting on the ruler.

Get the block.

Let it hang so that it is in equilibrium.

Why is it in equilibrium? Where is the centre of mass in relation to the string?

Using a strong piece of string, devise a simple experiment to find the centre of gravity of the chair you are sitting on (assuming it is an ordinary classroom or dining-type chair).

▶ Centre of gravity of chair!

Moments

Get the block.

Let it hang.

Now try to lift the block to the position shown, using one finger from the other hand.

▶ Moments – another basic theory step which we use countless times.

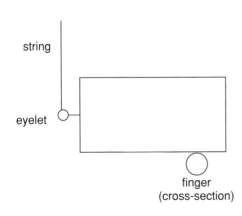

string

eyelet

finger
(cross-section)

Slide your finger from one end of the block to the other.

Do you notice a variation in the force you have to apply with your finger to keep the block in position?

Your block may be too light for you really to appreciate the effect. If so, repeat the performance with the set-up at the top of page 64.

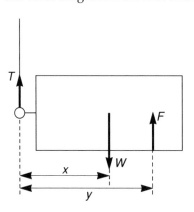

Now do you notice the variation?

For a further example of this effect close the door by pushing with one finger

- at the handle
- in the middle of the door
- 2 cm from the hinge.

In each of the cases described the mass being supported – or moved – is constant and yet varying forces are being felt in order to achieve the end result.

What is common to the types of motion described? They are all rotational; in each case the block, ruler, door moves about a pivot. In this work we are talking about the **turning effect** of forces, and the name for the turning effect of a force is the **moment** of the force.

▶ Moments

Let us return to the first situation described (the block on the string being supported by a finger).

If the block were to move, which point would it turn about? The eyelet.

The force diagram looks like this:

The force W has a turning effect about the eyelet given by $W \times x$ i.e. Wx.
F has turning effect given by Fy
For equilibrium $Fy = Wx$

▶ Clockwise and anti-clockwise

Turning effects are distinguished by being either clockwise or anti-clockwise with reference to the diagram we have drawn.

In this case Wx is a clockwise moment about the eyelet: it is trying to turn the block clockwise as we have drawn it. And Fy is an anticlockwise moment.

At the end of all this the important statement is:

▶ Moments defined

For equilibrium, clockwise moments equal anti-clockwise moments.

One final most important point on the distances involved: the distance must be the perpendicular distance from the line of action of the force to the point about which you are taking moments.

> **Units:**
> force × distance $\Rightarrow$ $M\,LT^{-2} \times L = ML^2T^{-2}$
> newtons × metres $\Rightarrow$ **newton metres**, Nm

▶ Units of moments

Considering the equation from above i.e. $Fy = Wx$ and remembering that Wx is constant, what type of graph would you expect if you plotted F against y?

Couples

▶ Couples

Get the block.

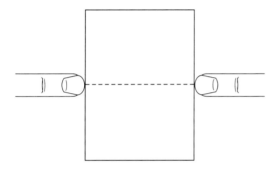

Push on opposite sides with the first finger of each hand. If you push harder with one finger than the other it will move. If you push equally the block is in equilibrium.

Now move your fingers so that you have:

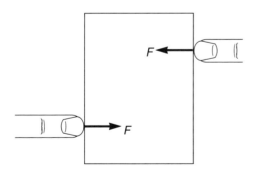

If you exert equal forces with each finger what happens?

The block does not move laterally but it turns or **rotates**.

An arrangement like this with equal, opposite, parallel (but not in line) forces is a **couple**.

▶ Couple

The effect of a couple we have seen: a turning effect.

► Moment of couple

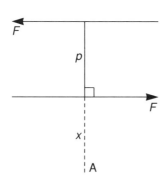

F, F are the forces
p is perpendicular distance
A is any point
Moments about A:
$F(p + x) - Fx = Fp$

► Every couple has its moment!

So the total moment about A is Fp – a result which is independent of where A is and this result Fp is the **moment of the couple**. It is a measure of the magnitude of the turning effect of the couple.

The direction of a couple obviously matters and the directions are defined as clockwise or anti-clockwise.

Consider this.

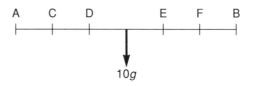

AB is a uniform rod of weight 10 g and length 6 cm smoothly hinged at A. What size of force is needed to maintain equilibrium?

30 at C   or 15 at D   or 10 at M   or $7\frac{1}{2}$ at E

or . . . or . . . in fact an infinite number of answers.

But they all have the same moment about A.

It is $10 \times 3 = 30$ and acts anti-clockwise.

Instead of a single force a couple could provide the same turning effect and it would be shown:

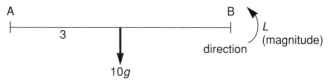

i.e. an anticlockwise couple of moment $L = 30$ is needed for equilibrium.

Now consider this.

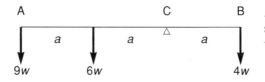

AB is a light rod on a support at C carrying weights as shown.

How can we find the magnitude and direction of the couple required to maintain equilibrium?

Moments about C: $9w \times 2a + 6w \times a - 4w \times a = 20wa$ anti-clockwise

∴   couple required is $L = 20wa$ clockwise.

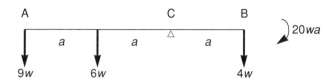

The rod is now in equilibrium.

Uniform bodies

The word 'uniform' is often used in mechanics. It means that the mass of a body is evenly distributed throughout it. The physics explanation is that the body has the same **density** throughout.

> ► Uniform bodies – constant density

A uniform beam has its centre of gravity at the middle of it; a uniform circular disc has its centre of gravity at the centre of the circle. 'Uniform' usually means that we can replace the mass of a body with a particle of the same mass at the geometric centre of the body in the case of rods, beams, circular discs. We make this statement with considerable hesitancy because although it is true and useful there are many exceptions, e.g. the centre of gravity of a uniform circular arc is not at the middle of the arc. Do not worry if this is causing some confusion at this stage. There is a later more detailed chapter on centre of gravity.

You should now have the idea of what is meant by 'uniform'.

(ACT) *Activity 1.11*

> ► Solutions on page 69

1

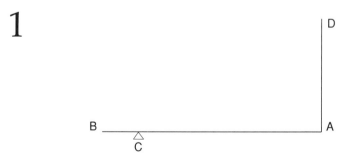

The diagram shows a uniform heavy beam AB of mass 50 kg and length 3 m.

It is supported by a wire AD (AB is horizontal and AD is vertical) and it rests on a support at C. Find the tension in the wire and the force on the beam at C. AC = 2.4 m.

2

C

60° ▷ B

A ⟋ 30°

AB is a uniform heavy beam of weight W and length 2*l*. It is smoothly pivoted at A and held in the position shown by a string BS.
Find the tension in the string.

3 A girl of mass 50 kg is on a seesaw at a distance of 10 feet from the pivot. At what distance must a man of mass 80 kg sit in order to make it balance?

4

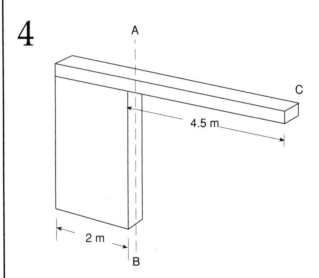

The diagram shows a lock gate on a canal. When it is opened the water extends up the gate for 1 m. If the resistance offered by the water were replaced by a single force at the middle of the area of contact what would be the value of this force if a man exerting a horizontal force of 625 newtons at C can just open the gate? The gate pivots about the line AB.

Explain why you do not need to know the weight of the gate (they are very heavy) to answer this question.

5 A uniform ladder of weight W is in limiting equilibrium with the upper end against a smooth wall and the lower end on a rough floor, coefficient of friction μ. If the ladder is inclined at θ to the wall, find the force of friction on the ladder and the normal reaction at the foot of the ladder. Also find μ in terms of θ.

Solutions to Activity 1.11

1

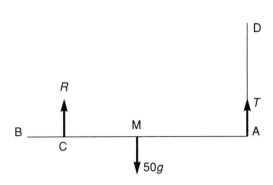

Which is the best point to take moments about?

Before deciding note:

moment = force × distance (make sure you have in mind the correct distance)

If distant is zero then moment is zero.

⇒ force has no moment about any point through which it acts.

▶ Uniform ⇒ CG at middle of beam M

▶ **Important**

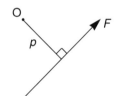

Moment of F about $O = Fp$.

If $p = 0$ we have

i.e. the conclusion reached above.

So, where do we take moments about?

▶ Considering the options

(a) About B ⇒ an equation involving R, T and $50g$
i.e. 2 unknowns, R and T.

(b) About C ⇒ an equation involving $50g$ and T
i.e. 1 unknown, solvable.

(c) About M ⇒ an equation involving R and T
i.e. 2 unknowns, R and T.

(d) About A ⇒ an equation involving R and $50g$
i.e. 1 unknown, solvable.

Of these **(b)** and **(d)** are most useful.

Hence: Moments about A ⇒ $R \times 2.4 = 50g \times 1.5$

⇒ $R = 50g \times \dfrac{1.5}{2.4}$

$= 306.25$ N

Resolving vertically for the beam: $T + R = 50g$

$$\therefore \quad T = 50g - R$$
$$= 50g - 306.25$$
$$= 183.75 \text{ N}$$

Further notes on the method

● Moments are taken about a point; not at a point, round a point, through a point etc. The word 'about' is the correct one to use.

● You could have answered the question by using either of equations **(a)** and **(c)**, together with the equation for resolving vertically and solving simultaneously! Think of the algebra involved. You are going to be concerned very much with finding the most efficient way to solve problems: you have just done an easy example.

▶ Uniform ⇒ CG at middle of beam, M

2

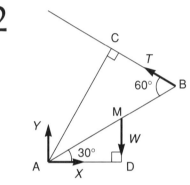

There is a force acting on AB at A; but in which direction?

You don't know. But whatever the direction in can be expressed in components X and Y as shown.

Now to form some equation (useful we hope!).

T wanted, W known therefore take moments about A for beam AB.

This will avoid any forces at A; so we didn't need to worry about the force there after all.

Moments about A:
$$T \times \text{AC} = W \times \text{AD}$$
$$T \times \text{AB}\sin60° = W \times \text{AM}\cos30°$$
$$T \times 2l \times \sqrt{\frac{3}{2}} = W \times l \times \sqrt{\frac{3}{2}}$$
$$T = \frac{W}{2}$$

You can see that in the end the equation and the algebra were easy: the hard part lies in deciding what to do in the first instance.

A variation on the same question

Resolving the forces T and W along and perpendicular to the beam gives the diagram shown at the top of page 71.

The components $W\cos60°$ and $T\cos60°$ have no moment about A.

Hence, taking moments about A:
$$W\cos30° \times l = T\cos30° \times 2l$$
$$T = \frac{W}{2}$$

▶ We have used two variations to answer this question: in the first we took the whole force and multiplied by appropriate distances worked out from the geometry of the diagram; in the second we used components of forces and multiplied by distances already known.

Always be prepared to consider these two variations: resolve the forces or resolve the distances.

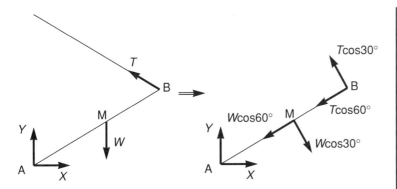

Again easy algebra following the main problem of sorting out the forces.

In this case one method is as good as the other but that will not always be so and you will have to be able to use either approach.

3

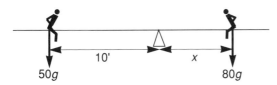

For balance moments about the pivot must be equal.

$50g \times 10 = 80g \times X$

$\Rightarrow \quad X = \dfrac{50 \times 10}{80} = 6.25 \text{ ft}$

► **Note** – mixing of metric and Imperial units, kg and feet. Justify for yourself why it does not matter in this case.

4

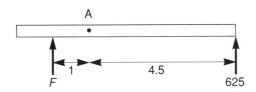

Taking moments about the pivot AB

$F \times 1 = 625 \times 4\frac{1}{2}$

$\Rightarrow \quad F = 2812.5 \text{ N}$

The weight of the gate is not needed because it is a vertical force and we are concerned here with horizontal forces.

In practice the weight is important because it plays a large part in the degree of friction at the pivot.

5

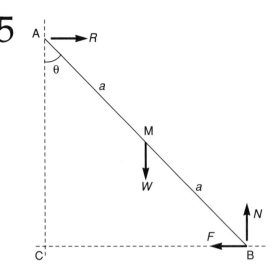

To find: F, N and μ

N: no problem

Resolving vertically: $N = W$

Resolving horizontally: $F = R$

not enough, another equation needed.

$\therefore$ consider moments.

About A: $\Rightarrow$ equation in F, N, W

About B: $\Rightarrow$ equation in R, W and we know $R = F$

About M: $\Rightarrow$ equation in R, F, N

Therefore taking moments about B for the ladder:

$$R \times 2a\cos\theta = W \times a\sin\theta \quad \Rightarrow \quad F = \frac{W}{2}\tan\theta$$

In limiting equilibrium $\quad \therefore \quad \mu = \frac{F}{N} = \frac{W}{2} \times \frac{\tan\theta}{W} = \frac{1}{2}\tan\theta$

Vectors

▶ Take the work on vectors slowly and carefully. Many students come unstuck on them: given time and thought, **you** won't!

Earlier in the chapter we considered various quantities and defined them as either vector or scalar. Now we are going to look at vector quantities in a bit more detail. Since we are going to quantify them a basic framework of axes is necessary.

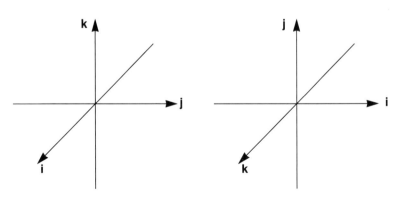

▶ Right-handed axes: a right-hand screw going positively along:
i would turn $j \rightarrow k$
j would turn $k \rightarrow i$
k would turn $i \rightarrow j$

The diagrams show two sets of right-handed axes representing three dimensions.

The unit vector in each of the directions is **i**, **j** or **k** and any other vector can be expressed in terms of these; e.g. a velocity made up of components 2 m s⁻¹ in the **i** direction, 5 m s⁻¹ in the **j** direction and 3 m s⁻¹ in the **k** direction would be written as

$$\mathbf{v} = 2\mathbf{i} + \mathbf{j} + 3\mathbf{k}$$

or $\mathbf{v} = \begin{pmatrix} 2 \\ 5 \\ 3 \end{pmatrix}$

which is the preferred form when it comes to working out problems.

The magnitude of this velocity is the speed, and this is given by

$$v = \sqrt{2^2 + 5^2 + 3^2}$$
$$= 38 \text{ m s}^{-1}$$

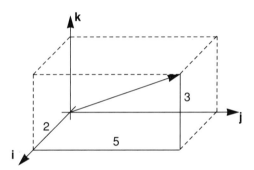

This diagram shows the vector $\begin{pmatrix} 2 \\ 5 \\ 3 \end{pmatrix}$ on a set of axes.

It can be seen that it is the diagonal of a cuboid and by applying Pythagoras' theorem:

$$\text{magnitude} = \sqrt{2^2 + 5^2 + 3^2}$$

All the vector quantities we have met so far can be expressed in **i**, **j**, **k** form: very often we are concerned with events all in one plane and then the **k** component is the one usually left out.

If distance is expressed in terms of time then the usual link with velocity and acceleration through calculus is used. This rather formal sentence simply means:

▶ Calculus and vectors

If $\mathbf{s} = t^3\mathbf{i} - 3t^2\mathbf{j} + 5\mathbf{k}$ or $\begin{pmatrix} t^3 \\ -3t^2 \\ 5 \end{pmatrix}$

then $\mathbf{v} = 3t^2\mathbf{i} - 6t\mathbf{j}$ or $\begin{pmatrix} 3t^2 \\ -6t \\ 0 \end{pmatrix}$ because $v = \dfrac{ds}{dt}$

and $\mathbf{a} = 6t\mathbf{i} - 6\mathbf{j}$ or $\begin{pmatrix} 6t \\ -6 \\ 0 \end{pmatrix}$ because $a = \dfrac{dv}{dt}$

► Solutions on this page

(ACT) *Activity 1.12*

1 $\mathbf{F}_1 = \begin{pmatrix} 3 \\ -1 \end{pmatrix}$ $\mathbf{F}_2 = \begin{pmatrix} 4 \\ 2 \end{pmatrix}$ $\mathbf{F}_3 = \begin{pmatrix} -2 \\ 7 \end{pmatrix}$

Find **(a)** $\mathbf{F}_1 + \mathbf{F}_2$ **(b)** $2\mathbf{F}_3 - \mathbf{F}_1$

2 $\mathbf{v} = \begin{pmatrix} t \\ 3 \end{pmatrix}$ Find **s** if $\mathbf{s} = \begin{pmatrix} 1 \\ 2 \end{pmatrix}$ initially.

3 What is the direction of the acceleration in question 2?

► The subject of vectors is endless and here you have the introductory bit.

4 If $\mathbf{s} = t^2\mathbf{i} + (2 - t)\mathbf{j}$ in what direction is the motion after 2 seconds?

5 A force F acts in the direction joining the point $(1, -2, 2)$ to the point $(5, 6, -4)$. Express F in vector form.

6 A particle starts from O and has velocity $\begin{pmatrix} 1 \\ 2 \\ 3 \end{pmatrix}$ after 3 seconds.

► Vectors are of considerable practical value throughout physics and engineering.

If the acceleration is $\begin{pmatrix} 2 \\ 2 \\ 0 \end{pmatrix}$ find the vector form of the distance after t seconds.

Solutions to Activity 1.12

1 When vectors are expressed in just two components like these it is the **k** component which is missing.

(a) $\mathbf{F}_1 + \mathbf{F}_2 = \begin{pmatrix} 3 \\ -1 \end{pmatrix} + \begin{pmatrix} 4 \\ 2 \end{pmatrix} = \begin{pmatrix} 7 \\ 1 \end{pmatrix}$

(b) $2\mathbf{F}_3 - \mathbf{F}_1 = 2\begin{pmatrix} -2 \\ 7 \end{pmatrix} - \begin{pmatrix} 3 \\ -1 \end{pmatrix} = \begin{pmatrix} -7 \\ 15 \end{pmatrix}$

2 $\mathbf{v} = \begin{pmatrix} t \\ 3 \end{pmatrix}$ $\therefore$ $\mathbf{s} = \begin{pmatrix} \frac{1}{2}t^2 + A \\ 3t + B \end{pmatrix}$

Initially $t = 0$ $\Rightarrow$ $A = 1, B = 2$

$\therefore$ $\mathbf{s} = \begin{pmatrix} \frac{1}{2}t^2 + 1 \\ 3t + 2 \end{pmatrix}$

3 $\mathbf{v} = \begin{pmatrix} t \\ 3 \end{pmatrix}$ $\therefore$ $\mathbf{a} = \begin{pmatrix} 1 \\ 0 \end{pmatrix}$

Therefore direction of acceleration is in direction of **i**-axis.

4 $\mathbf{s} = t^2\mathbf{i} + (2 - t)\mathbf{j}$

$\therefore$ $\mathbf{v} = 2t\mathbf{i} + -\mathbf{j}$ and, as we have seen before, it is velocity
                              which gives direction of travel.

When $t = 2$ $\mathbf{v} = 2\mathbf{i} - \mathbf{j}$

$\therefore$ direction is $\tan^{-1}(-\frac{1}{2})$ with the $\mathbf{i}$-axis.

i.e.

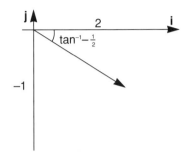

5   The vector joining the points is

$$\begin{pmatrix} 1-5 \\ -2-6 \\ 2--4 \end{pmatrix} \qquad = \begin{pmatrix} -4 \\ -8 \\ 6 \end{pmatrix} \qquad = 2\begin{pmatrix} -2 \\ -4 \\ 3 \end{pmatrix}$$

And it is the vector $\begin{pmatrix} -2 \\ -4 \\ 3 \end{pmatrix}$ which defines the direction.

However it would be wrong to say $\mathbf{F} = \begin{pmatrix} -2 \\ -4 \\ 3 \end{pmatrix}$

because that says the magnitude of $\mathbf{F}$ is $\sqrt{2^2 + 4^2 + 3^2} = \sqrt{29}$.
We do not know the magnitude of $\mathbf{F}$ so all we can say is

$\mathbf{F} = \lambda \begin{pmatrix} -2 \\ -4 \\ 3 \end{pmatrix}$

where λ is a constant.

6 $\mathbf{a} - \begin{pmatrix} 2 \\ 0 \\ 1 \end{pmatrix}$ $\therefore$ $\mathbf{v} = \begin{pmatrix} 2t + A \\ B \\ t + C \end{pmatrix}$

When $t = 3$ $\mathbf{v} = \begin{pmatrix} 1 \\ 2 \\ 3 \end{pmatrix}$ $\Rightarrow$ $A = -5, B = 2, C = 0$

$\mathbf{v} = \begin{pmatrix} 2t - 5 \\ 2 \\ t \end{pmatrix}$

$$\mathbf{s} = \begin{pmatrix} t^2 - 5t + D \\ 2t + E \\ \frac{1}{2}t^2 + F \end{pmatrix}$$

When $t = 0$ $\mathbf{s} = \begin{pmatrix} 0 \\ 0 \\ 0 \end{pmatrix}$ $\Rightarrow$ $D = E = F = 0$ and

$$\mathbf{s} = \begin{pmatrix} t^2 - 5t \\ 2t \\ \frac{1}{2}t^2 \end{pmatrix}$$

Chapter summary

We have now come to the end of the first chapter.

This has been a long chapter in which you have been introduced to most of the fundamental laws and principles which you need for this course. The majority of problems in mechanics involve two or three of these principles and I have mentioned them all in this first chapter so that we can more efficiently proceed to the usual mechanics problems rather than confining our work to problems based on one principle only.

It may all seem a little confusing now and so before continuing you should work through worksheets 1–6 to consolidate the work covered and prepare yourself for what follows.

Study the plan of the course (on page viii) which illustrates a recommended – but by no means essential – order of working through the book. You could now proceed to any chapter of the book, but in terms of maintaining interest and increasing difficulty the numerical order of the chapters is the preferred way.

Worksheet 1

▶ Solutions on page 87

1 Find the resultant of forces 12 N, 6 N, 2 N and 7 N acting on a particle in directions 12 o'clock, 4 o'clock, 6 o'clock and 9 o'clock.

2 A hammer of mass 2 kg falls from the top of a building of height 15 m. Find its speed and its kinetic energy when it hits the floor.

3 A mass of 10 kg is accelerating at 2 m s^{-2} up a smooth plane inclined at 40° to the horizontal. If the force acting on the mass is parallel to the plane find its magnitude.

4

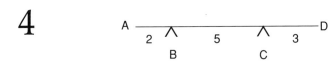

The diagram shows a heavy uniform beam of mass 30 kg resting on two supports B and C. A boy of mass 50 kg walks along the beam in the direction BA. Where is he when equilibrium is broken? (All lengths in m)

5 If $u = 0$, and $v = 6$ after 2 seconds find s after 5 seconds.

6 Find a and b if $2\begin{pmatrix} a \\ 6 \end{pmatrix} - 3\begin{pmatrix} -2 \\ b \end{pmatrix} = \begin{pmatrix} -2 \\ -9 \end{pmatrix}$

7

ACB is a rigid framework hinged at A and with AB horizontal. It has mass m per unit length.
   Find the magnitude and sense of the couple required to maintain equilibrium.

8 A ring is threaded on a smooth circular wire set in a vertical plane. Find, in terms of r, the radius of the wire, the speed of the ring when it is 30° below the horizontal.

9 A mass M is on a rough horizontal table, and is attached by a piece of string passing over a smooth pulley at the edge of the table to a mass m which is hanging vertically. Find the coefficient of friction in terms of m and M if the mass M is about to move.

10

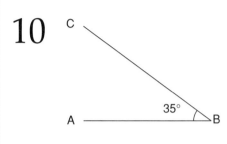

AB is a uniform beam of length 2 m and weight W, smoothly hinged at A. It is held horizontally by a string BC attached to a hook at C.

Find the force exerted on the hook by the string in terms of W.

► Solutions on page 90

Worksheet 2

1 A string passes over a smooth fixed pulley and carries at its ends massed of $4m$ and $7m$. Find the acceleration of the system and the distance either mass travels from rest in 3 seconds.

2

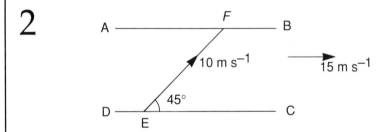

ABCD is a railway carriage travelling in the direction shown at 15 m s^{-1}, EF is the path of a marble which rolls at 10 m s^{-1} relative to the carriage and at an angle of 45° with the side of the carriage. Find the velocity of the marble relative to the track.

3 Find the resultant of forces represented by $2\mathbf{i} + 7\mathbf{j}$, $-5\mathbf{i} + 3\mathbf{j}$, $4\mathbf{i} - 9\mathbf{j}$ and $3\mathbf{i} + 2\mathbf{j}$. Also, find the magnitude of the resultant and its direction as an angle made with the i-axis.

4 A car accelerates uniformly from rest to a speed of 20 m s^{-1} in 30 seconds; it continues at constant speed for 90 seconds; and finally it slows down uniformly to stop in 10 seconds.

Show this information on a velocity–time graph. State the acceleration and retardation and find the distance travelled.

5

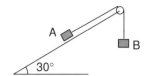

A is a mass of weight W on a rough sloping plane. It is attached by a string passing over a smooth pulley to a mass B, weight w, hanging freely. If A is about to move up the plane show that

$$\mu = \frac{2w - W}{w\sqrt{3}}.$$

6

The diagram shows a dog pulling on its lead which is 1 m long. The dog's collar is 0.4 m above the ground and the owner's hand is 0.9 m above the ground. If the dog exerts a forward force of 200 N on its collar find the magnitude and direction of the force exerted on the lead by the hand.

7 A ball of mass 0.1 kg falls 5 m vertically and rebounds to a height of 3 m. Find the ratio of its speeds before and after impact.

8

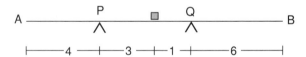

AB is a light rod carrying a mass M at C and resting on supports at P and Q. The maximum weight which can be placed at A is W and at B it is w, in each case maintaining equilibrium.

Find the ratio $\frac{W}{w}$.

9 A constant force P drives a car through a distance d from rest against a constant force R in t seconds.

Show that $2Md = (P - R)t^2$ where M is the mass of the car.

10 A small model engine drives at 30 km/h when the power of the engine is 7080 watts. Find the driving force.

▶ Solutions on page 92

Worksheet 3

1 A mass of $5m$, on a smooth plane inclined at α to the horizontal, is attached by a string passing over a smooth pulley at the top of the plane to a mass of $2m$ hanging freely. Find α if the system is in equilibrium.

2 Forces of 3 N, 4 N, 1 N and 7 N act in order round the sides of a square. Find the magnitude of the resultant and express its direction as an angle made with the force of 7 N.

3 A ball is projected vertically upwards with velocity $2u$.

At time $\dfrac{2u}{g}$ later a second ball is projected with velocity $3u$.

Find when and where the balls meet.

4

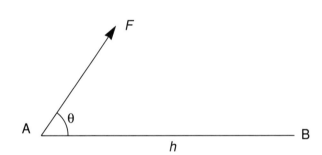

Show that the force through A can be replaced by an equal force through B together with a couple. Find the moment of the couple in terms of h and θ.

▶ This one is tricky!

5

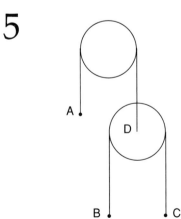

A string passes over the fixed smooth pulley E and carries at its ends a mass A, $12m$, and a light pulley D. Over D a string carries masses B, $6m$, and C, $8m$. Find the tension in each string and which masses rise and which fall.

6

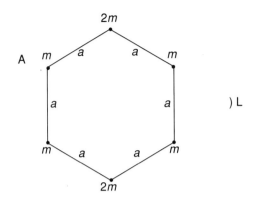

A light hexagonal frame carries masses at its vertices as shown. The hexagon is regular and it is arranged in a vertical plane, hinged at A and supported by a couple L. Find the magnitude and sense of L.

7 A mass of weight W is on a rough inclined plane, angle of inclination α. A force P parallel to the plane just prevents the mass from slipping down and a force Q parallel to the plane is just about to move the mass up the plane. Find the mean of P and Q in terms of W and α.

8 Find the equilibrant of forces of 15 NE, 10 NW, 8 S, 12 E and 4 N (all measured in newtons).

9 A body is sliding down a smooth slope inclined at 40° to the horizontal. Find the time taken for the velocity to increase from 3 m s^{-1} to 12 m s^{-1}.

10

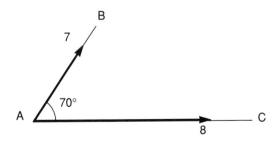

Find the resultant of the vectors **AB** and **AC** and relate it to the geometry of the parallelogram of which AB and AC are adjacent sides.

► Solutions on page 96

Worksheet 4

1 A is a mass M on a smooth sloping plane. B has mass m. A and B are connected by a light string passing over a smooth pulley. The masses are released from rest. Find the acceleration of B in terms of M, m and g. Find M in terms of m if A does not move.

2 $\mathbf{v} = \begin{pmatrix} 2t \\ 3 \\ 0 \end{pmatrix}$ Find an expression for $\mathbf{s}$ if $\mathbf{s} = \begin{pmatrix} 2 \\ 1 \\ 2 \end{pmatrix}$ when $t = 0$.

3 A car weighs one ton and its weight is evenly distributed between its four wheels. A man wishes to lift one wheel of the car by using a big lever.

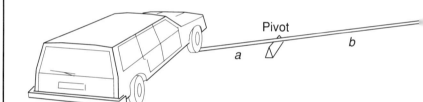

► Be careful: this last bit is a bit dodgy!

The maximum downward force he can exert is his own weight of 10 stones. Find the ratio $a : b$ for equilibrium (1 ton = 80 stones). Since the man wishes to lift the car, should the ratio be reduced or increased?

4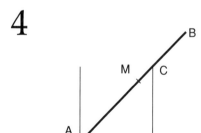
A uniform heavy rod rests in a cubical box as shown. All contacts are smooth. AM = 2, MC = CB = 1.

Find the horizontal and vertical conponents of the force exerted by the box on the rod at A, in terms of W, the weight of the rod.

5 A boat sails at 5 knots relative to the water. The boat aims due N but the water is running at 3 knots SE. Find the direction and speed of the boat.

6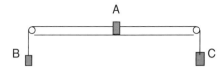

A is a mass of 5*m* attached by smooth strings to masses B, 2*m*, and C, 6*m*, which hang vertically.

The coefficient of friction between A and the table is 0.4. Find the tension in each string and the acceleration of A.

7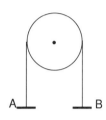

A and B are two pans, each of mass *m*, attached to a string passing over a smooth pulley. A carries a mass of 2*m* and B a mass of 4*m*. The system is moving at 12 m s^{-1} when the mass of 4*m* drops off B. How long is it before the system stops?

8 A particle is moving with constant acceleration such that when $t = 1$, $v = 5$ and when $t = 2$, $v = 1$. Given that when $t = 0$, $s = 0$ find the time(s) when the particle is 6 m from the start. All units in m, s and m s^{-1}.

9 A force of 8 N acts at (5, 3) in a direction 30° with the *x*-axis.

A force of 10 N acts at (–2, 4) in a direction 120° with the *x*-axis.

A force of 13 N acts at (1, –3) in a direction 240° with the *x*-axis.

Find the sum of their moments about the origin.

10 A parachutist descends at constant speed for 500 m. Find the work done by the resistance to the motion if the man weighs 75 kg. Assume $g = 10$ m s^{-2}.

Worksheet 5

► Solutions on page 99

1 A car has acceleration *f* and initial velocity *u*. A second car has acceleration $\frac{2}{3}f$ and initial velocity 2*u*. If they pass the same point simultaneously with the given initial velocities, when and where will the first one overtake the second? Give your answers in terms of *u* and *f*.

2 A heavy uniform door has width *x*. Find the force needed at the handle to push the door if the hinges offer a resisting couple of moment *L*.

3

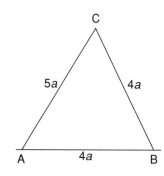

The diagram shows a heavy smooth beam AC, uniform and of length 5*a*, hinged at A and resting against a light supporting prop BC, length 4*a*. The length AB = 4*a*. Find the force exerted by the prop on the beam in terms of *W*, the weight of the beam.

4

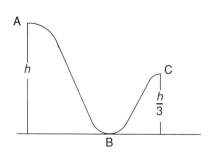

ABC is a roller coaster track. A car passes A with velocity *u*. Show that the velocity at C is $\frac{1}{3}\sqrt{5u^2 + 4gh}$, given that from A to B one sixth of the energy is lost overcoming resistances, and from B to C one third of the energy is lost overcoming resistances.

5

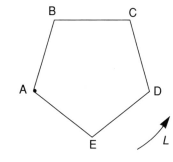

ABCDE is a light rigid regular pentagon in a vertical plane smoothly hinged at A with CD vertical. A mass *m* is placed at each vertex. The length of each side is *a*. An anti-clockwise couple of moment *L* is applied. Taking *g* as 9.81 m s^{-2} show that L = 42*ma*.

6

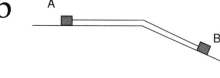

A is a mass of weight 2*W* on a rough horizontal surface. It is connected by a light smooth string to a mass B of weight *W* on a smooth plane inclined at 30° to the horizontal. The system is in equilibrium. Find the minimum value of μ, the coefficient of friction at A.

7 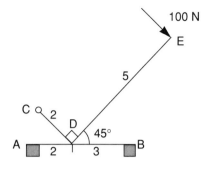 The diagram shows the cross-section of a plate AB held under pressure against a frame, shown shaded. It is held in place by a force of 100 N applied as shown to the arm CDE in which C is a smooth hinge and D is a smooth contact. Find the forces exerted by AB on the frame at A and B.

8 Two forces act on a point A and their lines of action include an angle of 60°. Their resultant is 15 N and one of the forces is 10 N. Find the other force.

9 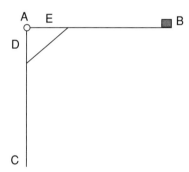 The diagram shows a uniform smooth beam AB of weight W carrying a mass of weight $2W$ at B. It is smoothly hinged to a fixed vertical pole AC and it rests at E on a fixed support DE. AE = AD and AB = 4AE. Find the force exerted on AB by the hinge.

10 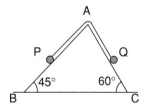 AB and AC are two fixed smooth planes sloping at the angles shown. P and Q are two equal masses connected by a light string passing over a smooth pulley at A. The system is released from rest. Find the speeds of P and Q after they have travelled 50 cm.

Worksheet 6

► Solutions on page 102

1 A rod leans against a rough wall and stands on rough level ground. The coefficient of friction at both contacts is $\frac{1}{2}$ and the rod makes an angle θ with the wall. Find the force of friction and the normal reaction at both contacts if equilibrium is limiting. The rod is uniform and of weight W.

2 Find the equilibrant of

$2(3\mathbf{i} + 4\mathbf{j}) - 3(-\mathbf{i} + 3\mathbf{j}) + (5\mathbf{i} - \mathbf{j}) - 2(4\mathbf{i} + 3\mathbf{j})$

3 A particle slows down uniformly from 30 m s⁻¹ to 20 m s⁻¹ in 5 seconds. It then continues for a time at constant speed after which it slows down uniformly to rest in 10 seconds. If the total distance travelled while slowing down is equal to the distance travelled at constant speed, find the total time of the journey.

4 A wire is in the form of a vertical circle of radius r. A smooth ring is threaded on it and it is at rest at the top. It is then gently displaced. Find the velocity of the ring when its potential energy is one quarter of its total energy. (Take the bottom of the wire as the level of zero potential energy.) Give your answer in terms of r and g.

5

P ————•——•——•——•——•——•———Q
     A B C D E F

A light rod PQ is 3.5 m long. Masses 1, 2, 3, 4, 5 and 6 kg are placed at A, B, C, D, E and F respectively where PA = AB = BC = CD = DE = EF = $\frac{1}{2}$ m. The whole system rests on two supports which exert equal forces on the rod. One support is at F, where is the other?

6

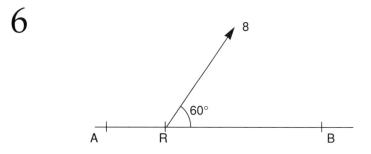

AB is a straight smooth wire and R is a ring threaded on it. The ring is moved from A to B by a force of 8 N acting at 60° to the wire. AB = 10 m. Find

(a) the work done on the ring by the force of 8 N

(b) the work done on the ring by the wire.

7 A football is travelling at 6 m s⁻¹. After 1 second it is given a kick in a direction perpendicular to its path. The kick would give a velocity of 8 m s⁻¹ to a still ball. The ball then travels for a further second. Find how far it then is from its starting point.

8 A particle is projected vertically upwards with velocity u and it returns to its starting point. Find where it is after one third of its total time.

9

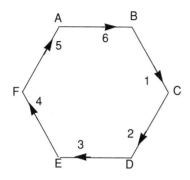

ABCDEF is a regular hexagon. Forces act along the sides as shown. Find the magnitude of the resultant and its direction as an angle made with AB.

10 The acceleration vector for a particle is

$$\mathbf{a} = \begin{pmatrix} t \\ 0 \\ 4 \end{pmatrix}$$

Find the distance vector given that when $t = 0$

$$\mathbf{v} = \begin{pmatrix} 0 \\ 2 \\ 1 \end{pmatrix} \text{ and } \mathbf{x} = \begin{pmatrix} 0 \\ 0 \\ 0 \end{pmatrix}$$

Solutions to Worksheet 1

1

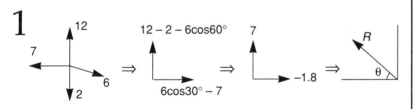

where $R = \sqrt{7^2 + 1.8^2} = 7.2$ N

and $\theta = \tan^{-1} \dfrac{7}{1.8} = 75.6°$ (11.30 approx)

▶ Resultant

2 Use v, s equation: $v^2 = u^2 + 2as$

$\Rightarrow \quad v^2 = 0^2 + 2 \times g \times 15 \quad \Rightarrow \quad v = 17.2$ m s^{-1}

$\text{KE} = \dfrac{1}{2} \times 2 \times 17.2^2 = 296$ J

▶ Uniform acceleration

3

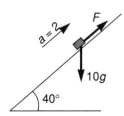

Using NL2 for mass:

$F - 10g\cos50° = 10 \times 2$

$\therefore \quad F = 20 + 63 = 83$ N

▶ NL2

► This avoids the need to find *P*.

4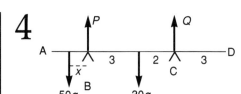

Equilibrium is broken when $Q = 0$.

Taking moments about B for the whole system:

$$50g \times x = 30g \times 3$$

$$\Rightarrow \quad x = 1.8 \text{ m}$$

► Uniform acceleration

5 To find s given $t \quad \Rightarrow \quad s = ut + \frac{1}{2}at^2$

We don't know a,

hence use the v, t equation $\quad \Rightarrow \quad v = u + at$ to find a

$$6 = 0 + a \times 2 \quad \Rightarrow \quad a = 3 \text{ m s}^{-2}$$

Now $\quad s = ut + \frac{1}{2}at^2 \quad \Rightarrow \quad s = 0 \times t + \frac{1}{2} \times 3 \times 5^2 = 37.5 \text{ m}$

► Vectors

6 $2\begin{pmatrix} a \\ 6 \end{pmatrix} - 3\begin{pmatrix} -2 \\ b \end{pmatrix} = \begin{pmatrix} 2a - 12 \\ 12 - 3b \end{pmatrix} = \begin{pmatrix} -2 \\ -9 \end{pmatrix}$

i.e. $\quad 2a - 12 = -2 \Rightarrow a = 5$

and $\quad 12 - 3b = -9 \Rightarrow b = -5$

7

► Couples

Taking moments about A for the whole system:

$$L = 4mga \times 2a\cos\theta + 3mga(4a\cos\theta + \frac{3a}{2}\sin\theta)$$

► Resolving the distances rather than the forces

$\qquad\qquad\quad$ AD $\qquad\qquad$ (AE $\;+\;$ EF)

This is a 3, 4, 5, triangle.

$\therefore \quad \cos\theta = \frac{4}{5}$ and $\sin\theta = \frac{3}{5}$

$\Rightarrow \quad L = \frac{187}{10} mga^2$ in the sense shown on the diagram.

8 The ring falls from A to B.

The system is free of constraints.
∴ conservation of energy

$\Rightarrow \quad \frac{1}{2}mv^2 = mg \times \text{AOC}$

$\Rightarrow \quad v^2 = 2g(r + r\sin30°)$

$\therefore \quad v = \sqrt{3gr}$

► COE

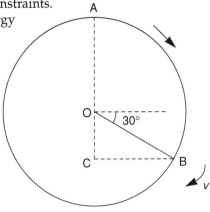

9

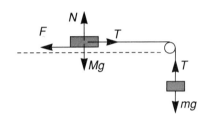

The block is about to move   ∴ $F = \mu N$
But, resolving vertically for M ⇒ $N = Mg$
and horizontally for m ⇒ $T = mg$ ⎫
and horizontally for M ⇒ $T = F$ ⎭ ⇒ $F = mg$

$\Rightarrow \quad mg = \mu Mg \quad \Rightarrow \quad \mu = \dfrac{m}{M}$

10

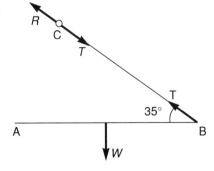

Force exerted on the hook is T.

Force exerted on the string by the hook is R ($R = T$)

∴ we need to find T.

► Tension

► Moments

► Resolving

► Eliminates need to know any forces at A.

► $T\sin35°$ is the vertical component of T at B.

Taking moments about A for AB: $T\sin35° \times 2 = W \times 1$

$\therefore \quad T = \dfrac{W}{2\sin35°} = 0.87W$

Solutions to Worksheet 2

▶ NL2

1

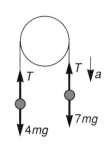

Using NL2 for $7m$: $7mg - T = 7ma$

Using NL2 for $4m$: $T - 4mg = 4ma$

$\Rightarrow$ $3mg = 11ma$ $\Rightarrow$ $a = \dfrac{3}{11} g$ m s^{-2}

Using the s, t equation:

$\Rightarrow$ $s = ut + \tfrac{1}{2}at^2$

$\Rightarrow$ $s = \dfrac{1}{2} \times \dfrac{3}{11} g \times 3^2 = \dfrac{27g}{22}$ m

▶ Resultant velocity

2

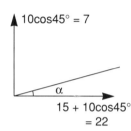

$10\cos45° = 7$

$15 + 10\cos45°$
$= 22$

Components of the velocity of the marble are as shown.

Speed of the marble
$= (7.1^2 + 22.1^2)^{\frac{1}{2}}$
$= 23.3$ m s^{-1} in a direction α to the track

where $\alpha = \arctan \dfrac{7.1}{22.1} = 17.8°$

3

$\mathbf{R} = 4\mathbf{i} + 3\mathbf{j}$

$|\mathbf{R}| = \sqrt{4^2 + 3^3} = 5$

at angle $\alpha = \tan^{-1} \dfrac{3}{4} = 36.9°$ with the $\mathbf{i}$-axis.

▶ Acceleration from slope

4

Acceleration $= \dfrac{20}{30} = \dfrac{2}{3}$ m s^{-2} Retardation $= \dfrac{20}{10} = 2$ m s^{-2}

The distance travelled is the area under the graph.

$x = \dfrac{1}{2} \times 30 \times 20 + 90 \times 20 + \dfrac{1}{2} \times 10 \times 20 = 2200$ m.

▶ The retardation could also be quoted as acceleration of -2ms^{-2}.

▶ Distance from area under graph

▶ Limiting equilibrium

5

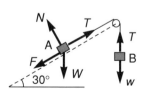

The system is about to move
$\Rightarrow$ limiting equilibrium
$\Rightarrow$ $F = \mu N$ **(1)**

Resolving $//$ plane for A:
$\Rightarrow$ $T = F + W\cos60° = F + \dfrac{W}{2}$ **(2)**

Resolving $\perp$ plane for A:
$\Rightarrow$ $N = W\cos30° = \dfrac{W\sqrt{3}}{2}$ **(3)**

Resolving vertically for B: $\Rightarrow$ $T = W$ (4)

Substituting from (4) and (1) in (2) $\Rightarrow$ $w = \mu N + \dfrac{W}{2}$

$\Rightarrow$ $w = \mu W \dfrac{\sqrt{3}}{2} + \dfrac{W}{2}$ $\Rightarrow$ $\mu = \dfrac{2w - W}{W\sqrt{3}}$

6

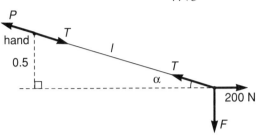

▶ Tension

▶ 30° since, from dimensions on the diagram $\alpha = 30°$

P is the force exerted by the hand on the lead.

For the hand: $P = T$

Resolving horizontally for the collar: $T\cos 30° = 200$

$\therefore$ $P = \dfrac{200 \times 2}{\sqrt{3}} = 230.9$ N.

▶ **NB:**   The downward force F appears on the diagram because T is the equilivant of the forces exerted by the dog on its collar.
   The value of F is not required in this solution.

7

Conservation of energy applied when the ball is falling:

$\Rightarrow$ $5mg = \dfrac{1}{2}mv_1^2$ $\Rightarrow$ $v_1^2 = 10g$

Conservation of energy applied when the ball is rising:

$\Rightarrow$ $\dfrac{1}{2}mv_2^2 = 3mg$ $\Rightarrow$ $v_2^2 = 6g$

$\dfrac{v^1}{v^2} = \sqrt{\dfrac{10}{6}} = 1.3$

▶ COE

8

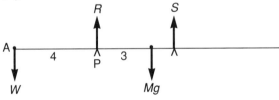

▶ Moments

With W at A equilibrium is about to be broken $\therefore$ $S = 0$

Taking moments about P $\Rightarrow$ $W \times 4 = Mg \times 3$ $\therefore$ $W = \dfrac{3Mg}{4}$

▶ About P $\because$ avoids using R

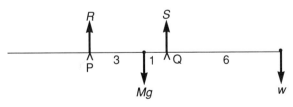

With w at B equilibrium is about to be broken $\therefore$ $R = 0$

Taking moments about Q $\Rightarrow$ $w \times 6 = Mg \times 1$ $\therefore$ $w = \dfrac{Mg}{6}$

▶ About Q $\because$ avoids using S

$\Rightarrow$ $\dfrac{W}{w} = \dfrac{3Mg}{4} \times \dfrac{6}{Mg} = \dfrac{9}{2}$

9

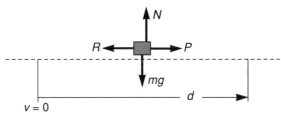

► NL2

Applying NL2 for the car: $P - R = Ma \Rightarrow a = \dfrac{P - R}{M}$

which is constant.

► Uniform acceleration

Using the s, t equation $\Rightarrow s = ut + \dfrac{1}{2}at^2$

► A result which seemed initially impossible from simple working – often the case.

$\Rightarrow d = \dfrac{1}{2} \times \dfrac{P - R}{M} \times t^2 \Rightarrow 2Md = (P - R)t^2$

10

► Power

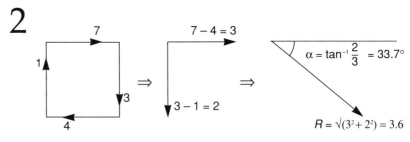

Power = force × velocity

$\therefore 7080 = F \times \dfrac{30 \times 1000}{60 \times 60}$

$\Rightarrow F = 850 \text{ N} (849.6)$

Solutions to Worksheet 3

1

The system is in equilibrium.

► Resolving

$\therefore$ resolving // plane:

$T = 5mg\sin\alpha$

and resolving vertically for B: $T = 2mg$

► **Remember:** arcsin means the same as $\sin^{-1}$ – you must know both terms.

$\Rightarrow 2mg = 5mg\sin\alpha$

$\alpha = \arcsin 0.4 = 23.6°$

► Resultant

2

$\alpha = \tan^{-1}\dfrac{2}{3} = 33.7°$

$7 - 4 = 3$

$3 - 1 = 2$

$R = \sqrt{(3^2 + 2^2)} = 3.6$

No words needed!

► Vertical motion under gravity

3

One idea is to find out where the first ball is after time $\dfrac{2u}{g}$.

► Uniform acceleration

$v = u + at \Rightarrow v = 2u - g\dfrac{2u}{g} = 0$ i.e. at maximum height

$v^2 = u^2 + 2gs \Rightarrow 0 = 4u^2 - 2gh \Rightarrow H = \dfrac{2u^2}{g}$

∴ we have

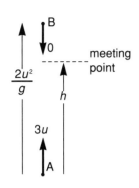

Nothing is known about v at the meeting point

hence $s = ut + \frac{1}{2}at^2$

$\Rightarrow \quad h = 3ut - \frac{1}{2}gt^2 \qquad$ for A

and $\frac{2u^2}{g} - h = \frac{1}{2}gt^2 \qquad$ for B

Adding: $\quad \frac{2u^2}{g} = 3ut$

$\Rightarrow \quad t = \frac{2u}{3g}$

Substituting for t: $h = 3u \times \dfrac{2u}{3g} - \dfrac{g}{2} \times \dfrac{4u^2}{9g^2} = \dfrac{16u^2}{9g}$

► Couples

4

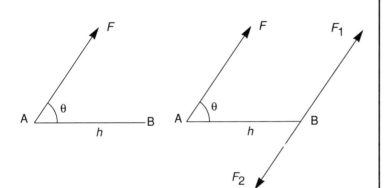

Adding equal and opposite forces F_1 and F_2 at B has not altered the system.

F_1 is the force equal to F which has been added at B. F and F_2 constitute a couple.

Moment of couple = $Fh\sin\theta$.

► NL2

5

a is relative to fixed pulley E.

f is relative to pulley D.

There are four unknowns a, f, T and T_1.

We can find four equations using NL2 for A, B, C and D.

Therefore a solution is possible!

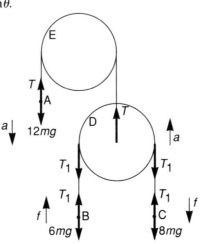

► 'light' ⇒ no mass

NL2 for A: $\quad 12mg - T = 12ma$ **(1)**

NL2 for D: $\quad T - 2T_1 = 0 \times a = 0$ **(2)**

NL2 for B: $\quad T_1 - 6mg = 6m(a + f)$ **(3)**

NL2 for C: $\quad 8mg - T_1 = 8m(f - a)$ **(4)**

Adding **(3)** and **(4)** $\quad \Rightarrow \quad 2g = 14f - 2a$

Substituting for T_1 from **(2)** and **(1)** $\quad \Rightarrow \quad 2g = 2a + f$

$f = \dfrac{4g}{15} \, , a = \dfrac{-2g}{15}$

Substituting for a in **(1)** $\quad \Rightarrow \quad T = \dfrac{68}{5}mg$ and $T_1 = \dfrac{34}{5}mg$

A rises with acceleration $\quad \dfrac{2g}{15}$

► The rather heavy algebra is unavoidable with these questions and consequently we have to be organized, be prepared to work 'slowly but surely' and keep checking our algebra.

B rises with acceleration $\quad \dfrac{4g}{15} - \dfrac{2g}{15} = \dfrac{2g}{15}$

C falls with acceleration $\quad \dfrac{4g}{15} - \dfrac{2g}{15} = \dfrac{2g}{15}$

6

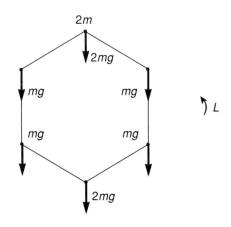

► Couples

The sense of L is shown: anti-clockwise.

Moments about A for the whole system give:

$L = 2 \times 2mg \times a\cos 30° + 2 \times mg \times 2a\cos 30°$

$= 4\sqrt{3}mga$

7

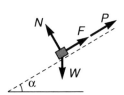 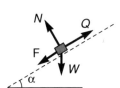

► Resolving

Resolving // plane: $\quad P + F = W\sin\alpha$ **(1)**

► Friction

$Q = F + W\sin\alpha$ **(2)**

In each case $F = \mu W \cos\alpha$

Therefore eliminating F from **(1)** and **(2)**

$\Rightarrow \quad P + Q = 2W\sin\alpha$

or $\dfrac{P + Q}{2} = W\sin\alpha$

8

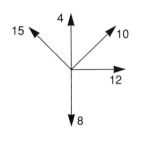

► Equilibrant

$\Rightarrow$ 15cos45° + 10cos45° + 4 − 8

12 + 10cos45° − 15cos45°

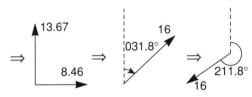

Resultant   Equilibrant

9 Acceleration on the body is $g\sin40°$

Using the v, t equation $\quad \Rightarrow \quad v = u + at$

$\Rightarrow \quad 12 = 3 + g\sin40° \times t \quad \Rightarrow \quad t = 1.4$ seconds

► Uniform acceleration

10

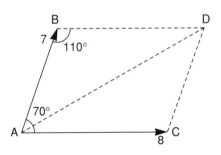

AD is the resultant of vectors 7 and 8.

By the cosine rule: $\quad AD^2 = 8^2 + 7^2 - 2 \times 8 \times 7\cos110°$

$= 8^2 + 7^2 + 2 \times 8 \times 7\cos70°$

$\therefore \quad AD = 12.3$

► Resultant

► NL2

Solutions to Worksheet 4

1

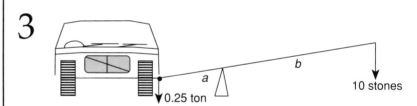

Using NL2 for B: $mg - T = ma$

Using NL2 for A:
$$T - Mg\sin30° = Ma$$

Adding $\Rightarrow$ $mg - \dfrac{Mg}{2} = ma + Ma$

$$\Rightarrow \quad a = \frac{g(2m - M)}{2(m + M)}$$

If A does not move $v = 0$ $\quad \therefore \quad a = 0$

i.e. $2m = M$

► Vectors

2 $\quad v = \begin{pmatrix} 2t \\ 3 \\ 0 \end{pmatrix} \quad \Rightarrow \quad s = \begin{pmatrix} t^2 + A \\ 3t + B \\ C \end{pmatrix}$

When $t = 0$ $\quad s = \begin{pmatrix} 2 \\ 1 \\ 2 \end{pmatrix} \quad \Rightarrow \quad A = 2, B = 1, C = 2$

$\therefore \quad s = \begin{pmatrix} t^2 + 1 \\ 3t + 1 \\ 2 \end{pmatrix}$

► Moments

3

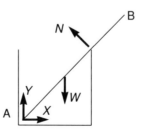

For equilibrium: $20 \times a = 10 \times b \quad \Rightarrow \quad a : b = 1 : 2$

To lift, b would have to be increased and hence the ratio becomes $1 : 2+$

i.e. the ratio is reduced because $\dfrac{1}{2+} < \dfrac{1}{2}$

► You were warned!

► Resolving

4

Resolving horizontally and vertically brings in X and Y, but also N. However, N is easily found by taking moments. Hence:

Moments about A for the rod:

$$N \times 3 = W \times 2\cos45°$$

therefore $N = 2W\cos45°$

► Moments

Resolving horizontally for the rod: $\quad x = N\cos45° = \dfrac{2W}{3}\cos45°$

$$\therefore \quad X = \frac{W}{3}$$

Resolving vertically for the rod: $\quad Y - N\cos45° = W$

$$\therefore \quad Y = \frac{2W}{3}$$

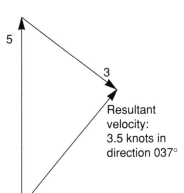

Resultant
velocity:
3.5 knots in
direction 037°

The questions did not specify any particular method. We have done this to remind you of the graphical method.

► Resultant by scale diagram

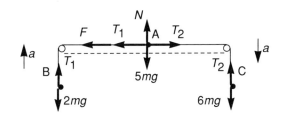

Using NL2 for B: $\quad T_1 - 2mg = 2ma$

Using NL2 for C: $\quad 6mg - T_2 = 6ma$

Adding $\quad \Rightarrow \quad T_1 - T_2 + 4mg = 6ma$ **(1)**

Using NL2 for A: $\quad \Rightarrow \quad T_2 - T_1 - F = 5ma$ **(2)**

Hence **(2)** becomes

$$4mg - 8ma - \mu N = 5ma$$

$$4mg - \frac{2}{5} \times 5mg = 13ma$$

$$\Rightarrow \quad a = \frac{2g}{13}$$

Substituting back: $\quad T_1 = 2mg + 2m \times \frac{2g}{13} = \frac{30mg}{13}$

and $\quad T_2 = 6mg - 6m \times \frac{2g}{13} = \frac{66mg}{13}$

► Tension

► Friction

► Now you can see why equation **(1)** is useful in the form it is in: looking at equation **(2)** we want to substitute for $T_2 - T_1$ and equation **(1)** gives us this without, at this stage, knowing T_1 or T_2.

7

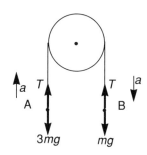

The diagram shows the system after the $4m$ mass has dropped off.

$\uparrow a$ $T\uparrow$ $T\uparrow$ $\downarrow a$

A   B

$3mg$ mg

► NL2

Using NL2 for A: $T - 3mg = 3ma$

Using NL2 for B: $mg - T = ma$ $\Biggr\}$ $\Rightarrow$ $a = -\dfrac{g}{2}$

► Uniform acceleration

We now have: $u = 12, v = 0, a = -\dfrac{g}{2}, t = ?$

$\therefore \quad v = u + at \quad \Rightarrow \quad 0 = 12 - \dfrac{gt}{2}$

$\therefore \quad t = \dfrac{24}{g}$ seconds $= 2.4$ seconds

8

► Uniform acceleration

Given s, find $t \quad \Rightarrow \quad s = ut + \frac{1}{2}at^2$ but u and a are unknown.

Hence use the v, t information.

Using $v = u + at$

$t = 1, v = 5 \quad \Rightarrow \quad 5 = u + a$

$t = 2, v = -1 \quad \Rightarrow \quad -1 = u + 2a$ $\Biggr\}$ $\Rightarrow \quad a = -6, u = 11$

Then $s = ut + \dfrac{1}{2}at^2$

$\Rightarrow \quad 6 = 11t - \dfrac{6}{2}t^2$

i.e. $3t^2 - 11t + 6 = 0$

$(3t - 2)(t - 3) = 0$

$\therefore \quad$ This particle is 6 m from start when $t = \dfrac{2}{3}$ and when $t = 3$.

9

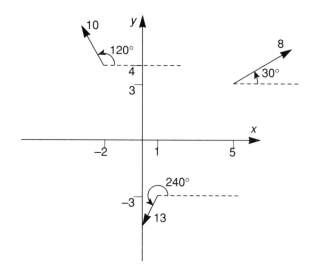

The diagram explains the angles. They are all made with the positive x-axis and measured anti-clockwise.

Taking moments about O:

▶ Moments

$M = 8\cos30° \times 3 + 10\cos30° \times 2 + 13\cos60° \times 3 + 13\cos30° \times 1$
$- 10\cos60° \times 4 - 8\cos60° \times 5$

$\Rightarrow \quad M = 28.9$ Nm (if distances were given in metres; not specified in the question)

10 The question slips into everyday language. The man has a mass of 75 kg and a weight of $75g$ N.

Since acceleration is zero

resistance = weight

$\therefore \quad R = 75g$

Work done = force × distance

▶ Work done

$\qquad = 75g \times 500$ m

▶ We have taken $g = 10$ here.

$\qquad = 375\,000$ joules

▶ kJ= kilojoules

$\qquad = 375$ kJ

▶ 1 kJ= 1000 J

Solutions to Worksheet 5

1 Given s and t, use the s, t equation.

$\Rightarrow \quad s = ut + \dfrac{1}{2}at^2$

▶ Uniform acceleration

For first car: $\quad d = ut + \dfrac{1}{2}ft^2$ **(1)**

For second car: $\quad d = 2ut + \dfrac{1}{2} \times \dfrac{2}{3}f \times t^2$ **(2)**

where d is the distance and t the time to overtaking.

Solving **(1)** and **(2)** $\Rightarrow \quad 0 = -ut + \dfrac{1}{6}ft^2$

$\Rightarrow \quad t = 0$ or $t = \dfrac{6u}{f}$

and then $d = u \times \dfrac{6u}{f} + \dfrac{1}{2}f \times \dfrac{36u^2}{f^2} = \dfrac{24u^2}{f}$

They overtake after $\dfrac{6u}{f}$ when they will have travelled a distance of $\dfrac{24u^2}{f}$.

2

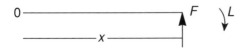

$0 \rule{6cm}{0.4pt}\,F \quad \downarrow L$

x

▶ Moments
▶ Couples

To move the door $Fx > L$

▶ There is a danger of complicating this question by introducing arbitrary forces. We have done all that is required.

$F > \dfrac{L}{x}$

► Moments

► Because ΔACB is isosceles

► COE

3

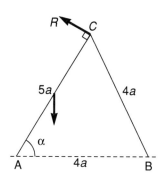

Because the beam is smooth reaction at C is ⊥ beam.

Taking moments about A for AC:

$$R \times 5a = W \times \frac{5a}{2}\cos\alpha$$

From the diagram

$$\cos\alpha = \frac{5a/2}{4a} = \frac{5}{8}$$

$$\therefore \quad R = W \times \frac{1}{2} \times \frac{5}{8} = \frac{5W}{16}$$

4 Energy at A:

$$\frac{1}{2}mu^2 + mgh$$

Energy at B:

$$\frac{5}{6}\left(\frac{1}{2}mu^2 + mgh\right)$$

Energy at C:

$$\frac{2}{3} \times \frac{5}{6}\left(\frac{1}{2}mu^2 + mgh\right)$$

But energy at C is also $\quad \frac{1}{2}mv^2 + \frac{mgh}{3}$

$$\therefore \quad \frac{1}{2}mv^2 + \frac{mgh}{3} = \frac{5}{9}\left(\frac{1}{2}mu^2 + mgh\right)$$

$$\Rightarrow \quad v = \frac{1}{3}\sqrt{5u^2 + 4gh}$$

5

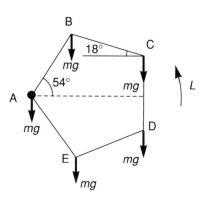

Taking moments about A for the whole:

$$M = 2mg \times a\cos54° + 2 \times mg \times (a\cos54° + a\cos18°)$$
$$= mga(1.17 + 1.17 + 1.90) = 4.24mga$$
$$\therefore \quad M = 41.59ma$$

$L = 42ma$ acting as shown would make the framework rotate anti-clockwise about A.

► Moments, couples

6

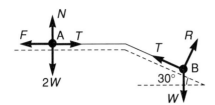

Resolving // plane for B: $T = W\sin30°$

and for A: $T = F$

$\therefore$ $F = \dfrac{W}{2}$

► Friction

For equilibrium $\mu \geq \dfrac{F}{N} = \dfrac{W/2}{2W} = \dfrac{1}{4}$

$\therefore$ minimum value of μ is $\dfrac{1}{4}$.

7

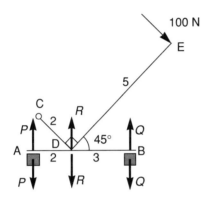

► Study the force diagram carefully: make sure you understand it. Newton's third law is much in evidence! The value of 'exploded' diagrams is highlighted.

Taking moments about C for CDE:

► Moments

$R \times 2\cos45° = 100 \times 5$ $\Rightarrow$ $R = 250\sqrt{2}$

Taking moments about A for plate AB:

► The working out was not too hard; but it was the diagram which made the difference.

$Q \times 5 = R \times 2$

$\Rightarrow$ $Q = \dfrac{250\sqrt{2} \times 2}{5} = 141.4 \text{ N}$

and $P = \dfrac{250\sqrt{2} \times 3}{5} = 212.1 \text{ N}$

8

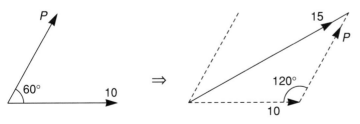

► Resultant

Using the cosine rule $\Rightarrow$ $15^2 = 10^2 + P^2 - 2 \times 10 \times P\cos120°$

$\Rightarrow$ $P^2 + 10P - 125 = 0$

$\Rightarrow$ $P = 7.2 \text{ N}$ (solving by the quadratic formula)

9

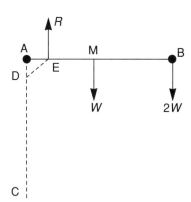

Since AB is smooth the force at E is ⊥ AB.

All forces, those at E, M and B, are ⊥ beam, hence the force at A must have no component // beam; if it had we would not have equilibrium.

Therefore the force at A on the beam is ⊥ AB.

Let this force be Y downwards.

Taking moments about E for AB: $Y \times AE = W \times EM + 2W \times EB$

∴ $Y = W + 6W \Rightarrow Y = 7W$

10 Using NL2 for P // AB:
$T - mg\cos45° = ma$

Using NL2 for Q // AC:
$mg\cos30° - T = ma$

Adding the two equations

$\Rightarrow mg(\cos30° - \cos45°) = 2ma$

$\Rightarrow a = \dfrac{9.81}{2}(\cos30° - \cos45°)$

$= 0.78$ ms^{-2}

We know $v, s \Rightarrow v^2 = u^2 + 2as \Rightarrow v^2 = 2 \times 0.78 \times 0.5$

$\Rightarrow v = 0.88$ m s^{-1}

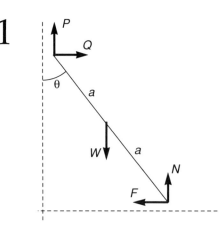

Solutions to Worksheet 6

1

Limiting friction, therefore $F = \mu N$ and $P = \mu Q$

Resolving horizontally for the rod: $F = Q$

and vertically: $P + N = W$

∴ $P = \mu Q = \mu F = \mu^2 N$

∴ $\mu^2 N + N = W$

$\Rightarrow N = \dfrac{W}{1 + \mu^2} = \dfrac{4}{5}W$

$\Rightarrow P = \dfrac{1}{5}W$

and $F = \mu N = \dfrac{2}{5}W$

and $Q = \dfrac{2}{5}W$

2 $2 (3\mathbf{i} + 4\mathbf{j}) - 3(-\mathbf{i} + 3\mathbf{j}) + (5\mathbf{i} - \mathbf{j}) - 2(4\mathbf{i} + 3\mathbf{j}) = 6\mathbf{i} - 8\mathbf{j}$ = resultant

∴ equilibrant is $-6\mathbf{i} + 8\mathbf{j}$

▶ Vectors

▶ Remember:
equilibrant = balancing force

3 Much information is given about s, v and t and a journey in three stages means that you could write down many equations – and easily get confused. With so much information it is a good idea to draw a v–t graph and see what is going on.

▶ Uniform acceleration

▶ Using the v-t graph

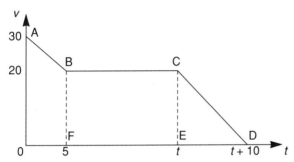

Given that area BCEF = area ABFO + area CED

then $20(t - 5) = \dfrac{1}{2}(30 + 20) \times 5 + \dfrac{1}{2} \times 20 \times 10$

$\Rightarrow \quad t = \dfrac{325}{20} = 16.25$

▶ Remember area under graph = distance travelled

Therefore total time of journey = 26.25 seconds.

After this simplification of a complicated sounding problem the moral is: Don't forget the graphical approach to uniform acceleration questions.

4

▶ Energy

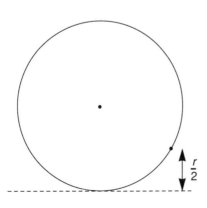

Initial energy is PE only and equal to $2mgr$.

When PE is $\dfrac{1}{4}$ of the total energy height is $\dfrac{r}{2}$ and then

$2mgr = \dfrac{mgr}{2} + \dfrac{1}{2}mv^2$

$\Rightarrow \quad v = \sqrt{3rg}$

► Moments

5

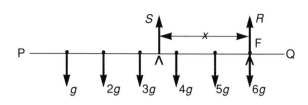

Resolving vertically for the whole: $R + S = 21g$

Since $R = S$ then $R = S = 10.5g$

Taking moments about F for the whole:

$10.5g \times x = 5g \times 0.5 + 4g \times 1 + 3g \times 1.5 + 2g \times 2 + g \times 2.5$

$\therefore \quad x = \dfrac{17.5}{10.5} = \dfrac{5}{3}\,\text{m}$

6

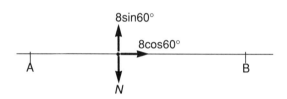

► Work done

(a)   Work done = force × distance

$= 8\cos60° \times 10 = 40$ joules

The component $8\sin60°$ moves the ring a zero distance in its direction therefore it does no work.

(b)   The wire exerts a force N on the ring.

Again no movement $\perp$ wire

$\therefore$ no work is done by N.

► Resultant velocity

7   Velocity diagrams

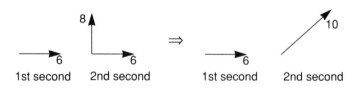

Distance diagram

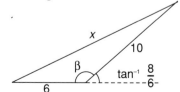

$x^2 = 6^2 + 10^2 - 2 \times 6 \times 10\cos\beta$

$= 36 + 100 + 120 \times \dfrac{6}{10}$

$\therefore \quad x = 14.4 \text{ m}$

► The cosine rule

8 Time to reach maximum height:

Use the v, t equation $\Rightarrow \quad v = u + at \quad \Rightarrow \quad 0 = u - gt$ i.e. $t = \dfrac{u}{g}$

► Vertical motion under gravity

Total time of flight $= \dfrac{2u}{g}$

One third of time of flight $= \dfrac{2u}{3g}$

$s = ut + \dfrac{1}{2}at^2 \quad \Rightarrow \quad h = u \times \dfrac{2u}{3g} - \dfrac{1}{2}g\left(\dfrac{2u}{2g}\right)^2 = \dfrac{4u^2}{9g}$

9

► Magnitude and direction of resultant

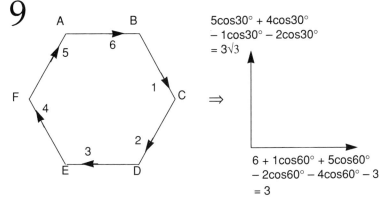

$5\cos30° + 4\cos30°$
$- 1\cos30° - 2\cos30°$
$= 3\sqrt{3}$

$\Rightarrow$

$6 + 1\cos60° + 5\cos60°$
$- 2\cos60° - 4\cos60° - 3$
$= 3$

$\therefore \quad r + \sqrt{3^2 + 3^2 \times 3} = 6$ in direction $\tan^{-1}\dfrac{3\sqrt{3}}{3}$

$= 60°$ with AB

10 $a = \begin{pmatrix} t \\ 0 \\ 4 \end{pmatrix}$

► Vectors

Integrating: $\mathbf{v} = \begin{pmatrix} \frac{1}{2}t^2 + A \\ B \\ 4t + C \end{pmatrix} \Rightarrow \mathbf{r} = \begin{pmatrix} \frac{1}{2}t^2 \\ 2 \\ 4t + 1 \end{pmatrix}$

because $\mathbf{r} = \begin{pmatrix} 0 \\ 2 \\ 1 \end{pmatrix}$ when $t = 0$

Integrating: $\mathbf{x} = \begin{pmatrix} \frac{1}{6}t^3 + D \\ 2t + E \\ 2t^2 + t + F \end{pmatrix} \Rightarrow \mathbf{x} = \begin{pmatrix} \frac{1}{6}t^3 \\ 2t \\ 2t^2 + t \end{pmatrix}$

because $\mathbf{x} = \begin{pmatrix} 0 \\ 0 \\ 0 \end{pmatrix}$ when $t = 0$

② *Impacts*

Chapter outline

Reminders

▐ Momentum

▐ Energy

▐ Resolving and combining

New theory in this chapter

▐ Conservation of momentum

▐ Newton's experimental law

▐ Relative velocity – simple

▐ Impacts including oblique

Pure mathematics needed

▐ Simultaneous equations

▐ Simple trigonometry

IMPACTS, DIRECT AND OBLIQUE, AND IMPULSE

Let us consider two snooker balls, A and B, on a table and quite free to move. They are both stationary. A is hit with the cue so that it strikes B directly, i.e. not a glancing blow. What happens when they collide?

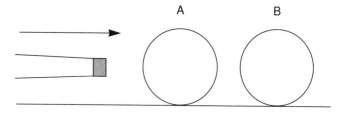

A	B
slows down, stops, rebounds	moves
loses velocity	gains velocity
loses momentum	gains momentum
loses kinetic energy	gains kinetic energy

Let's have a look at the velocities involved. In our work to date we have no law which covers the velocities in a problem of this type. However there is one and, once again, we have Newton to thank. This is known as **Newton's experimental law** or **Newton's law of**

impact or **Newton's law of restitution**: one law with various names and we shall use Newton's experimental law abbreviated to NEL. It is known as the experimental law because it is founded and justified purely by experiment and observation: there is not theoretical proof of the law.

To understand the law we need to know a little about relative velocity.

Relative velocity

Consider: walking speed 3 mph, train velocity 10 mph:
You walk towards the front of the train
your velocity relative to the train is 3 mph
your velocity relative to the track is 3 + 10 mph = 13 mph.
You walk towards the rear of the train
your velocity relative to the train is –3 mph
your velocity relative to the track is –3 + 10 = 7 mph.
Read through this last bit again noting particularly the use of the words 'speed', 'velocity' and 'relative' and the +3 and –3.
There is much more on relative velocity in Chapter 9 but we have enough knowledge here to continue with the present matter, NEL.

▶ 'Relative to' means considering the body that we are 'relative to' to be stationary.

> **Newton's experimental law states:**
> relative velocity after impact is equal to $-e$ times relative velocity before impact.

There are more formal variations on the wording of this law but this version is the simplest and most practical.

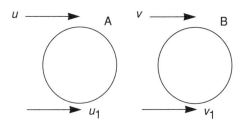

The diagram for questions on impacts really amounts to a table. For a simple situation of impact between different masses it would look like this:

	A	B	
$\rightarrow_+$ indicates positive direction	m_1	m_2	– names of masses
	•	•	– values of masses
	u	v	– velocities before impact
	u_1	v_1	– velocities after impact

▶ NEL: $v_1 - u_1 = -e(v - u)$

The algebra in these problems can soon become quite complicated and hence the need for an organized approach.

NEL in above case: $v_1 - u_1 = -e(v - u)$

▶ Ponder this equation carefully – you will use it often.

▶ Coefficient of restitution

Important note: when writing down the relative velocity we **must** follow the same order on both sides of the equation. In this case we used velocity of B – velocity of A.

You can't help but have noticed the sneaky bit where we have slipped the '–e' into the equation; e is a constant which exists for any two bodies and it is an indication of the elasticity of the bodies. If $e = 1$ they are perfectly elastic: a theoretical ideal but physically impossible (the nearest would be two superballs colliding); if $e = 0$ they are perfectly inelastic, as for putty colliding with dough. Hence e always has a value between 0 and 1, and it is called the **coefficient of restitution**.

The minus sign is necessary if we follow the guideline of keeping the same order when writing down the relative velocities. Without it there would be some wrong directions in the answers.

Momentum

Having considered velocities we shall now look at momentum. There are changes in momentum but are they linked by any law?

A butterfly doing 2 mph hitting a parked car (brakes off) would almost certainly not move the car (fatal injuries or at least a headache more likely for the butterfly).

A steam-roller doing 2 mph hitting the same car would send the car off at some considerable velocity and also carry on itself at 2 mph (nearly).

▶ Note the nearly!

Let's go back to the original impact of billiard balls at the beginning of this chapter.

A loses momentum   units MLT^{-1}

Rate of loss of momentum is $MLT^{-1} \times T^{-1} = MLT^{-2} =$ force
i.e. for the duration of the impact A experiences a force from B.

Newton's third law (NL3) $\Rightarrow$ B experiences the same force from A

i.e. it is force which changes momentum and since A and B experience the same force they experience the same change in momentum.

Hence the momentum lost by A is equal to the momentum gained by B; the total momentum does not change. This is known as the **conservation of momentum**, COM.

▶ Conservation of momentum, COM

Remember: we are talking about impacts where neither body is restrained in any way.

Applying conservation of momentum to the impact on page 107 we have

$$m_1 u + m_2 v = m_1 u_1 + m_2 v_1$$

Energy considerations

We shall consider what happens to energy as we look at some problems. Let us return to the original snooker ball problem. Given that the mass of each ball is 100 g and that A has initial velocity 3 m s^{-1} find the velocity of each ball after impact. Take $e = \frac{3}{4}$

$\rightarrow_+$

A	B
100	100
•	•
3	0
u	v

COM: $100 \times 3 \quad = \quad 100u \quad + \quad 100v$

► **Reminder:** most problems on impacts reduce to applying COM and NEL.

momentum of A before, momentum of A after, momentum of B after

$\Rightarrow \quad 3 = u + v$ $\hspace{2cm}$ **(1)**

NEL: $v \quad - \quad u \quad = \quad -\dfrac{3}{4} \quad (0 - 3)$ $\hspace{1cm}$

velocity of B after, velocity of A after, velocity of B before, velocity of A before

$\Rightarrow \quad 4v - 4u = 9$ $\hspace{2cm}$ **(2)**

Solving **(1)** and **(2)** simultaneously

$8v = 21 \quad \Rightarrow \quad v = \dfrac{21}{8} = 2\tfrac{5}{8} \text{ m s}^{-1}$

$u = \tfrac{3}{8} \text{ m s}^{-1}$

(ACT) *Activity 2.1*

► Solutions on page 110

1 A marble of mass 20 g travelling at 5 m s^{-1} hits another marble of the same size but mass 15 g travelling directly towards it at 8 m s^{-1}. If $e = \tfrac{5}{13}$, find the velocity of each after impact and investigate any changes in kinetic energy.

2 A football of mass 2 lb collides directly with another of mass $1\tfrac{1}{2}$ lb going in the opposite direction. The collison is direct and both balls are in the air. The first ball has speed of 25 ft/s and the second a speed of 10 ft/s. If $e = 0.6$ find their velocities after impact.

3 A smooth narrow tube is in the form of a vertical circle of radius r (something like a cycle inner tube set vertically). At the top and bottom are two stationary particles of masses $3m$ and $4m$ respectively. The top one is dislodged so that it falls and strikes the one at the bottom. If $e = \tfrac{2}{3}$ find, in terms of r, the maximum height the lower particle rises to.

4 A, B and C are three equally sized balls of masses $3m$, $4m$ and $5m$ respectively. They lie at rest in a straight line, in the order A, B, C, on a smooth horizontal surface. A is sent towards B with velocity u and $e = 0.5$ throughout. Show that there will be a third impact.

5 One bowl travelling at 3 m s^{-1} hits directly a stationary bowl of the same mass. The second one travels 2.5 m before stopping. Given that the coefficient of restitution is 0.6 find the acceleration (assumed constant) of the second bowl.

6 A snooker player hits the white ball directly onto a red one which she wishes to travel 3 m exactly before stopping. It is known that the deceleration of the red ball is $\frac{3}{2}$ m s^{-2}. What is the velocity of the white ball just before impact? Take $e = \frac{4}{5}$.

Solutions to Activity 2.1

1 $\rightarrow_+$

	A	B
	20 g	15 g
	•	•
	5	− 8
	u	v

► Note the − 8!

COM: $20 \times 5 + 15 \times -8 = 20u + 15v$

NEL: $v - u = -\dfrac{5}{13}(-5 - 8)$

∴   COM $\Rightarrow$ $4u + 3v = -4$
and NEL $\Rightarrow$ $v - u = 5$

$\Rightarrow$ $v = \dfrac{16}{7}$ and $u = -\dfrac{19}{7}$

i.e. both marbles change direction after impact. This is shown by the signs of the velocities.

Kinetic energy:

Before impact: $\dfrac{1}{2} \times 0.02 \times 5^2 + \dfrac{1}{2} \times 0.015 \times (1-8)^2 = 0.73$ J

After impact: $\dfrac{1}{2} \times 0.02 \times \left(-\dfrac{19}{2}\right)^2 + \dfrac{1}{2} \times 0.015 + \left(-\dfrac{16}{7}\right)^2 = 0.11$ J

► Remember this: students often try to apply conservation of energy to impacts, to their cost!

Hence kinetic energy is lost at the impact and the conservation of energy does not apply.

► Mechanics questions in Imperial units are rare but this question shows that sometimes the units do not matter so long as you are consistent throughout the question.

2 $\rightarrow_+$

	A	B
	2 lb	1.5 lb
	•	•
	25	−10
	u	v

COM: $25 \times 2 + 1.5 \times -10 = 2u + \dfrac{3}{2}u$

► To convert to SI units would only mean multiplying both sides of these equations by the same factors. The units in the momentum equation, in this case, are not, of course, Nm.

NEL: $v - u = -0.6(-10 - 25)$

COM: $\Rightarrow$ $4u + 3v = 70$

NEL: $\Rightarrow$ $v - u = 21$
  $\Rightarrow$ $v = 22$ ft/s and $u = 1$ ft/s

► The planning stage: do not fall into the trap of cluttering the diagram with all sorts of forces and then writing down every equation possible.

3   The diagram shows:
A, the top point from which the 3m mass is displaced
B, the bottom point where the particles collide
C, some point to which the second particle, mass 4m, rises as it stops.

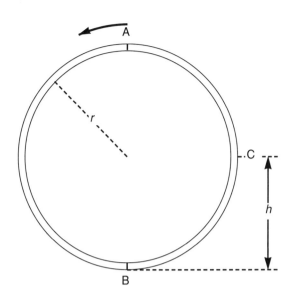

► Plan ahead using general principles; a bit like the rough notes preceeding any essay in other subjects.

Which principles apply?

► You cannot answer this if you don't know the principles covered in Chapter 1.

Forces, Newton's second law, acceleration? Not really. Forces act, of course, but we don't know much about them in this case.

Energy? Smooth surfaces therefore conservation of energy could apply.

Any good?

Loss in PE of $3m$ mass $\Rightarrow$ gain in KE

Impact at B $\Rightarrow$ gain in KE of $4m$ mass

The $4m$ mass rises and KE changes to PE – a more promising line of attack.

Hence for the $3m$ mass from A to B: gain in KE = loss in PE

$\Rightarrow \quad \dfrac{1}{2} \times 3m \times v^2 = 3m \times g \times 2r$

$\Rightarrow \quad v = \sqrt{4gr}$

► This value for v is now used when we consider the impact.

At B:

	$3m$	$4m$
$\rightarrow_+$	$\bullet$	$\bullet$
	$\sqrt{4gr}$	0
$e = \dfrac{2}{3}$		
	u	w

COM: $\quad 3m\sqrt{4gr} = 3mu + 4mw \quad \Rightarrow \quad 3\sqrt{4gr} = 3u + 4w$

NEL: $\quad w - u = -\dfrac{2}{3}(0 - \sqrt{4gr}) \quad \Rightarrow \quad \dfrac{2}{3}\sqrt{4gr} = w - u$

Solving $\quad \Rightarrow \quad 5\sqrt{4gr} = 7w \quad \therefore \quad w = \dfrac{5}{7}\sqrt{4gr}$

For the $4m$ mass, from B to C:

COE: $\dfrac{1}{2} \times 4m \times (\dfrac{5}{7}\sqrt{4gr})^2 = 4m \times g \times h$

$\Rightarrow \quad h = \dfrac{50}{49} r$

► The planning stage again

4 Consider the possibilities:

A hits B?	Yes
B then hits C?	Yes

The first two impacts are inevitable.
What is the condition for there to be a third impact? The velocity of A must be greater than that of B: hence the problem is to find velocities of A and B after the second impact.

First impact: COM: $3mu = 3\,mu_1 + 4mu$

$\Rightarrow \quad 3u = 3u_1 + 4v$ (1)

NEL: $v - u_1 = -e(0 - u)$

$\Rightarrow \quad u = 2v - 2u_1$ (2)

Second impact: COM: $4mv = 4mv_1 + 5mw$

$\Rightarrow \quad 4v = 4v_1 + 5w$ (3)

NEL: $w - v_1 = -e(0 - v)$

$\Rightarrow \quad v = 2w - 2v_1$ (4)

Time to pause: we have here four equations, four unknowns and it is easy to get in a mess.

► Planning again

Remember here that u which is given in the question is a known quantity. The ones we have introduced (u_1, v, v_1 and w) are the unknowns.
We want to find u_1 and v_1.
v is the unknown common to all four equations.

Hence   **(i)**   find v_1 in terms of v from **(3)** and **(4)**
      (ii)   substitute v_1 for v in **(1)** and **(2)**
      (iii)   solve **(1)** and **(2)** to get u_1 and v_1

$2 \times$ **(3)** $- 5 \times$ **(4)** $\Rightarrow \quad 3v = 18v_1 \quad \Rightarrow \quad v = 6v_1$

Substituting in **(1)** $\Rightarrow \quad 3u = 3u_1 + 24v_1 \quad \Rightarrow \quad u = u_1 + 8v_1$
and substituting in **(2)** $\Rightarrow \quad u = 12v_1 - 2u_1 \quad \Rightarrow \quad u = 12v_1 - 2u_1$

Solving now $\Rightarrow \quad 3u = 28v_1$,   i.e $v_1 = \dfrac{3u}{28}$

► After working through this question you should realize the value of planning.

and $u = 7u_1$ i.e. $u_1 = \dfrac{u}{7} = \dfrac{4u}{28}$

i.e. velocity of A is greater than that of B hence there is a third impact.

5

	A	B
	m	m
$\rightarrow_+$	•	•
	3	0
$e = 0.6$		
	u	v

COM: $3m = mu + mv \Rightarrow 3 = u + v$

NEL: $v - u = -\dfrac{3}{5}(0 - 3) \Rightarrow 9 = 5v - 5u$

$\left.\begin{array}{l} \\ \\ \end{array}\right\} \Rightarrow v = \dfrac{12}{5}$

Uniform acceleration, use the v, s equation $v_2^2 = u^2 + 2as$

$\Rightarrow 0 = \left(\dfrac{12}{5}\right)^2 + 2a \times \dfrac{5}{2} \Rightarrow a = -\dfrac{144}{125}$ m s^{-1}

A negative result as expected.

6

For the red ball:

$s = 3m \quad a = -\dfrac{3}{4}$ m s^{-2} $\quad v = 0 \quad u = ? \quad \therefore \quad$ use $v^2 = u^2 + 2as$

$0 = u^2 - 2 \times \dfrac{3}{2} \times 3 \Rightarrow u = 3$

Then:

	W	R
	m	m
	•	•
	v	0
	v_1	3

COM: $mv = mv_1 + 3m \Rightarrow v = v_1 + 3$

NEL: $3 - v_1 = -\dfrac{4}{5}(0 - v) \Rightarrow 4v = 15 - 5v_1$

Solving $\Rightarrow v = \dfrac{10}{3}$ m s^{-1}

Impulse

In the type of questions we have been looking at total momentum is unaltered but the momentum of each body changes at each impact. This change in momentum of a body is known as the **impulse**: if a body loses momentum it gives or delivers an impulse and if a body gains momentum it receives an impulse.

► Impulse means change in momentum

J is the letter often used to indicate the magnitude of an impulse. Many students are a bit baffled by the use of the letter J like this but all we need to remember is

► J indicates the magnitude of an impulse.

$J = mv - mu$

and if $u = 0 \Rightarrow J = mv$

or $v = \dfrac{J}{m}$

► Many students who are happy with the idea of momentum have a dread of impulse. Study the definition carefully and you will realize there is nothing to fear.

and knowing v is the starting point for many problems.

► Solutions on this page

> **(ACT)** *Activity 2.2*
>
> Go through Activity 2.1 and find the impulse received by the body which gains velocity at each impact.

> **Solutions to Activity 2.2**

1 B gains velocity

► But 154.3 what?

► Remember *J* is change in momentum so has the units of momentum, newton seconds, Ns.

Impulse $J = 15 \times \dfrac{16}{7} - 15 \times -8$

$= 154.3$

In this case $J = \dfrac{154.3}{1000} = 0.1543$ Ns.

► The units of *m* are not defined in the question hence you cannot give units to *J*.

2 $J = 1.5 (22 - -10) = 48$

3 $J = 4mw = 4m \times \dfrac{5}{7} \sqrt{4gr} = \dfrac{40}{7} m\sqrt{gr}$

4 For B: $J = 4mv = 4m \times 6v_1 = 24m \times \dfrac{3u}{28} = \dfrac{18mu}{7}$

For C: $J = 5mw_1 = \dfrac{5m}{2} (v + 2v_1) = 20m \times \dfrac{3u}{28} = \dfrac{15mu}{7}$

5 For B: $J = mv = \dfrac{12m}{7}$

6 For R: $J = 3m$

Oblique impact with a fixed surface

So far our impact work has involved impacts between bodies which are under no constraints. What about a ball hitting a wall?

The wall is not free to move and hence conservation of momentum **does not** apply.

Newton's experimental law **does** apply and this is the only principle we can use.

Consider a ball hitting a wall directly.

► Oblique impacts

► $v = -eu$ – a simple result, well worth remembering.

	Ball	Wall	
	m		NEL $\Rightarrow$ $(v - 0) = -e(u - 0)$
$\rightarrow_+$	•	•	$\Rightarrow$ $v = -eu$
	u	0	

The result means that if we know the velocity with which a body hits a fixed surface directly we can write down the velocity with which it leaves the surface.

Another feature of our work to date has been that all impacts have been direct. This means that in the case, for example, of two balls, the direction of impact has been along the line joining their centres.

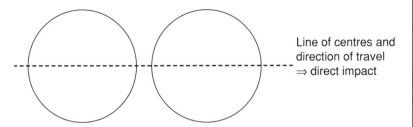

Line of centres and direction of travel
$\Rightarrow$ direct impact

More formally, it is motion where the direction of travel is normal to the surfaces at the point of contact.

If we have:

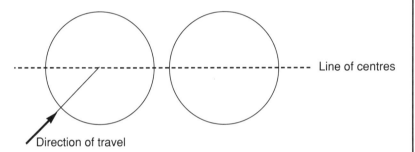

Line of centres

Direction of travel

then we have oblique impact.

So for a ball striking a smooth wall obliquely we have:

► In reality this is what happens most often but not in the case of A level Mechanics. With some boards, it is only on the Further Mathematics papers – check your syllabus.

Before

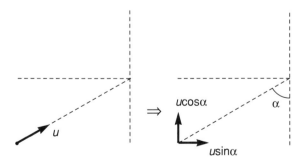

Resolving again: this time parallel to normal and tangent at contact.

After

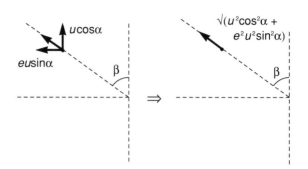

Component $//$ wall, $u\cos\alpha$, is unaltered because the wall is smooth, no forces along surface.

Component $\perp$ wall becomes $eu\sin\alpha$ (from above) and hence resultant velocity is $\sqrt{u^2\cos^2\alpha + e^2u^2\sin^2\alpha}$

▶ Don't make the mistake of having the 'before' and 'after' directions at the same angle to the surface of contact.

in a direction at β to the wall where $\tan\beta = \dfrac{eu\sin\alpha}{u\cos\alpha} = e\tan\alpha.$

Since $e < 1 \quad \Rightarrow \quad \beta < \alpha.$

▶ Solutions on page 117

(ACT) *Activity 2.3*

1 A ball falls vertically onto a concrete floor and rebounds to three-quarters of the height it fell. Find e, the coefficient of restitution.

▶ The problems of a snooker player!

2 A ball travelling horizontally rebounds from a fixed smooth wall in a direction perpendicular to its original direction. Originally the ball was 3 feet from the wall and it travelled 2 feet in a direction parallel to the wall before impact. Find e.

3

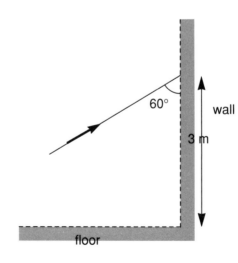

In a game of squash Fred hits the ball in a vertical plane perpendicular to the wall. The ball strikes the wall at the angle shown in the diagram and at velocity of 20 m s^{-1}.

Given that $e = \dfrac{\sqrt{3}}{2}$

and $g = 10$ find

(a) the horizontal and vertical components of the velocity after impact

▶ Does Fred work all this out every time he hits the ball?

(b) the maximum height the ball reaches

(c) how far from the base of the wall it hits the floor.

4 Richard's gun fires ping-pong balls. He fires a ball horizontally at a smooth plane which slopes at 60° to the horizontal. The ball rebounds and its second impact with the plane is at the same point as the first. If the ball was fired with velocity 10 m s^{-1} find e.

5 A ball strikes a fixed smooth wall at a speed of 10 m s^{-1} and at an angle of $\tan^{-1}\frac{4}{3}$ with the wall. After the impact, where $e = \frac{1}{2}$, the ball decelerates at 0.5 m s^{-2}. Find when and where it stops.

Solutions to Activity 2.3

1 A diagram for this question is more of a table:

Falling   Rising

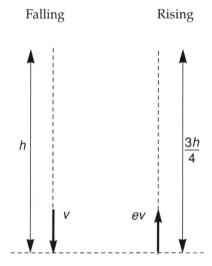

h $\dfrac{3h}{4}$

v ev

► Putting given information into a more comprehensible form

We know, v, h, use $v^2 = u^2 + 2as$

Falling: $u^2 = 2gh$

and rising: $e^2 v^2 = 2g \times \dfrac{3}{4} h$

dividing $\Rightarrow \dfrac{1}{e^2} = \dfrac{4}{3}$ – routine algebra

$\Rightarrow e = \dfrac{\sqrt{3}}{2}$

► The key stage: letting given information suggest what to do next.

2 The ball starts from A, hits the wall at B, rebounds through C. DB is the interpretation of the second sentence in the question. Make sure you understand this.

Now, from page 116 $\tan\beta = e\tan\alpha$

Also $\tan\beta = \cot\alpha$ ∴ $\alpha + \beta = 90°$

► Complicated sounding question: the second sentence in particular needs careful reading.

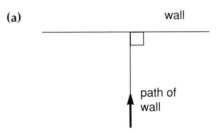

$$\therefore \; e = \frac{1}{\tan^2\alpha}$$

$$\therefore \; e = \frac{4}{9} \qquad \tan\alpha = \frac{3}{2} \text{ from the diagram.}$$

► 'Vertical plane perpendicular to wall' – a bit more heavy but necessary wording. In most rooms the walls are vertical planes and in a rectangular room one plane is perpendicular to the other at the corner.

3 In our question here, looking from above the ball hits the wall at 90°.

(a)

The diagram shows what is happening in the vertical plane.

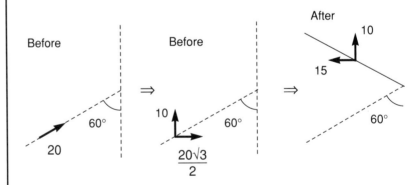

↑ 10 because 20cos60° = 10

$\rightarrow \dfrac{20\sqrt3}{2}$ because $20\cos30° = \dfrac{20\sqrt3}{2}$

↑ 10 because there is no change // wall

← 15 because $\dfrac{20\sqrt3}{2} \times e$

$= 15$

Vertically the ball experiences acceleration g downwards.

(b) We wish to find h, we know v therefore use $v^2 = u^2 + 2as$

$\Rightarrow$ $\quad 0 = 10^2 - 2 \times 10 \times h \quad v = 0$ at maximum height
$\Rightarrow$ $\quad h = 5$ m

The ball strikes the wall 3 m from the floor
$\therefore$ maximum height reached is 8 m.

(c) Horizontally the ball has zero acceleration.
Therefore it travels at constant speed 15 m s^{-1} all the time it is in the air.

To find the time in the air return to vertical considerations.
Impact with wall to top: $v = u + at \quad \Rightarrow \quad 0 = 10 - 10t$
$\Rightarrow$ $\quad t = 1$ s

Top to floor: $\quad s = ut + \dfrac{1}{2} at^2 \quad \Rightarrow \quad 8 = \dfrac{10}{2} t^2 \quad \Rightarrow \quad t = \sqrt{1.6}$ s

$\therefore$ total time in air $= 1 + \sqrt{1.6} = 2.26$ s
Now horizontally: $\quad x = 15 \times 2.26 = 33.9$ m

► Big squash court!

Points to note:
- Although this was a longer question, possibly seeming impossible at first reading, it has been answered by using easily understood principles: this is usually the case in mechanics.
- The value of resolving, again!
- Remember the horizontal/vertical technique; you will meet it again.

4

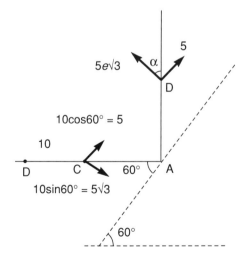

For the ball to strike the plane at A a second time it rebounds vertically at the first impact.

The ball is fired at B and C shows its velocity in component form before impact, D shows it after impact.

It is necessary to resolve // and ⊥ to the plane as in previous questions.

$$\tan\alpha = \frac{5}{e5\sqrt{3}} = \sqrt{3} \text{ because } \alpha = 60°$$

$$\therefore \quad e = \frac{1}{3}$$

► We could have quoted the result from question 2 to reach the same conclusion.

What is the minimum slope of the plane for which the original condition (second impact at the same point as the first) is possible?

5

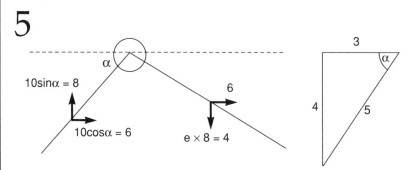

10sinα = 8
10cosα = 6
e × 8 = 4
6
3
4
5
α

If v is the velocity after rebound $v = \sqrt{4^2 + 6^2} = \sqrt{52}$

Time to stop? use the t, v equation $\Rightarrow v = u + at$

$$\therefore \quad 0 = \sqrt{52} - 2 \times \frac{1}{2} \times s \quad \Rightarrow \quad s = 52 \text{ } m$$

Therefore it stops after travelling 52 m in a direction $\tan^{-1}\frac{2}{3}$ with the wall.

Oblique impacts between unconstrained objects
Let's now consider oblique impact between two balls which are not constrained. As we go through this work, we find that we are not learning any new theory or principles: we are using the knowledge we already have to solve a harder problem.

EXAMPLE

► You could try this question yourself without reading further, given the hints:
● resolving plays a large part,
● combine the ideas of activities 2.1 and 2.2.

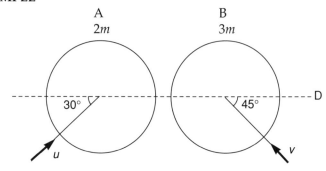

A
2m

B
3m

30°
45°
D
u
v

A and B are two smooth balls of the same size but with masses $2m$ and $3m$ respectively. They are moving in the directions shown when they collide. If $u = 4\sqrt{3}$, $v = 3\sqrt{2}$ and $e = \frac{1}{2}$ what happens next?

Solution

The line CD, which is the line joining the centres, is one line of reference and the other is the line perpendicular to it at the point of contact, the common tangent.

The diagram then becomes:

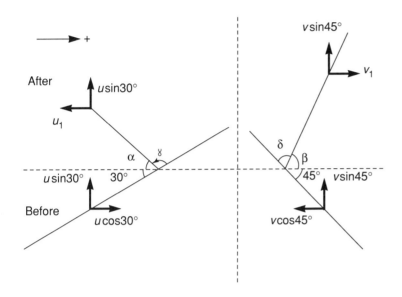

We can find the final velocities when we know u_1 and v_1.
Working along the line of centres:

COM: $2mu\cos30° - 3mv\cos45° = 2mu_1 + 3mv_1$

NEL: $v_1 - u_1 = -e(-v\cos45° - u\cos30°)$

COM: $\Rightarrow \quad 2u_1 + 3v_1 = u\sqrt{3} - \dfrac{3v}{\sqrt{2}}$

$\Rightarrow \quad 2u_1 + 3v_1 = 12 - 9 = 3$

NEL: $\Rightarrow \quad v_1 - u_1 = \dfrac{u\sqrt{3}}{4} + \dfrac{v}{2\sqrt{2}}$

$\Rightarrow \quad v_1 - u_1 = 3 + \dfrac{3}{2} = \dfrac{9}{2}$

Solving $\Rightarrow \quad v_1 = \dfrac{12}{5}$ and $u_1 = -\dfrac{21}{2}$

A further note on signs

In the NEL equation, on the right hand side, we have written $-v\cos45°$: this $-ve$ sign is because we know definitely that the component parallel to the line of centres is in the negative direction. Study the use of the signs carefully.

► **Sign of momentum**
u_1 and v_1 are written as positive quantities until we know their value. The diagram shows u_1 as $-ve$ but it could also be $+ve$.

Hence, after impact we have:

Referring back to the original diagram:

► Angle turned through by direction of motion

the angle γ (= 180° – (30° + α)) is the angle which the direction of motion of A has turned through and similarly so is δ for the motion of B. These angles are quite often asked for in examination questions.

► Solutions on page 123

(**ACT**) *Activity 2.4*

1

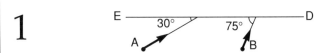

The diagram shows the directions of travel of two spheres of the same size but A has mass 10 kg and B has mass 8 kg. They collide and CD is the line joining the centres. Find the velocities of A and B after impact and the angle each has turned through. Take $e = 0.4$.

2

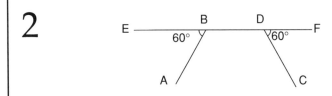

A mass of $4m$ is travelling in the direction AB and a mass of $3m$ is travelling in the direction CD, both at a speed of 6 m s⁻¹. They collide where EBDF is the line joining the centres. After the collison the $4m$ mass is moving perpendicular to EF. Find the coefficient of restitution and the final velocity of the $3m$ mass.

3

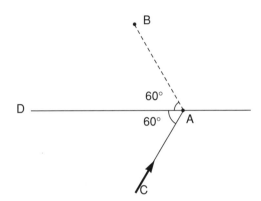

A and B are two circular pins on a bagatelle board and they have negligible diameter. AB = 20 cm. A ball of radius 1 cm is fired at A with a speed of 10 m s⁻¹ in the direction CA. It hits A where DA is the line joining the centres. Does the ball then hit pin B? Take $e = 0.8$.

▶ Allow plenty of time for this one. The geometry needs careful consideration.

Solutions to Activity 2.4

1

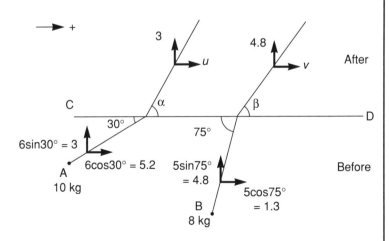

Along CD:

COM: $10 \times 5.2 + 8 \times 1.3 = 10u + 8v \quad \Rightarrow \quad 5u + 4v = 31.2$

NEL: $v - u = -0.4(1.3 - 5.2) \quad \Rightarrow \quad v - u = 1.56$

Solving: $\Rightarrow \quad 9v = 31.2 + 7.8 \quad \Rightarrow \quad v = 4.33, u = 2.77$

Velocity of A: $\sqrt{3^2 + 2.77^2} = 4.1$ m s^{-1}

in direction $\alpha = \tan^{-1} \dfrac{3}{2.77} = 47.3°$

Velocity of B: $\sqrt{4.8^2 + 4.33^2} = 6.5$ m s^{-1}

in direction $\beta = \tan^{-1} \dfrac{4.8}{4.33} = 47.0°$

A is turned through an angle of $(\alpha - 30°) = 17.3°$

B is turned through an angle of $(75° - \beta) = 27.1°$

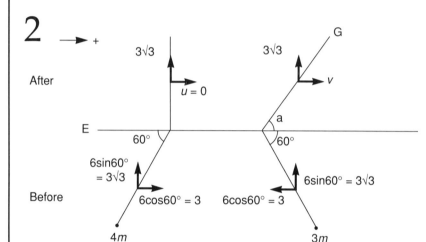

2

► **Remember:** once the velocity components perpendicular to the line joining centres before impact have been decided they can immediately be transferred to the situation after impact.

Along EF:

COM: $4m \times 3 - 3m \times 3 = 4m \times 0 + 3mv$

$\Rightarrow \quad 3 = 3v \quad \Rightarrow \quad v = 1$

NEL: $v - u = -e(-3 - 3)$

$\Rightarrow \quad v = 6e$

$v = 1$

$\therefore \quad e = \dfrac{1}{6}$

$\therefore$ after impact the $3m$ mass is travelling in the direction DG with speed $\sqrt{(3\sqrt{3})^2 + 1^2} = \sqrt{28} = 5.3$ m s^{-1}

► **Remember:** arctan and tan^{-1} mean the same. You should know them both.

and where $\alpha = \arctan \dfrac{3\sqrt{3}}{1} = 79.1°$

3

This problem has two main components:

- to find the direction of the ball after impact
- by considering the geometry to investigate whether or not B is in the path of the ball.

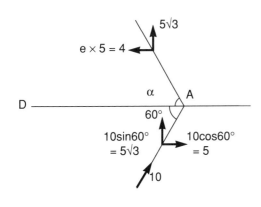

Along DA: velocity after $= -e \times$ velocity before

in the case of impact with a solid surface.

► See pages 106–108 if you have forgotten this.

∴ component after
$= -0.8 \times 5$

$= -4$ along DA

i.e. 4 along AD

$$\alpha = \arctan \frac{5\sqrt{3}}{4} = 65.2°$$

Now for the geometry:

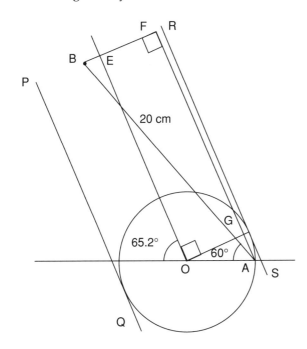

The ball will hit B provided B is between PQ and RS.
OE is the path of the centre of the ball and for a hit
BE < radius of ball.

If BE = x then $x < 1$ for a hit.

EF = OG = OAsin65.2° = 0.9

BF = x + EF = x + 0.9 = ABsinBÂF

$= 20\sin(65.2° - 60°)$

$= 1.8$

∴ $x = 1.8 - 0.9 = 0.9$

i.e. $x < 1$ therefore the ball hits B.

► **NB** Most students would find the second part of this question harder than the first, i.e. the pure mathematics being harder than the mechanics. This is often the case and is something you must be prepared for.

3 *Mostly Newton's Second Law*

Chapter outline

Reminders

▮ NL2

▮ Uniform acceleration

▮ Relative motion

▮ Limiting friction

New theory in this chapter

▮ Problems involving connected particles

Pure mathematics needed

▮ Simple trigonometry

▮ Simultaneous equations

INTRODUCTION

In this chapter you will be using mainly the principles of:

● Newton's second law, NL2
● Uniform acceleration.

Other points which you need to remember:

● Significance of the word 'smooth' – no frictional or other forces
● Meaning of 'light' – no mass and hence no weight
● Meaning of 'relative to' – see page 107
● Limiting friction.

► Solutions on page 129

(ACT) *Activity 3.1*

1

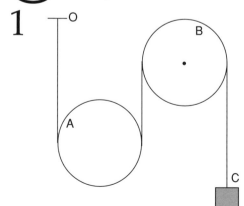

The diagram shows a string passing round two smooth pulleys, A and B, and carrying a mass of 5*m* at C. The string is fixed at O and the pulley B rotates on a smooth fixed axle through its centre.

The pulley A is not fixed and it has mass $3m$. Find the acceleration of C and the force exerted on the pulley B by the axle. B is a light pulley.

2

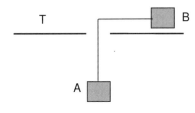

The figure shows a table top T with a smooth-edged hole in it. A is a mass of m below the table, attached by a string passing through a smooth pulley to a mass B, of mass $2m$, on the table. B is 3 m from the hole. The surface of the table is rough and variable. Investigate what happens if μ, the coefficient of friction, takes the values **(a)** $\frac{1}{4}$ **(b)** $\frac{1}{2}$ **(c)** $\frac{3}{4}$. If B moves find the time taken to reach the hole.

3

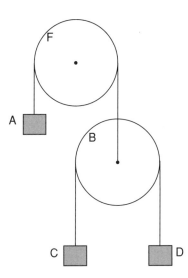

Pulley F is fixed but free to rotate smoothly about its axis. A smooth string passing over F carries a mass A of $5m$ at one end and a light pulley, B, at the other. Over B, which is free to rotate about its axis, passes another smooth string, carrying masses C of $2m$, and D of $3m$, at its ends. Find the accelerations of A, B, C and D.

► Ponder carefully before you start this one – equilibrium?

4 A girl of mass 50 kg stands on some bathroom scales on the floor of a lift. Find her apparent weight, as shown by the scales, when the lift accelerates at **(a)** 10 m s^{-2} **(b)** 2 m s^{-2} **(c)** –5 m s^{-2} **(d)** –12 m s^{-2} upwards. $g = 10$ m s^{-2}.

► Towards the realms of weight-lessness – think about this carefully and you will see how weight varies.

5

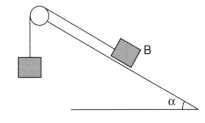

The diagram shows a rough plane inclined at α to the horizontal. A is a mass of weight W connected by a light rope passing over a smooth pulley, C, to a mass B, weight $2W$, on the plane. B moves very slowly down the plane. If $\mu < 1$ show that $\sin \alpha - \cos \alpha < \frac{1}{2}$.

6

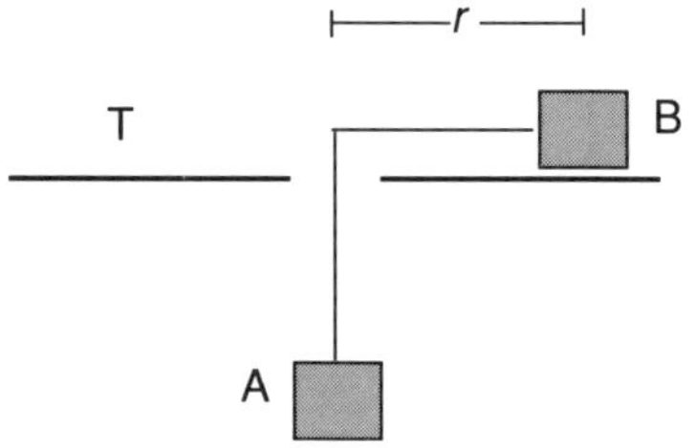

As in question 2, T is a horizontal table with a hole in it, but this time the table is smooth.

A, mass m, hangs in equilibrium. B, mass M, is going round in a circle, radius r, centre the hole, at constant speed.

Find the acceleration of B in terms of M, m and g.

► Coalesce = stick together

7 A string passes over a smooth fixed pulley and on its ends it has masses of $2m$ and m. They are held at the same level with the string taut. They are then released. When the mass m has risen 1 metre it has an inelastic collision with a mass of $3m$ and the two coalesce. Find

(a) the velocity of the combined mass, m and $3m$, after the impact
(b) the time that elapses from impact before the system is stationary
(c) the time taken from impact until once again all the masses are at the same level.

► **Remember:** large, clear diagrams and clearly labelled diagrams

8

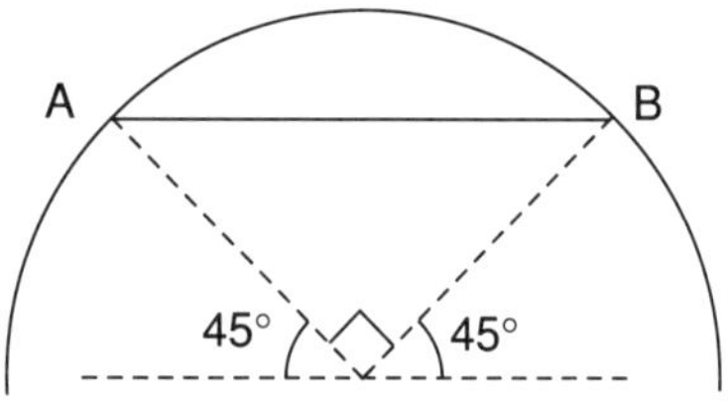

The diagram shows two small rings, A of mass m and B of mass M ($M > m$), threaded on a smooth circular wire which is set in a vertical plane.

They are connected by a light string AB and initially they are in the positions shown. They are released and they move on the wire until the radius to A makes an angle α with the horizontal.

Find the tangential acceleration of A in terms of M, m, α and g, and find the condition in terms of m, M and α for this motion to occur.

► Equilibrium? Remember question 3.

9 A pulley, A, is fixed with its axis horizontal. Over A passes a smooth string carrying at its ends two light pulleys, B and C. Over B passes a smooth string with masses $6m$ and $4m$ at its ends; similarly over C passes another smooth string with masses $3m$ and $7m$ at its ends. Find the force exerted by the axis of A on A.

10

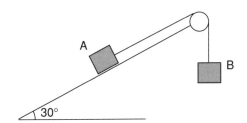

The diagram shows an inclined rough plane on which is a mass A, 3*m*. A is connected by a light string passing over a smooth pulley at the top of the plane and carrying a mass B, 4*m*, at its free end. Given that B accelerates downwards at $\frac{8}{5}$ m s⁻² find the coefficient of friction between A and the plane.

Solutions to Activity 3.1

1

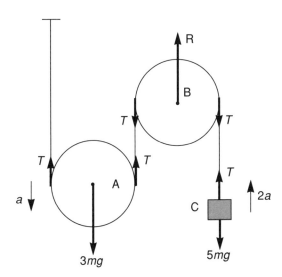

Study the diagram carefully; before you carry on make sure you understand:

- why the tension, *T*, is the same throughout the length of the string
- why the acceleration of C is 2*a* if the acceleration of A is *a*
- the force *R* is the force exerted on the pulley by the axle.

► Because the pulleys are smooth

► See solution 8, page 135

Vertically B is in equilibrium therefore $R = 2T$

NL2 for A: $3\,mg - 2T = 3ma$

NL2 for C: $T - 5mg = 10ma$

Eliminating T: $\Rightarrow\ -7mg = 23ma\ \Rightarrow\ a = -\dfrac{7g}{23}$

► The negative result is no surprise really, considering the masses involved.

► NB Units: We can only give units to our answers if the units of the quantities have been defined in the question. It is quite common for units not to be defined and hence we can give the answers without units (as in this question).

$$T = 5mg + 10ma = 5mg - \frac{70mg}{23} = \frac{45mg}{23}$$

Hence acceleration of C = $\frac{14g}{23}$ downwards

and $R = \frac{90mg}{23}$

2

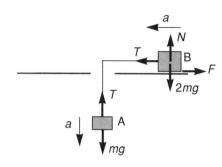

The force diagram is the same for all three cases.

Motion will occur if $T > F$

Remember, for equilibrium, $F \le \mu N$

Resolving vertically for B: $N = 2mg$

Hence, for equilibrium $F \le 2\mu mg$ i.e. $F_{max} = 2\mu mg$

Let us now assume that there is motion, i.e. a has value.

NL2 for A: $mg - T = ma$

NL2 for B: $T - F_{max} = 2ma$

$\Rightarrow mg - F_{max} = 3ma$

$\Rightarrow a = \frac{mg - 2\mu mg}{3m} = \frac{g(1 - 2\mu)}{3}$

When μ has the value

(a) $\frac{1}{4}$ $\qquad a = -\frac{g}{3}\left(1 - \frac{1}{2}\right) = \frac{g}{6}$

i.e. B has acceleration $\frac{g}{6}$ towards the hole.

We know t, s therefore use $s = ut + \frac{1}{2}at^2$

$\Rightarrow 3 = \frac{g}{12}t^2 \Rightarrow t = \frac{\sqrt{36}}{g} = 1.89$ s

(b) $\frac{1}{2}$ $\qquad a = \frac{g}{3}(1 - 1) = 0$

i.e. equilibrium

► A surprising result?

(c) $\frac{3}{4}$ $\qquad a = \frac{g}{3}\left(1 - \frac{3}{2}\right) = \frac{-g}{6}$

B accelerates away from the hole! Can this be true? No. Remember friction comes in to play to oppose motion, in this case to negate T and it can never be greater than T. From part **(b)** the maximum value T can take is mg (by considering A) and hence the maximum force of friction is mg. The statement that

► Common sense prevails!

$F = \dfrac{3}{2}mg$ is therefore wrong in this case.

Another view would be that, if B moves away from the hole, T and F would reverse directions: a piece of string pushing?!

3

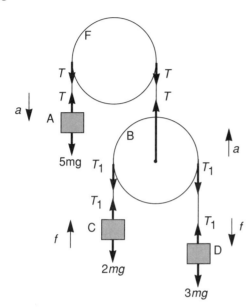

The string passing over pulley F carries a total mass of $5m$ at each end, therefore it is in equilibrium and does not move! Or does it? Common sense suggests that what we have just said is true. Let's proceed by giving A an acceleration of a: if the foregoing argument is true we should get $a = 0$.

The acceleration, f, of C and D is relative to the pulley B.

NL2 for A: $5mg - T = 5ma$ **(1)**

NL2 for B: $T - 2T_1 = 0 \times a$ **(2)**

NL2 for D: $3mg - T_1 = 3m(f - a)$ **(3)**

NL2 for C: $T_1 - 2mg = 2m(f + a)$ **(4)**

▶ B is a light pulley   ∴ $m = 0$

▶ Relative accelerations

▶ Make sure you understand the $(f - a)$ and the $(f + a)$

D accelerates at f downwards relative to B; but B accelerates at a upwards relative to F, which is fixed therefore D accelerates at $(f - a)$ downwards relative to F i.e. $(f - a)$ is the absolute acceleration of D.

Eliminate T from **(1)** and **(2)**   ⇒   equation including T_1 and a

Eliminate f from **(3)** and **(4)**   ⇒   equation including T_1 and a

Eliminate T_1 from new equations   ⇒ a found!

▶ Planning!

Hence: from **(1)** and **(2)** $5mg - 2T_1 = 5ma$ **(5)**

and from **(3)** and **(4)** $12mg - 5T_1 = -12ma$ **(6)**

From **(5)** and **(6)** $\qquad mg = 49ma \Rightarrow a = \dfrac{g}{49}$

From **(3)** and **(4)** $\qquad mg = 5mf - ma$

Substituting $a = \dfrac{g}{49} \Rightarrow f = \dfrac{10g}{49}$

Hence A accelerates downwards at $\dfrac{g}{49}$ m s^{-2}

B accelerates upwards at $\dfrac{g}{49}$ m s^{-2}

C accelerates upwards at $\dfrac{9g}{49} + \dfrac{10g}{49} = \dfrac{11g}{49}$ m s^{-2}

D accelerates downwards at $\dfrac{10g}{49} - \dfrac{g}{49} = \dfrac{9g}{49}$ m s^{-2}

4 When you stand on some bathroom scales the force diagram for the forces acting on you is that shown on page 2. The scales actually record the force R which they exert on you and which is equal to your weight when the system is in equilibrium.

At equilibrium the girl has apparent weight 500 N = Ma. In this problem the girl is not in equilibrium because she is being accelerated.

▶ Apparent weight

▶ The algebra is simple but the reasoning required in this question is quite deep. Expect to have to return to the ideas here before you really understand them.

R = force exerted on girl (shown by scales)

a = acceleration

M = mass of girl

Let us firstly consider the general situation.

NL2 for girl: $R - Mg = Ma$

$\Rightarrow \quad R = Mg + Ma$

(a) $a = 10$: $R = 50 \times 10 + 50 \times 10$
$= 100 \times 10 = 1000$ N

Her apparent weight is doubled.

(b) $a = 2$: $R = 50 \times 10 + 50 \times 2 = 60 \times 10 = 600$ N
Her apparent weight is increased by 20%.

(c) $a = -5$: $R = 50 \times 10 - 50 \times 5 = 25 \times 10 = 250$ N
Her apparent weight is halved.

(d) $a = -12$: $R = 50 \times 10 - 50 \times 12 = -10 \times 10 = -100$ N
negative weight! at least weightless.

In this case the girl accelerates downwards at g (= 10 m s^{-2}) but the lift goes at 12 m s^{-2} therefore the girl leaves the floor (and bangs her head on the ceiling of the lift).

5 This type of question throws many students. After reading a description of a mechanics situation they are asked to show a result relating only to the angle of slope; nothing to do with any mechanics quantities, weights, velocities etc. Invariably you will only arrive at the required result by considering the mechanics of the situation.

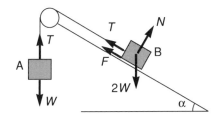

F = friction

N = normal reaction

T = tension

The significance of the 'very slowly' in the question is that it says the acceleration is negligible. Since B is moving, however, the force of friction is a maximum.

We have three unknowns, T, F and N, so we must have three equations before we can do anything towards finding them.

NL2 for A: $T - W = 0$ $\therefore$ $T = W$

NL2 along plane for B: $2W\sin\alpha - F - T = 0$ **(1)**

$\perp$ plane: $N = 2W\cos\alpha$

Since friction is a maximum $F = \mu N = \mu \times 2W\cos\alpha$

Substituting for T and F in **(1)**:

$2W\sin\alpha - 2\mu W\cos\alpha - W = 0$

$\Rightarrow$ $2\sin\alpha - 2\mu\cos\alpha - 1 = 0$

$\Rightarrow$ $\mu = \dfrac{2\sin\alpha - 1}{2\cos\alpha}$

$\mu < 1$ $\Rightarrow$ $\dfrac{2\sin\alpha - 1}{2\cos\alpha} < 1$

$\Rightarrow$ $\sin\alpha - \cos\alpha < \dfrac{1}{2}$ – Well, what do you know?

► Finding the unknowns in terms of common quantities in this case *W*.

► Each term is a term in *W*; *W* cancels out ⇒ an equation without any forces i.e. something towards what we want.

► You may wonder at the significance of this result. The result itself is purely academic and of no value in its own right but to achieve it you have shown that you know how to handle the mechanics of the problem.

6

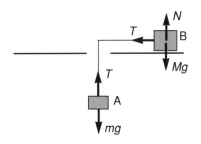

A is in equilibrium

$\therefore$ $T = mg$

NL2 for B: $T = Ma$

a is acceleration

$\therefore$ $a = \dfrac{mg}{M}$

► The words 'constant speed' may make you think that there is zero acceleration but that would be faulty thinking. To see why look at page 47.

Hence we have a value for the acceleration. What about is direction? It acts in the direction of T i.e. towards the centre of the circle the mass is moving on.

▶ Planning

7

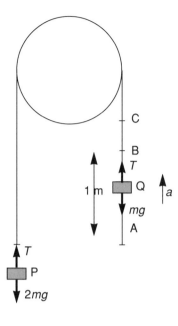

Q starts at A and rises to B.

Collides with $3m$ mass at B.

Continues to rise and stops at C.

Falls to A.

(a) Use conservation of momentum to find the velocity after impact.

We need to know velocity before impact.

$\therefore$ we need the acceleration.

Hence: NL2 for Q $\Rightarrow$ $T - mg = ma$

and NL2 for P $\Rightarrow$ $2mg - T = 2ma$

$\Rightarrow$ $a = \dfrac{g}{3}$

▶ Thinking and planning

For the velocity at B: we know s, we want v

so use $v^2 = u^2 + 2as$

$\Rightarrow$ $v^2 = 2 \times \dfrac{g}{3} \times 1$ $\Rightarrow$ $v = 2.6$ m s^{-1}

COM for system: $3m \times 2.6 = 6m \times v_1$

$\Rightarrow$ $v_1 = 1.3$ m s^{-1}

▶ Thinking and planning

(b) For B to C: we know v, u. We want t so use $v = u + at$. Firstly we need the new acceleration.

NL2 for Q: $T_1 = 4mg = 4ma$

NL2 for P: $2mg - T_1 = 2ma$

$\Rightarrow$ $a = \dfrac{g}{3}$

Hence: $0 = 1.3 - 3.3t$ $\Rightarrow$ $t = 0.39 \approx 0.4$ s

▶ Thinking and planning

(c) We want t_2 (time from C to A). We know a, u but not s, v.

It is necessary first to find the distance B to C.

s, v $\Rightarrow$ $v^2 = u^2 + 2as$

▶ Is this the value you expected?

$\Rightarrow$ $0 = 6.5 - 6.5s$ $\Rightarrow$ $s = 1$ m

$\therefore$ CA = 2 m

$s = ut + \dfrac{1}{2}at^2$ $\Rightarrow$ $2 = \dfrac{1}{2} \times \dfrac{9}{3} \times t_2^2$

$\Rightarrow$ $t_2 = 1.2$ s

8

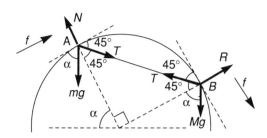

N, R are normal reactions.

T is the tension in the string.

Consider A and B to be in the positions shown where the radius to A makes an angle α with the horizontal.

NL2 along tangent for A: $T\cos 45° - mg\cos\alpha = mf$

NL2 along tangent for B: $Mg\sin\alpha - T\cos 45° = Mf$

Solving for f:

$\Rightarrow \quad Mf + mf = Mg\sin\alpha - mg\cos\alpha$

$\Rightarrow \quad f = \dfrac{g(M\sin\alpha - m\cos\alpha)}{M + m}$

For motion to occur $f > 0$

i.e. $M\sin\alpha - m\cos\alpha > 0$

$\Rightarrow \quad \tan\alpha > \dfrac{m}{M}$

▶ What a heavy question this was at first reading! Being asked to find 'tangential acceleration' and 'conditions for motion' is enough to make anyone pack up and go home.

But look back now and see what was involved:
(i) clear diagram
(ii) NL2
(iii) Some algebra.

And with the information given what else could we have done anyway?

Moral: don't be put off by the formal, but necessary, language used in questions.

9

Refer to the diagram on page 136.

a is the acceleration of B relative to A

f_1 is the acceleration of the $6m$ mass relative to B

f is the acceleration of the $7m$ mass relative to C.

A is in equilibrium vertically.

$\therefore \quad R = 2T$

NL2 for B: $T - 2T_1 = 0 \times a$

and for C: $-T + 2T_2 = 0 \times a$

$\therefore \quad T = T_1 + T_2$

NL2 for:

$7m$ mass	$\Rightarrow \quad 7mg - T_2 = 7m(f + a)$	**(1)**
$3m$ mass	$\Rightarrow \quad T_2 - 3mg = 3m(f - a)$	**(2)**
$6m$ mass	$\Rightarrow \quad T_1 - 6mg = 6m(a - f_1)$	**(3)**
$4m$ mass	$\Rightarrow \quad T_1 - 4mg = 4m(a + f_1)$	**(4)**

Eliminating f from **(1)** and **(2)** and f_1 from **(3)** and **(4)** will give two equations with T_1, T_2 and a. Then eliminating T_1 and T_2 will give T and a which we want because we then eliminate a to find T.

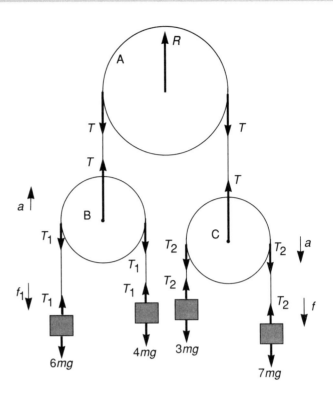

Hence: from **(1)** and **(2)**

$$42mg - 10T_2 = 42ma \qquad \text{(5)}$$

from **(3)** and **(4)**

$$10T_1 - 48mg = 48ma \qquad \text{(6)}$$

Substituting for T_2 in **(5)**

$$42mg - 5T = 42ma \qquad \text{(7)}$$

and for T_1 in **(6)**

$$5T - 48mg = 48ma \qquad \text{(8)}$$

Adding equations **(8)** and **(7)**

$$\Rightarrow \quad -6mg = 90ma$$

i.e. $a = \dfrac{-g}{15}$

Substituting in **(8)**

$$\Rightarrow \quad 5T - 48mg = -\frac{48mg}{15}$$

$$\Rightarrow \quad T = \frac{224}{25}\,mg$$

$$\therefore \quad R = \frac{448}{25}\,mg$$

▶ Once we have a good diagram the mechanics of this question are not too difficult to apply. However we cannot stress too much the need for clarity and order in handling the amount of algebra which follows.

10

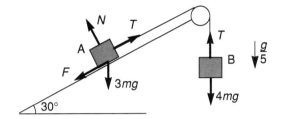

NL2 for A along plane: $T - F - 3mg\sin30° = \dfrac{3mg}{5}$ **(1)**

NL2 for B: $4mg - T = \dfrac{4mg}{5}$

$\therefore\quad T = \dfrac{16mg}{5}$ **(2)**

Since A is moving F is a maximum i.e. $F = \mu N$

$\therefore\quad F = \mu 3mg\cos30°$ **(3)**

Substituting for F and T from **(3)** and **(2)** in **(1)** we get

$\dfrac{16}{5}mg - 3\mu mg\dfrac{\sqrt{3}}{2} - 3mg\times\dfrac{1}{2} = \dfrac{3mg}{5}$

$\Rightarrow\quad \dfrac{16}{5} - \dfrac{3}{2} - \dfrac{3}{5} = \dfrac{3\sqrt{3}}{2}\mu$

$\Rightarrow\quad \mu = \dfrac{11}{10}\times\dfrac{2}{3\sqrt{3}} = 0.4$

More Friction than Anything

► See page 30

► See page 63
► See pages 53 and 58

Chapter outline

Reminders

▮ Friction

▮ μ is the coefficient of friction between two surfaces

▮ For equilibrium $F \leq \mu N$

▮ Limiting (maximum) friction $= \mu N$

▮ $\mu < 1$

▮ Smooth = no friction

▮ Friction resists motion

▮ Moments

▮ Energy and work

New theory in this chapter

▮ Static and dynamic friction

▮ Angle of friction

▮ Three force problems

Pure mathematics required

▮ Simple trigonometry

▮ Simultaneous equations

▮ Compound angles – $\sin(A + B)$ etc

FRICTION

On page 32 there is a graph like this:

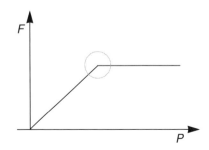

Do you remember how we arrived at this graph?

Now if we had made accurate measurements of P and F we could have drawn an accurate graph.

Static and dynamic friction

An enlargement of the part inside the circle of such a graph would look like this:

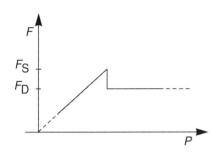

This graph shows that friction increases to a value F_s.

When movement occurs friction drops slightly to F_D.

F_s is known as **static friction** and F_D is known as **dynamic friction**.

▶ Static and dynamic friction

The difference between them is very small (it has been exaggerated in this graph) and, as has been the case so far, we consider them to be equal in our work.

Angle of friction

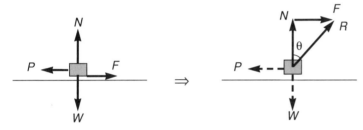

W = weight

P = applied force

F = force of friction

N = normal reaction

This diagram indicates that we are turning our attention solely to the forces F and N. It shows them drawn as a triangle of forces in which R is the resultant of F and N. It is also the equilibrant of P and W.

In the first diagram W and N remain constant.

As P increases F increases ⇒ θ increases on the second diagram
θ is a maximum when F is a maximum and then

$$\tan\theta = \frac{F}{N}$$

but $\mu = \frac{F}{N}$

$\therefore$ $\tan\theta = \mu$

Angle of friction
The maximum value of θ is usually indicated by λ, hence $\mu = \tan\lambda$ and λ is known as the **angle of friction**.

▶ Angle of friction defined

The angle of friction should not cause any real problem: it is an alternative way of representing μ.

▶ In mechanics we are looking at real situations and tackling problems, even if we make assumptions – 'smooth' etc. – to make life easier. In reality it is difficult to think of a situation where friction does not play a part other than items at rest on a level surface. Friction is active in all dynamic and in many static situations.

▶ Solutions on page 142

▶ A long question involving:
COM
NEL
NL2
$F = \mu N$
$v^2 = u^2 + 2as$
– good revision!
Planning is important.

 *Activity 4.1*

1

ABC is a horizontal surface in which AB is smooth and AB = 1 m. BC is rough and BC = 10 m. An impact occurs at A between particle P, mass 2*m* kg, travelling in direction AB at 5 m s⁻¹ and Q, mass *M* kg, which is at rest. Q comes to rest at C. The coefficient of restitution at the impact is 0.6.

Find the force of friction acting on Q and find where P stops, assuming the coefficient of friction is the same for P and Q on the rough surface.

2 A light ladder rests against a smooth wall and stands on rough horizontal ground. The ladder is inclined to the wall at 30° and a man of weight *W* climbs three-quarters of the way up the ladder. Find the coefficient of friction between the ladder and the ground if the ladder is in limiting equilibrium.

3 A particle of weight *W* is placed on a rough sloping plane of which the angle of slope may be varied. By considering a position of limiting equilibrium find a relationship between the angle of friction and the angle of slope.

4 Using a ruler only, find the coefficient of friction between your block and **(a)** this book **(b)** some other rougher surface.

5

▶ Why not? It is a useful way of moving a very heavy object given limited facilities.

This picture shows a man dragging a garden spade with a car engine on it.

By transforming the picture into the following diagram create a force diagram to represent what is happening.

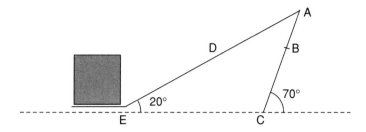

ABC is the man from shoulder to foot. AC = 1.6 m

B is the centre of gravity (CG) of the man who has weight W. BC = 1 m.

AD is the man's arm and DE is the spade handle: ADE is a straight line.

The engine is a uniform block of weight w.

μ is the coefficient of friction between spade and floor and is 0.8.

By keeping his feet still and leaning back, the man can reach a situation where the engine just moves.

Find w as a fraction of W.

6 A particle of weight W is placed on a rough plane, angle of friction λ. A force P, acting at angle β to the upward direction of the plane, is about to move the particle. Find the value of β in terms of λ when P is a minimum, and also the value of this minimum. The plane makes angle α with the horizontal.

▶ A harder question, featuring expansions of sin $(A + B)$ and sin $(A - B)$.

7 A mass m is on a rough plane at the point A. The plane is inclined at 30°. The mass has an initial velocity of 5.7 m s⁻¹ down the plane. Take $\mu = 0.8$ and $g = 9.8$.

Find where the mass is after 3 seconds, its velocity at that time and the work done against friction in getting there.

▶ Work done and energy are involved in this one.

8

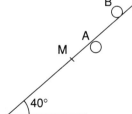

A uniform heavy beam rests on a fixed rough peg, A, and passes under a smooth fixed peg B. It is inclined at 40° to the horizontal. If equilibrium is limiting and $\mu = \frac{1}{2}$ show that BA : AM = 3 : 2.

► If you have the chance you could approach local industries and see if they will tell you of some examples in their work where friction can be a help and where it can be a hindrance. Enlightened industry is only too happy to cooperate with students in this way. If your course involves coursework this would be a possible topic of study.

9

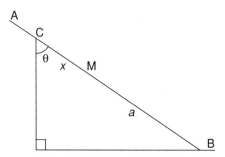

A uniform beam, weight W, rests on the floor of an ice-rink which is smooth and it overhangs a wall, as shown, where the contact is rough.

$\mu = \dfrac{1}{\sqrt{3}}$, CM $= x$, MB $= a$, M is the centre of gravity.

Find, in terms of W, a, x and θ

(a) the force on the beam at B

(b) the force of friction at C

(c) the normal reaction at C.

(d) Find the minimum value of θ for equilibrium to be possible.

Solutions to Activity 4.1

1 There are several bits to this question and a little planning will help:

► A good planning plan!

		Knowing	Use	To find
(i)	**(a)**	impact at A	COM, NEL	velocity of P and Q
	(b)	velocity of Q, distance BC	v, s	acceleration of Q
	(c)	acceleration at Q	NL2	F_Q
(ii)	**(a)**	F on Q	$F = \mu N$	μ
	(b)	μ	$F = \mu N$	F on P
	(c)	F_P	NL2	acceleration of P
	(d)	acceleration of P	v, s	s

(i) At A, COM: $2m \times 5 = 2mu + mu \quad \Rightarrow \quad 10 = 2v + u$

$$u - v = -0.6 \times -5 \quad \Rightarrow \quad 3 = u - v$$

$$\Rightarrow \quad u = \frac{16}{3}, v = \frac{7}{3}$$

For Q: $v, s \quad \Rightarrow \quad v^2 = u^2 + 2as \quad \Rightarrow \quad 0 = \left(\frac{16}{3}\right)^2 + 2a \times 10$

$\Rightarrow \quad a = -1.4 \text{ m s}^{-2}$

i.e. Q is retarding at 1.4 m s^{-2}

NL2 $\quad \Rightarrow \quad F_Q = m \times 1.4$ where F_Q is force of friction on Q

i.e. $F_Q = 1.4m$ N

▶ We can state it in newtons because the information was given.

(ii) P arrives at B with velocity $\frac{7}{3}$ m s^{-1}.

For P on BC: $\quad F_P = \mu N_P \quad \Rightarrow \quad F_P = \mu \times 2mg$

For Q on BC: $\quad F_Q = \mu N_Q \quad \Rightarrow \quad 1.4m = \mu mg$

$\therefore \quad F_P = 2 \times 1.4m = 2.8m$

NL2 $\quad \Rightarrow \quad -2.8m = 2mf$

▶ f is the acceleration of P

$f = -1.4 \text{ m s}^{-2}$

$v, s \quad \Rightarrow \quad v^2 = u^2 + 2as$

$\Rightarrow \quad 0 = \left(\frac{7}{3}\right)^2 - 2 \times 1.4 \times s$

$\Rightarrow \quad s = 1.9 \text{ m}$

Therefore P stops at D where BD = 1.9 m

2

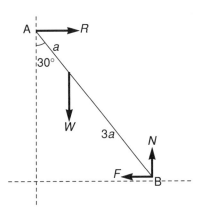

▶ You could develop a good study topic by trying to find the safest angle for a ladder in practice. It is possibly about 30° to the vertical. With a little effort and research you should be able to reach a good conclusion.

Resolving vertically: $\quad N = W$

Resolving horizontally: $\quad F = R$

Taking moments about B for the ladder:

$R \times 4a\cos30° = W \times 3a\sin30°$

$\therefore \quad R = \frac{3W}{4}\tan30°$

Limiting equilibrium $\quad \Rightarrow \quad F = \mu N$

$\Rightarrow \quad \mu = \frac{3W}{4}\tan30° \times \frac{1}{W} = 0.4$

3

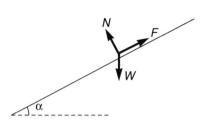

The system is in equilibrium, therefore R, the resultant of F and N, is the equilibrant to W.

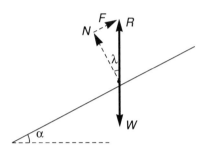

F and N are dotted because they should not really be there: they are replaced by R.

Since equilibrium is limiting, the angle of friction, λ, is as shown. By the geometry of the diagram $\lambda = \alpha$.

► A neat solution – not an equation in it!

4

  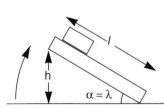

► Question 3 put into immediate practice!

The block is just about to slip.
Then $\alpha = \lambda$
Measure h and l.

$$\mu = \tan \lambda = \frac{h}{\sqrt{l^2 - h^2}}$$

5

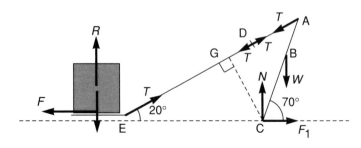

Forces are as shown.

T is the tension in the man's arms and the spade handle.

Why is it the some in both?

Point D is in equilibrium, therefore tensions are equal.

Resolving horizontally for the engine/spade: $F = T\cos20°$

Limiting equilibrium, $\therefore$ $F = \mu R = \mu w$

Hence $T\cos20° = \mu w$ **(1)**

Taking moments about C for AC: $T \times CG = W \times 1\cos70°$

$\therefore$ $T \times 1.6\cos40° = W\cos70°$ **(2)**

Eliminating T from **(1)** and **(2)**:

$$\frac{\mu w}{\cos20°} = \frac{W\cos70°}{1.6\cos40°}$$

$\therefore$ $w = \dfrac{W\cos70°\cos20°}{1.6 \times 0.8 \times \cos40°} = 0.3W$

▶ It is necessary to find a link between T and W.

▶ Why is this a fairly easy way of moving a heavy weight? Consider the forces acting on the weight, compared with pushing with your hands.

6

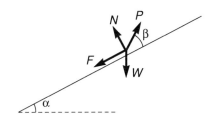

Resolving // plane: $P\cos\beta = F + W\sin\alpha$ **(1)**

Resolving $\perp$ plane: $N + P\sin\beta = W\cos\alpha$ **(2)**

Limiting equilibrium: $F = \mu N$ **(3)**

Substituting from **(3)** in **(1)**: $P\cos\beta = \mu N + W\sin\alpha$ **(4)**

Substituting for N from **(2)** in **(4)**:

$P\cos\beta = \mu(W\cos\alpha - P\sin\beta) + W\sin\alpha$

$\Rightarrow$ $P\cos\beta + \mu P\sin\beta = \mu W\cos\alpha + W\sin\alpha$

$\Rightarrow$ $P(\cos\lambda\cos\beta + \sin\lambda\sin\beta) = W(\sin\lambda\cos\alpha + \cos\lambda\sin\alpha)$

since $\mu = \tan\lambda$

$\Rightarrow$ $P\cos(\lambda - \beta) = W\sin(\alpha + \lambda)$

$\Rightarrow$ $P = \dfrac{W\sin(\alpha + \lambda)}{\cos(\lambda - \beta)}$

P is minimum when $\cos(\lambda - \beta) = 1$

i.e. when $\lambda = \beta$ and then $P = W\sin(\alpha + \lambda)$.

7

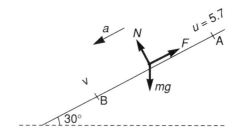

NL2 // plane:
$mg\sin\alpha - F = ma$

Limiting equilibrium:
$F = \mu N = \mu mg\cos\alpha$

Eliminating F:
$mg\sin30° - 0.8mg\cos30° = ma$

$\Rightarrow \quad a = -1.9 \text{ m s}^{-2}$

Using the v, t equation:
$\Rightarrow \quad v = u + at$

$\Rightarrow \quad v = 5.7 - 1.9 \times 3$

$\therefore \quad v = 0$

i.e. stationary

Using the v, s equation:
$\Rightarrow \quad v^2 = u^2 + 2as$

$\Rightarrow \quad 0 = 5.7^2 - 2 \times 1.9 \times s$

$\Rightarrow \quad s = 8.6 \text{ m}$

i.e. after 3 seconds the mass is stationary at B where AB = 8.6 m.

Energy lost = loss in PE + loss in KE

$= m \times 9.8 \times 8.6\sin30° + \dfrac{1}{2} \times m \times 5.7^2$

= 58 joules (if m is in kg)

Work done = force × distance

$= F \times AB$

$= \mu mg\cos30° \times 8.6$

$= 0.8 \times m \times 9.8 \times \cos30° \times 8.6$

= 58m joules (if m is in kg)

► So far this question has not proved so bad but we now come to the part which many students find harder to understand.

In going from A to B the mass loses kinetic and potential energy. This is because of the external forces acting in the direction of travel which in this case amount to the force of friction. The energy lost is a measure of the work done overcoming the force of friction.

We have two ways of calculating it.

We can either find the energy lost or use the force × distance rule.

We have actually found the work done by the force but this is equal to the work done against the force by the mass sliding.

► So many different principles involved in question 7 – we really are getting into the mechanics now!

8 Let MA = x and
   AB = y.

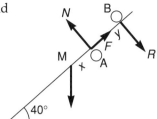

Again we have to derive a purely geometrical result and again
all we can do is look at the mechanics of the problem.
The result involves distances, x and y, which suggests using
moments. About where? When deciding upon the point to take
moments about, we look for the point which eliminates
quantities we don't want, and includes those we do.

(a) Taking moments about A
     gives an equation connecting W, R
     Resolving ⊥ rod gives an
     equation connecting W, N, R
     Resolving // rod gives an
     equation connecting W, F
     Using limiting friction gives
     an equation connecting F, N

(b) Taking moments about B gives
     an equation connecting W, N
     Resolving // the rod gives an
     equation connecting F, W
     Using limiting friction gives an
     equation connecting F, N

Hence plan **(b)** looks like the better one to try.

▶ $\left.\begin{array}{l} F, W \\ F, N \end{array}\right\}$ W, N

means from two equations, one in
F and W, and one in F and N, F can
be eliminated to give an equation
in W and N.

Taking moments about B for the beam:

$Ny = W\cos40° \times (x + y)$ **(1)**

Resolving // rod: $W\sin40° = F$ **(2)**

Using limiting friction: $F = \dfrac{1}{2} N$ **(3)**

From **(2)** and **(3)**: $W\sin40° = \dfrac{1}{2} N$

Substituting for N in **(1)**: $2W\sin40° \times y = W\cos40° \times (x + y)$

Hence $y \times 2\sin40° = x\cos40° + y\cos40°$

$y(2\sin40° - \cos40°) = x\cos40°$

$\therefore \dfrac{y}{x} = \dfrac{\cos40°}{2\sin40° - \cos40°} = \dfrac{0.76}{0.52}$

$\therefore \dfrac{y}{x} \approx \dfrac{3}{2}$

▶ Algebraically this is what we
wanted; an equation with the
same force, in this case W, in every
term because W can be cancelled
out and we shall be left with x and
y only.

▶ NB This solution well illustrates
the value of planning. Method **(a)**
would be correct and would score
as many marks but while you are
spending more time to score the
same number of marks the student
who used method **(b)** has moved
on and is scoring more marks else-
where.

9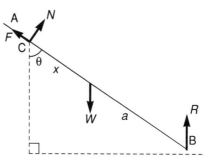

The beam tends to slip down and hence F acts in the direction shown.

(a) Taking moments about C for AB (because it will not include F and N which are not required at this stage)

$$R(a + x)\sin\theta = W \times \sin\theta \quad \Rightarrow \quad R = \frac{Wx}{a + x}$$

(b) Resolving // the beam: $F + R\cos\theta = W\cos\theta$

$$\Rightarrow \quad F = W\cos\theta - \frac{Wx\cos\theta}{(a + x)}$$

$$= \frac{Wa\cos\theta}{a + x}$$

(c) Taking moments about B for AB (because it excludes F and R)

$$N(a + x) = Wa\sin\theta$$
$$\Rightarrow \quad N = \frac{Wa\sin\theta}{a + x}$$

(d) Finding maximum/minimum values suggests inequalities and an obvious one is:

► **Remember:**

$\dfrac{1}{\tan\theta} = \text{cotangent}\theta = \cot\theta$

$\dfrac{1}{\cos\theta} = \text{secant}\theta = \sec\theta$

$\dfrac{1}{\sin\theta} = \text{cosecant}\theta = \text{cosec}\theta$

For equilibrium $\dfrac{F}{N} \leq \mu$

$$\Rightarrow \quad \frac{Wa\cos\theta}{a + x} \times \frac{a + x}{Wa\sin\theta} \leq \frac{1}{\sqrt{3}}$$

$$\Rightarrow \quad \cot\theta \leq \frac{1}{\sqrt{3}}$$

$$\Rightarrow \quad \tan\theta \geq \sqrt{3}$$

► Go back to the diagram and, without any working out, state the direction of the resultant of F and N.

$$\Rightarrow \quad \theta \geq 60°$$

$$\therefore \quad \text{minimum value of } \theta \text{ is } 60°$$

Three-force problems

Some of the problems we have considered in the last activity fall into the category of three-force problems, because there are three and only three forces acting on the body under consideration.

Consider your block.

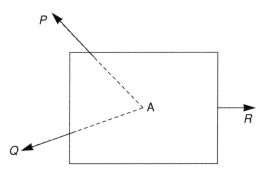

► This bit of theory is often asked for in examinations.

Suppose it is acted on by three forces P, Q and R.

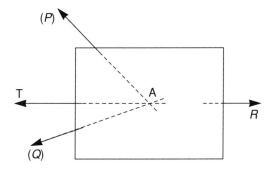

P and Q may be replaced by their resultant which acts through A, the point of intersection of their lines of action. The block is now acted on by two forces, T and R. If it is in equilibrium under the action of two forces they must be equal and opposite and colinear (in line). Hence the line of action of R must pass through A.

Reverting back to the first diagram: if the block is in equilibrium under the action of three forces they are concurrent: their lines of action meet in the same point.

EXAMPLE – a three-force problem
Using the set-up in question 2 of Activity 4.1 on page 140 find the reaction exerted by the ground on the ladder.

► Example – a three-force problem

Solution
P is the resultant of F and N at B (see the diagram on page 143).

The lines of action of R and W are known and they meet at C.

∴   the line of action of P is through C because the ladder is in equilibrium under three forces which are concurrent.

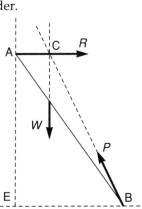

Looking at the geometry of the diagram we can highlight the triangle CDB:

► Always be on the lookout for possible use of geometry to solve these problems.

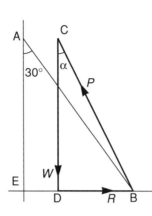

The sides of △CDB are in the directions of the forces and hence it can be considered as the triangle of forces where

CD represents W

BC represents P

and DB represents R.

Now DB $= \dfrac{3}{4}$ BE $= \dfrac{3}{4} \times 4a\cos60° = \dfrac{3a}{2}$

and CD = AE = $4a\cos30° = 2a\sqrt{3}$

$\Rightarrow$ BC = 3.8a by Pythagoras' theorem

► This may seem long-winded but it can be a very quick way of solving these problems.

From △CDB $W = P\cos\alpha$ $\Rightarrow$ $P = \dfrac{W3.8}{2\sqrt{3}} = 1.1W$

► Solutions on page 151

(ACT) *Activity 4.2*

1

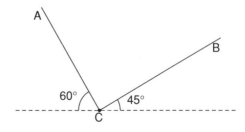

The diagram shows the cross-section of two smooth surfaces set perpendicular to each other. The line of intersection is horizontal (something like a food trough on a level field). AB is a uniform rod of weight W. Show that the line of action of W passes through the intersection of the planes.

2

AC and BC are two strings fixed at A and B and supporting a weight W at C. Without resolving or drawing a scale diagram find the tensions in the strings.

3 A rod AB of length $2a$ and weight W is hinged at A and supported at $60°$ to the upward vertical by a string, of length $2a$, attached to B and to a point $2a$ vertically above A. Find the tension in the string and the reaction on the rod at the hinge.

Solutions to Activity 4.2

1

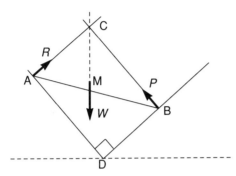

AB is in equilibrium under three forces W, R and P.
R and P are perpendicular to DA and DB respectively and their lines meet at C, thus forming a rectangle ACBD.
The line of action of W passes through C for equilibrium.
But MC is half the diagonal DC of the rectangle.
Therefore the line of action of W is along the diagonal and passes through D.

2

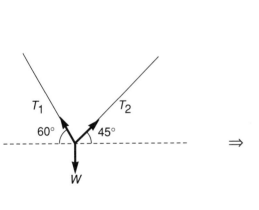

$\Rightarrow$

► Triangle of forces

The triangle of forces

Sine rule $\Rightarrow \dfrac{T_1}{\sin 45°} = \dfrac{T_2}{\sin 30°} = \dfrac{W}{\sin 105°}$

$\Rightarrow T_1 = 0.7W$ and $T_2 = 0.5W$

► Sine rule:
$\dfrac{a}{\sin A} = \dfrac{b}{\sin B} = \dfrac{c}{\sin C}$

3

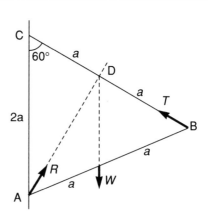

Directions of W and T are known. Therefore R acts through D.
The triangle of forces can be seen in the diagram in $\triangle$ADC.

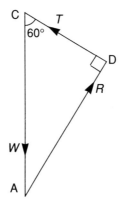

$$T = W\cos 60° = \frac{W}{2}$$

$$R = W\cos 30° = \frac{W\sqrt{3}}{2}$$

Reactions at Joints

► See page 5

► See page 63

► See page 4

> **Chapter outline**
>
> **Reminders**
>
> ▌ Resolving
>
> ▌ Taking moments
>
> ▌ Equilibrium
>
> **New theory in this chapter**
> None
>
> **Pure mathematics required**
>
> ▌ Simple trigonometry
>
> ▌ Simultaneous equations

Reactions at joints

Quite often we meet the situation where rods, beams, etc. are joined together, usually by a smooth hinge or pivot, or they are held together by strings and our problem is to find the forces acting at the joint. Consider an ordinary stepladder which can be represented like this:

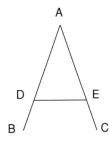

AB is the heavier side, with the steps smoothly jointed at A to the lighter side. DE is a piece of rope which prevents the whole system from doing the splits.

Smoothly jointed means no rotational resistance, friction, etc. in the joint.

In this work we are particularly interested in what is happening at A.

Method

1 Explode the joint.

2 Put in the forces in component form.

Since the joint is in equilibrium the force exerted on AB by AC is equal and opposite to the force exerted on AC by AB.

At this stage, if the problem indicates directions for X and Y, then make use of the fact. If you haven't a clue on directions, as in this case, don't worry, just guess! If your guess is wrong it will be sorted out in the algebra.

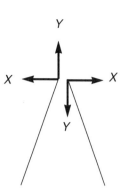

3 Use resolving and moments to find X and Y.

4 Find the resultant of X and Y.

Let's consider the stepladder again. We'll see that there is more to point 3 than meets the eye.

► This work shows how easy it is to disappear under a mountain of algebra and fail to reach any conclusion. Planning is the secret to success!

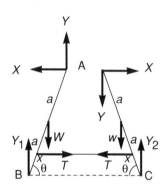

Method for equation	Forces involved	Equation
Resolve horizontally for AB	T, X	$T = X$
Resolve horizontally for AC	T, X	$T = X$
Resolve horizontally for the whole	none	none – see note opposite
Resolve vertically for the whole	Y_1, Y_2, W, w	$Y_1 + Y_2 = W + w$
Resolve vertically for AB	Y_1, Y, W	$Y_1 + Y = W$
Resolve vertically for AC	Y_2, Y, w	$Y_2 = w + Y$
Moments about B for the whole	W, w, Y_2	$4Y_2 = 3w + W$
Moments about C for the whole	w, W, Y_1	$4Y_1 = 3W + w$
Moments about B for AB	T, W, X, Y	$Wa\cos\theta + Tx\sin\theta$ $= X2a\sin\theta + Y2a\cos\theta$
Moments about C for AC	T, W, X, Y	$wa\cos\theta + Tx\sin\theta + Y2a\cos\theta$ $= X2a\sin\theta$
Moments about A for AB	Y_1, T, W	$Y_12a\cos\theta = T(2a - x)\sin\theta + W a\cos\theta$
Moments about A for AC	Y_2, T, w	$Y_22a\cos\theta = T(2a - x)\sin\theta + w a\cos\theta$
Moments about A for the whole	Y_1, Y_2, W, w	$2Y_1 + w = 2Y_2 + W$

. . . and that's not all!

We could continue by considering moments about the centres of gravity of AB and AC and the points where the rope is attached to AB and AC.

None of the equations is difficult to form in its own right but it is easy to see that without some sort of plan we would end up with algebraic chaos and a lack of direction – a lot of equations and no answer. So once again we are stressing the value of planning solutions constructively.

▶ **Note:** Resolving horizontally for the whole system gives no equation because there are no external horizontal forces on the whole system. *T* and *X* are forces internal to the system (and it is easy to see that the two *T*s and the two *X*s cancel each other out when the whole is considered).

Vertically *W*, *w*, Y_1 and Y_2 are external forces, Y_1 and Y_2 being external reactions to *W* and *w*.

▶ Solutions on page 156

(ACT) *Activity 5.1*

1

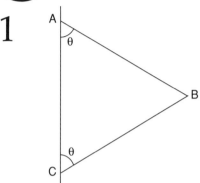

The diagram shows a rod BC, weight *W* and length 2*a*, smoothly pivoted to a wall at A and smoothly jointed to a light rod AB, also of length 2*a*. AB is fastened to the same wall at A.

Find the reactions in horizontal and vertical component form on BC at B and at C.

2

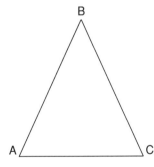

AB and BC are two equal, uniform legs of a stepladder, each of weight *W* and length 2*a*, and inclined at *θ* to the horizontal. They are held in position by a rope AC which is taut, and B is a smooth joint.

Find   **(a)**   the tension in the string

   (b)   the force acting on BC at the joint B.

3   A man of weight 10*W* climbs three-quarters of the way up the side BC of the stepladder in question 2.

Find the vertical and horizontal components of the force exerted on BC by AB.

4

A ———————— B ———————— C ———————— D

The diagram shows three uniform rods of equal length $2a$. AB has mass $2m$, BC has mass $4m$ and CD has mass $3m$. The rods are horizontal with AB on a support at a distance x from B and CD on a support at a distance y from C. The joints at B and C are smooth. Find x and y in terms of a.

5

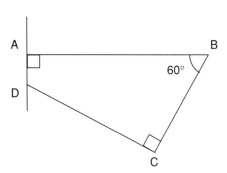

The diagram shows a framework of three rods, AB, BC and CD, smoothly jointed at B and C and fastened to a wall at A and D. The rods are uniform and AB = $2a$, BC = $2b$ and DC = $2c$. Their masses are W, $2W$ and $2W$ respectively.

Find the reactions at B and C.

Solutions to Activity 5.1

1

▶ A useful, easy equation

▶ For X_1 and Y_1 – planning again!

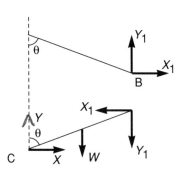

X, Y, X_1 and Y_1 are the required components.

Resolving horizontally for BC:
$\Rightarrow \quad X = X_1$

Moments about A for AB
$\Rightarrow$ equation in X_1, Y_1

and moments about C for BC
$\Rightarrow$ equation in X_1, Y_1, W

Taking moments about A for AB

$\Rightarrow \quad Y_1 \times 2a\sin\theta + X_1 \times 2a\cos\theta = 0$

$\Rightarrow Y_1\sin\theta + X_1 \cos\theta = 0$ $\qquad$ **(1)**

Taking moments about C for BC

$\Rightarrow \quad Y_1 2a\sin\theta + Wa\sin\theta = 2aX_1\cos\theta$

$\Rightarrow \quad 2Y_1\sin\theta + W\sin\theta = 2X_1\cos\theta$ $\qquad$ **(2)**

Substituting for $Y_1\sin\theta$ from **(1)** in **(2)**:

$\Rightarrow \quad -2X_1\cos\theta + W\sin\theta = 2X_1\cos\theta$

$\Rightarrow \quad X_1 = \dfrac{W}{4}\tan\theta$

Substituting in **(1)** for X_1: $\Rightarrow \quad Y_1\sin\theta + W\tan\theta\cos\theta = 0$

$\Rightarrow \quad Y_1 = -\dfrac{W}{4}$

$X = X_1 \quad \Rightarrow \quad X = \dfrac{W}{4}\tan\theta$

Now we have only to find Y.

Resolving vertically for BC: $Y = W + Y_1$

$$\therefore \quad Y = W - \frac{W}{4} = \frac{3}{4}W$$

Hence the components are:

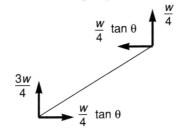

► **Note:** The original guess of direction for Y_1 was wrong but was corrected by the algebra.

► State the force on AB at A, in component form!

2

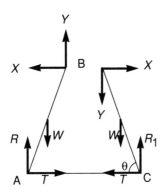

Resolving vertically for the whole system: $R + R_1 = 2W$

By symmetry: $R = R_1$

$$\therefore \quad R = W$$

Taking moments at B for BC: $T \times 2a\sin\theta + Wa\cos\theta = R_1 2a\cos\theta$

$$T = \frac{W}{2}\cot\theta$$

Resolving horizontally for BC: $X = T$

$$\therefore \quad X = \frac{W}{2}\cot\theta$$

Resolving vertically for BC: $Y + W = R_1$

$$\therefore \quad Y = 0$$

$\therefore$ force on BC at B is $\dfrac{W}{2}\cot\theta$ horizontally as shown.

► At each stage, ask yourself why we decided to do what we have done – when you can answer that you will be making good progress.

3

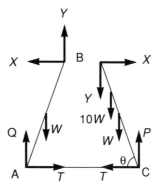

The length of each side is $2a$.

Taking moments about A for the whole system will give P.

Resolving vertically for BC will give Y.

Taking moments about C for BC will give X – question finished!

Hence:

Taking moments about A for the whole system:

$$Wa\cos\theta + 10W\frac{5a}{2}\cos\theta + W\times 3a\cos\theta = P\times 4a\cos\theta$$

$$\therefore\quad P = \frac{29}{4}W$$

► Why?

Resolving vertically for BC:

$$Y + 10W + W = \frac{29}{4}W$$

$$\therefore\quad Y = -\frac{15}{4}W$$

► Why?

Taking moments about C for BC:

$$X2a\sin\theta = Wa\cos\theta + 10W\frac{3a}{2}\cos\theta - \frac{15}{4}W\times 2a\cos\theta$$

$$\Rightarrow X = \frac{17}{4}W\cot\theta$$

$\therefore$ components of force on BC at B are

$\frac{17}{4}W\cot\theta$ horizontally to the right

$\frac{15}{4}W$ vertically upwards.

► Why? (margin, left)

4

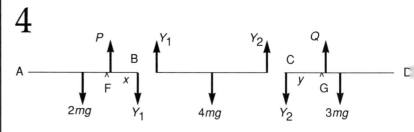

No horizontal forces on AB and CD
$\Rightarrow$ no horizontal components at B and C.

Thoughts:
- moments about F for AB will give an equation in mg, Y, a and x
- a similar equation can be found for CD.

These are OK if we know Y_1 and Y_2.

► See BC

Hence:

Resolving vertically for BC: $Y_1 + Y_2 = 4mg$

$$\text{but } Y_1 = Y_2$$

by symmetry or by taking moments about one end

$$\therefore \quad Y_1 = Y_2 = 2mg$$

Taking moments about F for AB: $2mg(a - x) = Y_1 x$

$$\therefore \quad a - x = x$$

$$\Rightarrow \quad x = \frac{a}{2}$$

Taking moments about G for CD: $Y_2 y = 3mg(a - y)$

$$\therefore \quad 2y = 3a - 3y$$

$$\Rightarrow \quad y = \frac{3a}{5}$$

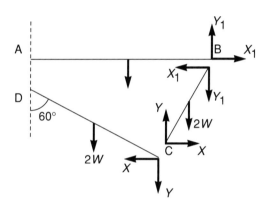

Taking moments about D for CD and about B for BC will give two equations in X and Y.

► Planning again!

Hence:

Taking moments about D for CD:

$2W \times c\sin 60° + Y \times 2c\sin 60° + X \times 2c\cos 60° = 0$

$W\sqrt{3} + Y\sqrt{3} + X = 0$ $\qquad\qquad$ **(1)**

Taking moments about B for BC:

$2Wb\cos 60° + X \times 2b\sin 60° - Y \times 2b\cos 60° = 0$

$W + X\sqrt{3} - Y = 0$ $\qquad\qquad$ **(2)**

Multiply **(1)** by $\sqrt{3}$ and subtract **(2)**:

$2W + 4Y = 0 \quad \Rightarrow \quad Y = -\dfrac{W}{2}$

$$\text{and } X = -\frac{W\sqrt{3}}{2}$$

► Notice that we couldn't have been more wrong in guessing the directions of the components at B and C, but the algebra has saved the day again!

Resolving horizontally for BC: $X = X_1 \Rightarrow X_1 = -\dfrac{W\sqrt{3}}{2}$

Resolving vertically for BC: $Y_1 = Y - 2W \Rightarrow Y_1 = -\dfrac{5W}{2}$

At C: the reaction on DC is

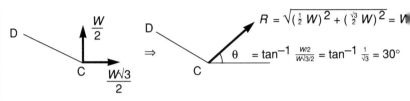

$R = \sqrt{(\tfrac{1}{2}W)^2 + (\tfrac{\sqrt{3}}{2}W)^2} = W$

$\theta = \tan^{-1}\dfrac{W/2}{W\sqrt{3}/2} = \tan^{-1}\dfrac{1}{\sqrt{3}} = 30°$

and at B on BC we get

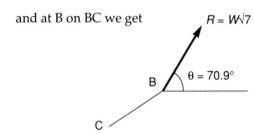

$R = W\sqrt{7}$

$\theta = 70.9°$

6 *Projectiles*

Chapter outline

Reminders

▮ Uniform acceleration equations

▮ Centre of mass

▮ NEL

New theories in this chapter
None – the chapter concentrates on method

Pure mathematics required

▮ Simple trigonometry

▮ Simultaneous equations

▮ Equation of parabola, $y = ax^2 + bx + c$

► See page 39

► See page 61

► See page 107

PROJECTILES – HORIZONTAL AND VERTICAL MOVEMENT

We have already met problems where projectiles (particles, bullets, stones, balls, things, etc.) are projected (sent, thrown, fired, hit, kicked, etc.) vertically upwards. We shall now look at cases where the angle of projection is not vertically upwards, which means that there is both horizontal and vertical movement.

This last statement sums up how we deal with the problems – once again our skill in resolving into two directions comes to the rescue.

There is not much new theory here – we just need to concentrate on the methods used. The last question in this chapter summarizes some standard results – but it is best to leave it until last!

► Resolving again!

(ACT) *Activity 6.1*

► Solutions on page 164

1 A stone is thrown at an angle of 60° to the horizontal with a speed of 20 m s⁻¹. Find

(a) how long it is before it lands
(b) where it is after 1 second
(c) the direction it is travelling after 1 second
(d) the maximum height it reaches
(e) its horizontal range.

Take $g = 10$ m s⁻².

► You may think this is a steep problem to start with, but you really do know all the theory that you need. The problem lies in the application of that theory.

2 A golf ball is at A on a steep bank alongside the green BC. C is the hole. The angle of the slope is 60°, AB = 20 m and BC = 8 m. (See diagram overleaf.)

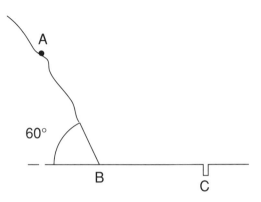

The golfer selects an iron which will send the ball at an angle of 40° to the horizontal. What speed must he give the ball if it is to hit the hole without touching anything else first?

► Would it be valid if it bounced straight out? Who knows?

3 A ball is thrown with horizontal and vertical components of velocity of u and w respectively. The coefficient of restitution between the ball and the ground is $\frac{1}{2}$. If d is the horizontal distance travelled to the first impact with the ground, find how far it is to the second impact. Find also the ratio of the maximum heights reached by the ball between the two bounces.

► Let's hope the stone doesn't destroy the conker!

4 A catapult fires a stone at 25 m s⁻¹. The target is a conker 15 m away and 10 m above the ground. Find the angle of projection.

5

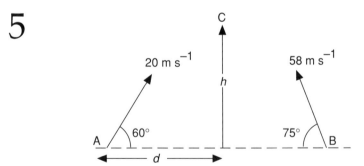

The diagram shows the initial speeds and directions of two projectiles, fired at different times. One has mass $2m$ and is fired from A, the other has mass m and is fired from B.

They collide directly at C, when both are at their highest points, h above the level AB. Find, in terms of h and g, their distance apart when they reach the level of AB again. The coefficient of restitution between them is $\frac{2}{5}$.

6

The diagram shows a boy skimming small flat stones on water.

When the stone leaves his hand it is 1 m above water level and travelling horizontally at 20 m s⁻¹. The coefficient of restitution between stone and water is $\frac{1}{4}$. How far does the stone go before it sinks?

▶ Barnes Wallace did a lot of research on this – the result of his labours was the destruction of the Moehne and Eder dams by the 'Dam Busters' in World War 2.

7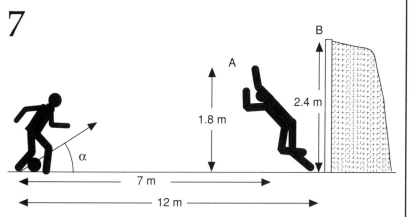

The diagram shows Pat about to score a goal! He kicks the ball at 15 m s⁻¹ and he will score a goal if the ball falls between A and B (the goalkeeper's fingertips and the crossbar). Distances are as shown. Find the range of choice of angles of projection, α on the diagram.

▶ Solution 4 will help!

8 Do raindrops fall in straight lines? Justify your answer by finding an equation linking horizontal and vertical distances travelled. (Time is the common factor in both directions.)

▶ How many times have you pondered this very question?

9 From a point A in a plane sloping at 20° to the horizontal, a ball is thrown up the plane at an angle of 40° to the plane, and with a speed of 15 m s⁻¹. If the ball hits the plane again at B, find the distance AB.

10 You are standing on the extreme tail end of an open deck on a ship travelling at 25 knots (powerful ship!). You throw a golf ball vertically upwards at 15 m s⁻¹. Who catches the ball, you or the sea? Justify your answer.

11 A particle is projected, from a horizontal plane, with speed V at an angle α to the horizontal. Find, in terms of V, α and g

(a) the time of flight, T

(b) the maximum height reached, H

(c) the range, R

(d) the value of α for maximum R

(e) Find the equation connecting horizontal and vertical distance travelled and show that the path of the projectile is a parabola.

Solutions to Activity 6.1

1

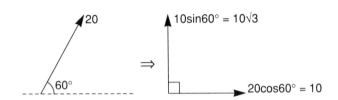

(a) Vertically:

$$v = u + at \quad \Rightarrow \quad 0 = 10\sqrt{3} - 10t \quad \Rightarrow \quad t = \sqrt{3} \text{ seconds}$$

i.e. $\sqrt{3}$ s to the highest point

$\therefore$ full time of flight $= 2\sqrt{3}$ s

(b) Vertically:

$$s = ut + \frac{1}{2}at^2 \quad \Rightarrow \quad y = 10\sqrt{3} \times 1 - \frac{10}{2} \times 1^2 = 12.32 \text{ m}$$

Horizontally: $s = ut \quad \Rightarrow \quad x = 10 \times 1 = 10$ m

Distance from origin $= \sqrt{12.32^2 + 10^2} = 15.9$ m

(c) Direction is found from velocity after 1 second.

> ► Direction of travel is always found from the velocity – a statement of the obvious but a point that students often miss.

Vertically: $v = u + at \quad \Rightarrow \quad \dot{y} = 10\sqrt{3} - 10 \times 1 = 7.3 \text{ m s}^{-1}$

Horizontally: $\dot{x} = 10$

If the direction is θ to the horizontal $\quad \theta = \tan^{-1}\left(\frac{7.3}{10}\right) = 36.1°$

(d) Maximum height is when $\dot{y} = 0$

$$v^2 = u^2 + 2as \quad \Rightarrow \quad 0 = (10\sqrt{3})^2 - 2 \times 10 \times h$$

$$\Rightarrow \quad h = 15 \text{ m}$$

> ► This question shows well the technique of working in two directions, horizontally and vertically, and combining when necessary. This is the method we are going to use throughout work on projectiles.

(e) To find the range, R:

$$s = ut \quad \Rightarrow \quad R = 10 \times 2\sqrt{3} = 34.6 \text{ m}$$

($t = 2\sqrt{3}$ from part **a**)

2

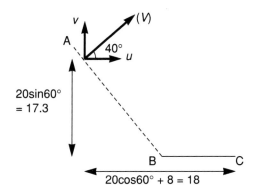

Let the initial components of velocity be u and v as shown.

Think horizontally and vertically and look for a factor which links the two: result – time, t. The time taken between A and C vertically must be the same as the time taken between A and C horizontally. Let's see what we can do with time!

Horizontally: $s = u + at$ $\Rightarrow$ $18 = ut$ **(1)**

Vertically: $s = ut + \dfrac{1}{2}\,at^2$ $\Rightarrow$ $-17.3 = vt - \dfrac{1}{2}\,gt^2$ **(2)**

Substituting from **(1)** into **(2)** for t: $-17.3 = 18\tan40° - \dfrac{1}{2}\,g\left(\dfrac{18}{u}\right)^2$

$u = \sqrt{\dfrac{5 \times 18^2}{18\tan40° + 17.3}} = 7.1$

If v is the initial speed, $v = \dfrac{u}{\cos40°} = 9.2 \text{ m s}^{-1}$

▶ Does all this go through Nick Faldo's mind as he prepares to play a shot?

3

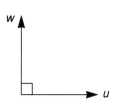

Vertically: $v = u + at$ $\Rightarrow$ $T = 2gw$
T = time of flight

$v^2 = u^2 + 2as$ $\Rightarrow$ $H_1 = \dfrac{w^2}{2g}$

H_1 is the maximum height and occurs when $v = 0$

Horizontally: $x = d$ when $t = \dfrac{2w}{g}$

After impact the vertical velocity is v_1.

NEL: $v_1 = -e \times -w = ew$

Vertically: $v = u + at$ $\Rightarrow$ $T_1 = e \times \dfrac{2w}{g}$

$v^2 = u^2 + 2as$ $\Rightarrow$ $H_2 = \dfrac{e^2w^2}{2g}$

$e = \dfrac{1}{2}$ horizontally: $d_1 = u \times \dfrac{w}{g} = \dfrac{d}{2}$

and vertically: $\dfrac{H_2}{H_1} = \dfrac{e^2 w^2}{2g} \times \dfrac{2g}{w^2} = e^2 = \dfrac{1}{4}$

4

25 m s⁻¹ · 10 m · 15 m · α

If t is the time taken to reach the target:

Horizontally: $15 = 25\cos\alpha \times t$

(1)

Vertically: $10 = 25\sin\alpha \times t - \dfrac{1}{2}gt^2$

(2)

Substituting for t from **(1)** in **(2)**:

$$10 = \dfrac{25\sin\alpha \times 15}{25\cos\alpha} - \dfrac{1}{2}g\left(\dfrac{15}{25\cos\alpha}\right)^2$$

$$10 = 15\tan\alpha - \dfrac{1}{2}g \times \dfrac{15^2}{25^2}(1 + \tan^2\alpha)$$

since $\dfrac{1}{\cos^2\alpha} = \sec^2\alpha = 1 + \tan^2\alpha$

$\therefore$ $1.8\tan^2\alpha - 15\tan\alpha + 11.8 = 0$ taking $g = 9.8$

Using the quadratic formula, $\tan\alpha = 7.45$ or 0.88 giving
$\alpha = 82.3°$ or $41.3°$ (the two possible angles of projection).
At the lower angle the stone is still rising towards the target. At the greater angle it is falling.

► Are there any conditions in which only one angle of projection is possible? What are they?

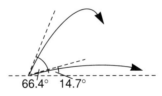

66.4°   14.7°

5

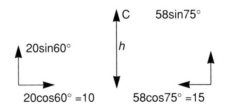

C   58sin75°

20sin60°   h

20cos60° =10   58cos75° =15

For the impact at C:

	2m	m	
	●	●	
	10	−15	horizontal
	v	w	vertical

COM: $2m \times 10 - m \times 15 = 2mv + mw$ $\Rightarrow$ $5 = 2v + w$

NEL: $-\dfrac{2}{5}(-15 - 10) = w - v$ $\Rightarrow$ $10 = w - v$

Solving the two equations gives $v = -\dfrac{5}{3}$, $w = \dfrac{25}{3}$

We now have, after impact at C:

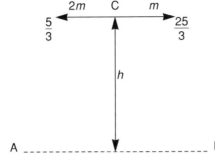

► A complex problem: projectiles, then impacts, then projectiles again – but quite reasonable when taken step by step.

To find the time to fall vertically from C to AB:

$s = ut + \dfrac{1}{2}at^2$ $\Rightarrow$ $h = \dfrac{1}{2}gt^2$ $\Rightarrow$ $t = \sqrt{\dfrac{2h}{g}}$

Horizontally the $2m$ mass travels $\dfrac{5}{3}\sqrt{\dfrac{2h}{g}}$ to the left and

the m mass travels $\dfrac{25}{3}\sqrt{\dfrac{2h}{g}}$ to the right.

Distance apart $= \dfrac{30}{3}\sqrt{\dfrac{2h}{g}} = 10\sqrt{\dfrac{2h}{g}}$ m

6

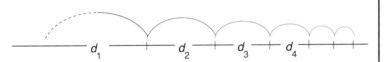

► How often have you tried this?

Horizontal velocity = 20 m s^{-1}

The time of flight of one bounce is e times the preceding time.

Similarly $d_2 = ed_1$ $d_3 = ed_2$ and so on.

► From question 3!

$\therefore$ distance travelled $= (d_1 + d_2 + d_2 + d_3) - \dfrac{1}{2}d_1$

$= (d_1 + ed_1 + e^2d_1 + ...) - \dfrac{1}{2}d_1$

$= d_1(1 + e + e^2 + e^3 + ... - \dfrac{1}{2})$

$1 + e + e^2 + e^3 + ... = $ the sum to infinity (S_∞) of a GP with $a = 1, r = e$

► More pure mathematics!

$= \dfrac{1}{1-e} = \dfrac{4}{3}$

Now to find d_1:

Time taken to fall: $s = ut + \dfrac{1}{2}at^2$ $\Rightarrow$ $1 = \dfrac{1}{2}gt^2$

$$t = \sqrt{\frac{2}{8}}$$

$$\therefore \quad d_1 = 2 \times 20 \times \sqrt{\frac{2}{8}} = 40\sqrt{\frac{2}{8}}$$

$$\therefore \quad \text{distance travelled} = 40\sqrt{\frac{2}{8}}\left(\frac{4}{3} - \frac{1}{2}\right)$$

$$= \frac{100}{3}\sqrt{\frac{2}{8}} = 15 \text{ m}$$

► 3 pm Saturday afternoon and time for a mechanics lesson – some hope! But you can see that mechanics is all around you!

7

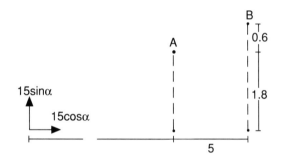

Considering A:

Horizontally: $s = ut \implies 7 = 15\cos\alpha \times t \implies t = \dfrac{7}{15\cos\alpha}$

Vertically: $s = ut + \dfrac{1}{2}at^2 \implies 1.8 = 15\sin\alpha \times t - \dfrac{1}{2}gt^2$

Substituting for $t \implies 1.8 = 7\tan\alpha - \dfrac{1}{2}g(1 + \tan^2\alpha)\dfrac{7^2}{15^2}$

$\implies \tan^2\alpha - 7\tan\alpha + 2.8 = 0$

$\implies \alpha = 23° \text{ or } 81.3°$

Since the ball needs to be falling to score, the angle is 81.3°.

Considering B by the identical method, we get $\alpha = 73.3°$.

$\therefore \quad$ for a goal, $73.3° < \alpha < 81.3°$

8

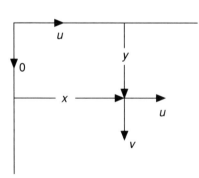

u = velocity of the cloud.

Horizontally: $x = ut$

Vertically: $y = \dfrac{1}{2}gt^2$

Eliminating t:

$y = \dfrac{1}{2}g \times \dfrac{x^2}{u^2}$ $\Rightarrow$ $2u^2y = gx^2$

which is not a straight line – it is a parabola.
If $u = 0$ (cloud stationary) then $x = 0$ and rain ralls in a straight line.

▶ In reality the problem is more complex but when we see rain falling at an angle we are seeing the resultant of two vectors: the horizontal velocity of the cloud and the velocity due to falling.

9

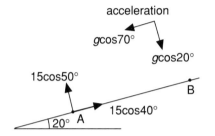

Note the use of 'plane' and 'normal to plane' as lines of reference, not horizontally and vertically as usual.

▶ Method for range etc. up sloping planes

Parallel to the plane: $s = ut + \dfrac{1}{2}at^2$

$\Rightarrow$ $x = 15\cos40° \times t - \dfrac{1}{2}g\sin20° \times t^2$

Perpendicular to the plane: $s = ut + \dfrac{1}{2}at^2$

$\Rightarrow$ $y = 15\sin40° \times t - \dfrac{1}{2}g\cos20° \times t^2$

When on the plane $y = 0$, hence

$0 = 15\sin40° \times t - \dfrac{1}{2}g\cos20° \times t^2$

$0 = 9.6t - 4.6t^2$ $\Rightarrow$ $t = 0$ at A

$t = \dfrac{9.6}{4.6} = 2.09$ at B

Then $x = 15\cos40° \times 2.1 - \dfrac{1}{2}g\sin20° \times (2.1)^2$

$\therefore$ AB $= 16.7$ m

10

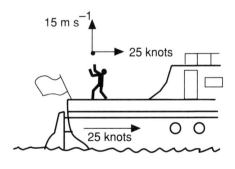

Vertically: the ball rises, stops and then falls.

Horizontally: throughout the vertical motion the ball travels horizontally at 25 knots; you are also travelling at 25 knots, so you catch the ball.

▶ In the same way this answers the problem of whether or not you land on the exactly the same spot if you jump vertically upwards on a train travelling at 60 mph.

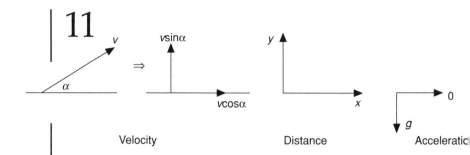

| Velocity | Distance | Acceleration |

(a) Vertically: $v = u + at \Rightarrow 0 = V\sin\alpha - gt$

So time to highest point $= \dfrac{V\sin\alpha}{g}$

▶ Time of flight

$\therefore$ time of flight is $t = \dfrac{2V\sin\alpha}{g}$

(b) Vertically: $v^2 = u^2 + 2as \Rightarrow 0 = V^2\sin^2\alpha - 2gH$

▶ Maximum height

$\therefore$ maximum y = is given by $H = \dfrac{V^2\sin^2\alpha}{2g}$

(c) Horizontally: $s = ut \Rightarrow R = V\cos\alpha \times \dfrac{2V\sin\alpha}{g}$

▶ Range

where R = maximum x $R = \dfrac{V^2\sin^2\alpha}{g}$

(d) From **(c)**: If V is constant but R is variable, then

▶ Maximum range

maximum R occurs when $\sin^2\alpha = 1 \Rightarrow 2\alpha = \dfrac{\pi}{2}$

maximum R is when $\alpha = 45°$

(e) Horizontally: $x = V\cos\alpha \times t$

Vertically: $y = V\sin\alpha \times t - \dfrac{1}{2}gt^2$

Eliminating t: $y = \dfrac{V\sin\alpha}{V\cos\alpha} \times x - \dfrac{1}{2}\dfrac{gx^2}{V^2\cos^2\alpha}$

▶ x, y equation

$y = x\tan\alpha - \dfrac{g\sec^2\alpha}{2V^2} \times x^2$

▶ Trajectory

this is a parabola, known as the trajectory.

Standard notation

This last question, number 11, establishes various results in standard notation. You should be aware of these and be able to derive them. Many students take the wrong approach to this work by learning them parrot-fashion and then repeatedly trying to apply them to all problems.

Stick to the method we have used throughout, applying uniform acceleration equations vertically and horizontally (or parallel to and perpendicular to the plane) as necessary, according to the demands of the problem. This way you will have a far greater understanding, and knowing that the problems can be resolved into these simple dimensions will give you the confidence to tackle them.

Centre of Gravity

► See page 61

► See page 63

CENTRE OF GRAVITY

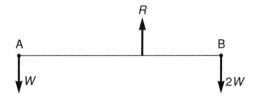

AB is a light rod of length l. At A there is a mass of weight W and at B there is a second mass of weight $2W$.

The rod is in equilibrium under the action of these weights and their equilibrant, R.

Problem: at which point does R act?

Taking moments about A:

$Rx = 2Wl \quad \Rightarrow \quad 3Wx = 2Wl$

i.e. $x = \dfrac{2l}{3}$

Or taking moments about B:

$R(l - x) = Wl \quad \Rightarrow \quad 3l - 3x = l$

$x = \dfrac{2l}{3}$

This result tells us that W and $2W$ could be replaced by $3W$ acting at a point $\frac{2l}{3}$ from A i.e.

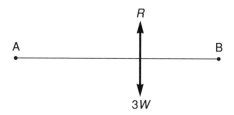

or put another way

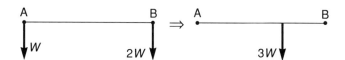

► Centroid – another name for centre of gravity

G is the **centre of gravity** of the system as described i.e. rod AB with W at A and $2W$ at B. In finding the position of G we have used a principle which is the main feature of the work in this chapter. In this case no matter which point we take moments about, the moment of the force $2W$ acting at G is equal to the sum of the moments of the separate forces W and $2W$ acting at A and B respectively. This long explanation can be reduced to:

moment of sum (of various components) acting through centre of gravity = sum of moments of separate components

Which is reduced further to:

► Moment of sum = sum of moments ⇒ the important principle behind this work.

moment of sum = sum of moments

This may seem a bit woolly but a few questions will make it clear.

► Solutions on page 173

(ACT) Activity 7.1

1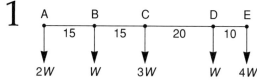

A light rod ABCDE has weights attached as shown. Find the position of the centre of gravity.

► Further new technique is introduced in this question but have a go first. **Hint:** once again consider two directions at right angles.

2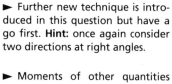

ABC is a light triangular framework with masses of $2m$ at A, $3m$ at B and $4m$ at C.

Find the position of the centre of gravity.

► Moments of other quantities are defined in this question.

3

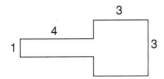

The diagram shows a lamina of mass m per unit area. Find the position of the centre of gravity.

4

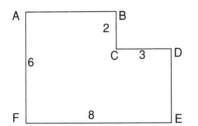

A uniform lamina has the shape shown. Find the position of its centre of gravity.

5

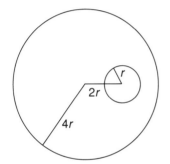

A circular lamina has a smaller circle cut from it. Find the position of the centre of gravity of the remainder.

▶ And this one!

▶ A lamina is a flat sheet, often with an odd shape – very popular in mechanics!

Solutions to Activity 7.1

1

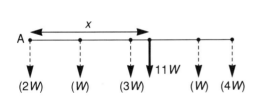

The diagram shows the original five forces replaced by a single force of $11W$ (equal to the sum of the others) acting at a distance x from A.

Moment of sum = sum of moments
Taking moments about A:

$$11W \times x = W \times 15 + 3W \times 30 + W \times 50 + 4W \times 60$$

$$\Rightarrow 11x = 15 + 90 + 50 + 240$$

i.e. $x = \frac{395}{11} = 35\frac{10}{11}$

i.e. the whole system could be replaced by a single weight of $11W$ acting at a point $35\frac{10}{11}$ units from A.

2

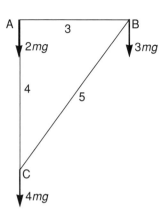

Firstly we find the position of the centre of gravity from the line AC by taking moments about the line AC.

Moment of sum = sum of moments

$\Rightarrow \quad 9mg\bar{x} = 2\ mg \times 0 + 4\ mg \times 0 + 3\ mg \times 3$ (moments of forces)

$\Rightarrow \quad 9m\bar{x} = 9m$ (moments of masses)

$\Rightarrow \quad \bar{x} = 1$

▶ $\bar{x}$ – pronounced '$\bar{x}$-bar' is used to indicate the distance to the centre of gravity.

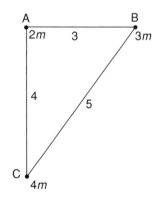

▶ $\bar{y}$ is y-bar, the distance of the centre of gravity from AB.

Taking moments about AB:
$9m\bar{y} = 4m \times 4 + 3m \times 0 + 2m \times 0$

$\Rightarrow \quad \bar{y} = \dfrac{16}{9}$

– much more efficient than in the first case.

Hence the system can be replaced by:

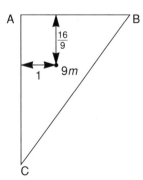

3

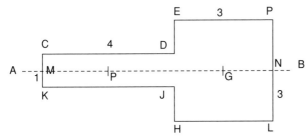

By symmetry, the centre of gravity is on the line AB.

Consider the shape to be made of two parts, CDJK and EFLH.

The centre of gravity of CDJK is at P where MP = 2 and

centre of gravity of EFLH is at Q where NQ = $\frac{3}{2}$.

The mass of CDJK is $4 \times 1 \times m = 4m$ and
the mass of EFLH is $3 \times 3 \times m = 9m$

Taking moments about CK for the whole:

$(4m + 9m)\bar{x} = 4m \times 2 + 9m \times (4 + \frac{3}{2})$

$13m\bar{x} = 8m + \dfrac{99m}{2}$ (moments of areas)

$13\bar{x} = 8 + \dfrac{99}{2}$ (moments of areas)

$\Rightarrow \quad \bar{x} = \dfrac{115}{26}$

i.e. the centre of gravity is on AB, $4\frac{11}{26}$ units from CK.

> ▶ Notice how the 'moments of masses' equation became the 'moments of areas' equation. By now you should be realizing that we can take moments for many quantities; force, mass, area, volume and even momentum, although this latter one will not come up in this course.

4

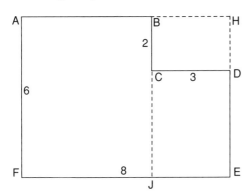

Taking moments about AF:

area AHEF $\times 4$ = area BHCD $\times (5 + \frac{3}{2})$ + area ABCDEF $\times \bar{x}$

$(6 \times 8) \times 4 - (2 \times 3) \times \dfrac{13}{2} = \{(6 \times 8) - (2 \times 3)\}\bar{x}$

$\Rightarrow \quad \bar{x} = 3\frac{9}{14}$

Taking moments about FE:

$48 \times 3 - 6 \times 5 = 42 \times \bar{y}$

$\Rightarrow \quad \bar{y} = \dfrac{114}{42} = \dfrac{19}{7}$

i.e. the centre of gravity is $3\frac{9}{14}$ from AF and $2\frac{5}{7}$ from FE.

> ▶ We have got this result by considering the shape to be a rectangle AHEF with rectangle BHDC removed to illustrate the idea. The question could have been answered as in question 3, by considering rectangles ABJF and CDEJ added together.

▶ The – sign is quite correct: the centre of gravity is $\frac{2r}{15}$ to the left of O as the diagram is drawn. The minus sign arises because we considered the moments of the removed circle and the shape left to be in the same sense about 0, when they are not. It also highlights that the algebra takes account of wrong assumptions made: we have met this before.

5

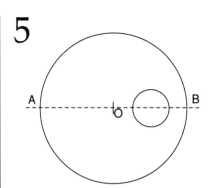

By symmetry the centre of gravity is on AB.

Taking moments about O:

$\pi(4r)^2 \times 0$

$= \pi r^2 \times 2r + (\pi(4r)^2 - \pi r^2) \times \bar{x}$

$0 = \pi r^2 \times 2r + 15\pi r^2 \times \bar{x}$

$\Rightarrow \quad \bar{x} = -\dfrac{2r}{15}$

Centres of gravity of triangular laminae

We shall now find the centre of gravity of a uniform triangular lamina and, at the same time, introduce a variation of the technique.

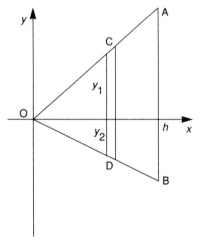

The triangle, which is assumed scalene, is arranged with a vertex at the origin and the opposite side, AB, parallel to the y-axis.

The triangle can be considered to be made up of strips, like CD, of length $y_1 + y_2$ and width δx.

The equation of the line OA is $y = ax$ and the equation of OB is $y = bx$.

Then the length of CD is $(a + b)x$ and its width is δx.

Therefore its area is $(a + b)x\delta x$

Now, apply 'moment of sum = sum of moments'.

Taking moments about Oy

$\Rightarrow \quad$ area OAB $\times \bar{x} = \displaystyle\sum_{x=0}^{h} (a + b)x \times x\delta x$ $\qquad$ (1)

area of OAB $= \frac{1}{2} \times$ AB $\times h$

▶ **NB** $\displaystyle\sum_{x=0}^{h} \underbrace{(a + b)x\delta x}_{} \times \underbrace{x}_{}$

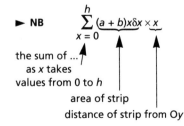

the sum of ...
as x takes
values from 0 to h

area of strip

distance of strip from Oy

$= \frac{1}{2} \times (ah + bh) \times h = = \frac{1}{2} (a + b)h^2$

(1) now becomes, as $\delta x \to 0$

$$\frac{1}{2}(a + b)h^2 \times \bar{x} = \int_0^h (a + b)x^2 \, dx$$

$$\Rightarrow \quad \frac{1}{2}(a + b)h^2 \, \bar{x} = \frac{(a + b)h^3}{3}$$

$$\Rightarrow \quad \bar{x} = \frac{2h}{3}$$

But the centre of gravity of each strip is at the midpoint of the strip. i.e. the centres of gravity of all the strips lie on line joining the midpoints of the strips, i.e. the median of the triangle.

So the centre of gravity of OAB is on the median.

Hence the centre of gravity is on the median $\frac{2}{3}$ of the distance from the vertex.

It follows that the centre of gravity must lie on all three medians.

Hence the medians are concurrent $\frac{2}{3}$ of the distance along each from the respective vertex.

Medians meet at the **centroid** which is another name for the centre of gravity.

And so calculus comes into our work. It is used when the object concerned cannot readily be subdivided into components, as they could in Activity 7.1.

▶ The **median** is the line joining the vertex to the midpoint of the opposite side.

▶ Centroid defined

(ACT) *Activity 7.2*

▶ Solutions on page 179

▶ Moments of areas are needed in this question.

1

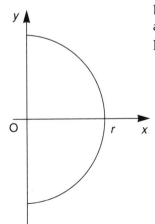

By setting up a semicircle on axes as shown in the diagram, find the position of its centre of gravity.

► Moments of volumes

2

By rotating the part OA of a straight line through 360° about the x-axis, a cone ABO is generated, height h and base radius r.

Using a similar technique as in question 1, find the position of its centre of gravity.

► Moments of volumes

3 By a similar method to that used in question 2, find the position of the centre of gravity of a solid hemisphere.

4 A uniform wire, mass m per unit length, is bent to form three sides of a square of side $2a$. The wire is suspended by a string attached to one end of it. Find the angle the parallel sides make with the vertical.

5 If the cone in question **2** and the hemisphere in question **3** have the same size of circular base, their bases may be joined so that a new solid is formed. The height h of the cone is equal to kr. Both parts have the same density.

Find the position of the centre of gravity of the new solid.

Find k if the solid can be placed in equilibrium with any part of the hemispherical surface on a smooth horizontal plane.

6 A solid is generated by rotating the curve $y^2 = 4x$ through 360° about the x-axis, the extremities being the origin and $x = 4$. Find the position of the centre of gravity of the solid.

7 Find the position of the centre of gravity of a wire bent to form the perimeter of a sector of a circle which subtends an angle of 2α at the centre of the circle.

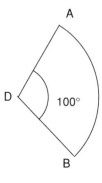

A uniform wire is bent to make the shape shown, where O is the centre of the circle of which AB is an arc. Find the position of the centre of gravity.

Solutions to Activity 7.2

1 Area of the strip is $2y\delta x$

$= 2\sqrt{(r^2 - x^2)}\delta x$

because the equation for the circle is $y^2 + x^2 = r^2$

Taking moments about the y-axis:

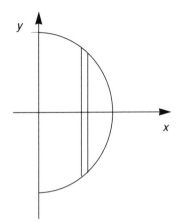

$$\frac{1}{2}\pi r^2 \bar{x} = \sum_{x=0}^{r} 2\sqrt{(r^2 - x^2)}\delta x \times x$$

i.e. $\dfrac{1}{2}\pi r^2 \bar{x} = \displaystyle\int_0^r 2\sqrt{(r^2 - x^2)}x\,\delta x$

$\Rightarrow \dfrac{1}{2}\pi r^2 \bar{x} = \left[-\dfrac{2}{3}(r^2 - x^2)^{3/2} \right]_0^r$

$\Rightarrow \bar{x} = \dfrac{4r}{3\pi}$

Hence the centre of gravity is on the x-axis (by symmetry) at a distance $\dfrac{4r}{3\pi}$ from the centre of the circle.

2

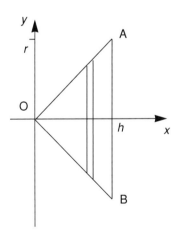

A thin element of the cone is a disc, radius y.

The volume of the disc $= \pi y^2 \delta x$

Taking moments about Oy:

$$V \times \bar{x} = \sum_{x=0}^{h} \pi y^2 \delta x \times x$$

i.e. $\dfrac{1}{3}\pi r^2 h\bar{x} = \int_0^h \pi\left(\dfrac{rx}{h}\right)^2 x\,\delta x$

because for OA $y = \dfrac{rx}{h}$

$\therefore \quad \dfrac{1}{3}\pi r^2 h\bar{x} = \dfrac{\pi r^2}{h^2} \times \dfrac{h^4}{4}$

$\Rightarrow \quad \bar{x} = \dfrac{3h}{4}$

3

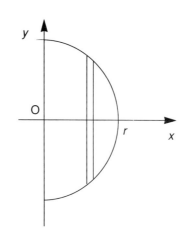

Volume of element $= \pi y^2 \delta x$

$= \pi(r^2 - x^2)\mathrm{d}x$

Moment of element about $Oy = \pi(r^2 - x^2)x\delta x$

Taking moments about Oy:

$\dfrac{2}{3}\pi r^3 \bar{x} = \int_0^r \pi(r^2 - x^2)x\,\mathrm{d}x$

$\therefore \quad \dfrac{2}{3}\pi r^3 \bar{x} = \dfrac{\pi r^4}{4}$

$\Rightarrow \quad \bar{x} = \dfrac{3r}{8}$

i.e. the centre of gravity is on Ox $\dfrac{3r}{8}$ from O.

4

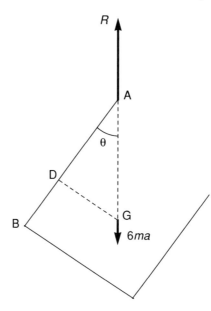

The wire is suspended as shown.

For equilibrium $R = 6ma$ and the force R and the force $6ma$ are in the same vertical line.

θ is the required angle.

Where is G? This is our first problem.

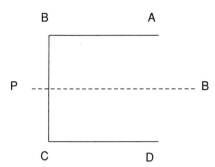

G is on PQ.

Taking moments about BC:

$6a\bar{x} = 2a \times a + 2a \times a$

$\Rightarrow \quad \bar{x} = \dfrac{2a}{3}$

Referring to the first diagram:

$DG = a$

$AD = AB - DB$

$\quad = 2a - \dfrac{2a}{3} = \dfrac{4a}{3}$

$\therefore \quad \tan\theta = \dfrac{DG}{AD}$

$\quad = \dfrac{a}{4a/3} = \dfrac{3}{4} \quad \Rightarrow \quad \theta = 36.9°$

5

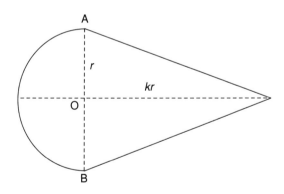

Volume of hemisphere
$\frac{2}{3}\pi r^3$

Volume of cone
$\frac{1}{3}\pi k r^3$

CG of hemisphere
$\dfrac{3r}{8}$ from O

CG of cone
$\dfrac{kr}{4}$ from O

Taking moments about AB:

$\left(\dfrac{2}{3}\pi r^3 + \dfrac{1}{3}\pi k r^3\right)\bar{x} = \dfrac{2}{3}\pi r^3 \times \dfrac{3r}{8} - \dfrac{1}{3}\pi k r^3 \times \dfrac{kr}{4}$

$\Rightarrow \quad \bar{x} = \dfrac{r(3 - k^2)}{4(2 + k)}$

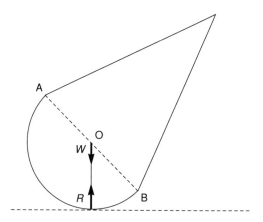

Smooth plane, therefore R is normal to the plane.

Therefore R passes through O   (by geometry).

For equilibrium, the weight of the mass passes through O

i.e. centre of gravity is at O.

Therefore $\bar{x}$ (as found above) is zero.

$$\Rightarrow \quad \bar{x} = \frac{r(3 - k^2)}{4(2 + k)} = 0$$

$$\Rightarrow \quad k = \sqrt{3}$$

6

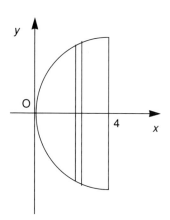

Volume of solid $= \pi \int_0^4 y^2 \, \mathrm{d}x \quad = \pi \int_0^4 4x \, \mathrm{d}x = \pi \times 2 \times 4^2$

Moments for the element $\quad \Rightarrow \quad \pi y^2 \delta x \times x = \pi 4 x^2 \mathrm{d}x$

Taking moments about Oy:

$$\pi \times 2 \times 4^2 \times \bar{x} = \pi \int_0^4 4x^2 \, \mathrm{d}x$$

$$= 4^4 \times \frac{\pi}{3}$$

$$\Rightarrow \quad \bar{x} = 4^4 \times \frac{\pi}{2} \times 3$$

7

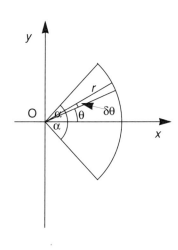

Consider an element of the arc subtending an angle of $\delta\theta$ at O.

The length of the element $= r\delta\theta$

▷ This is true only if θ is in radians.

Moment of element about Oy
$= r\delta\theta \times r\cos\theta$

Therefore taking moments about Oy for the whole:

$$2r\alpha \times \bar{x} = \int_{-\alpha}^{\alpha} r^2\cos\theta \, d\theta$$

▶ This integration is also only accurate if θ is in radians.

$\therefore \quad 2r\alpha\bar{x} = r^2(\sin\alpha - \sin{-\alpha})$

$\therefore \quad 2r\alpha\bar{x} = 2r^2\sin\alpha$

$\therefore \quad \bar{x} = \dfrac{r\sin\alpha}{\alpha}$

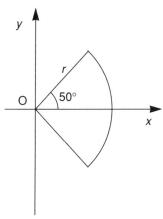

In the work done so far in this question θ and α have been in radians and we should firstly find the angle here in radians.

$50° = 0.87$ rad

Taking moments about Oy:

$(2r + 2 \times r \times 0.87)\bar{x} = 2r \times \dfrac{r}{2}\cos0.87 + 2r \times 0.87 \times \dfrac{r\sin0.87}{0.87}$

$3.74r\bar{x} = r^2(0.64 + 1.52)$

$\bar{x} = r \times \dfrac{2.16}{3.74} = 0.58r$

Vectors Again

► See page 58

► See page 59

► See page 72

► See page 73

> **Chapter outline**
>
> **Reminders**
>
> ▌ Work done; force × distance; joules
>
> ▌ Power; force × velocity; watts
>
> ▌ Vectors
>
> ▌ $a = \dfrac{dv}{dt} \quad v = \dfrac{ds}{dt}$
>
> **New theory in this chapter**
>
> ▌ Work done by scalar product
>
> ▌ Power by scalar product
>
> **Pure mathematics needed**
>
> ▌ Simple differentiation/integration
>
> ▌ Scalar products

VECTOR AND THE WORK OF FORCES

Continuing our work using vector form, we'll have a look at work done by a force.

If the force is constant we earlier had the definition that work done = force × distance.

In this definition we must stress that the force factor means the force acting in the direction of the distance travelled. A simple example will illustrate this.

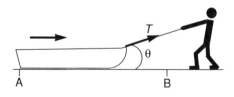

The diagram shows a child dragging a sledge. The value of T, the force exerted on the sledge, is 50N. $\theta = 40°$. If AB = 15 m the work done by the force T is

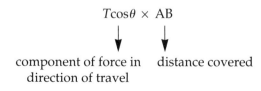

$T\cos\theta \times$ AB

component of force in   distance covered
direction of travel

∴   work done = $50\cos40° \times 15$ = 574.5 joules

From the definition of a scalar product:

$T\cos\theta \times AB = \mathbf{T} \cdot \mathbf{AB}$

and hence we can find the work done when the force and distance are in vector form.

Scalar products

Scalar products are well covered in any pure mathematics course but as a reminder of the main points:

1   Definition: $\mathbf{a} \cdot \mathbf{b} = ab\cos\theta$
2   $\mathbf{i} \cdot \mathbf{i} = \mathbf{j} \cdot \mathbf{j} = \mathbf{k} \cdot \mathbf{k} = 1$
3   $\mathbf{i} \cdot \mathbf{j} = \mathbf{j} \cdot \mathbf{k} = \mathbf{k} \cdot \mathbf{i} = \cdots = 0$

4   $\begin{pmatrix} a \\ p \\ k \end{pmatrix} \cdot \begin{pmatrix} b \\ q \\ l \end{pmatrix} = ab + pq + kl$

5   The product is a scalar quantity.

Work done = $\mathbf{F} \cdot \mathbf{s}$

$= Fs\cos0$ if F and s are in the same direction

$= mas$ using $F = ma$, NL2

$= \tfrac{1}{2}m(v^2 - u^2)$ using $v^2 = u^2 + 2as$

$= $ change in KE

► A point we have made before but neatly reinforced here.

(ACT) *Activity 8.1*

► Solutions on page 186

1 Express a force of 39 N in the direction of the vector $\begin{pmatrix} 3 \\ 4 \\ 12 \end{pmatrix}$ in vector form.

2 A point has position vector $\mathbf{r} = t^2\mathbf{i} + 2t\mathbf{j} - t\mathbf{k}$. It is acted on by a force given by $\mathbf{F} = t\mathbf{i} + 2t\mathbf{j} + \mathbf{k}$.

(a) Find the velocity $\mathbf{v}$.

(b) Find an expression for the power in terms of t.

(c) Find the work done by $\mathbf{F}$ as t varies from 1 to 3.

$\mathbf{F}$ is in newtons, $\mathbf{r}$ in metres, t in seconds.

3 The acceleration of a particle of mass m is

$\mathbf{a} = \begin{pmatrix} 1 \\ 2t \\ -1 \end{pmatrix}$ m s^{-2}

If $\mathbf{v} = \begin{pmatrix} 1 \\ 0 \\ 0 \end{pmatrix}$ when $t = 0$, find the power at time t.

Find the change in energy in the first three seconds and find where the particle is after 5 seconds if it is originally at the origin.

4 The position vector of a particle of unit mass is given by

$$\mathbf{r} = \begin{pmatrix} \sin t \\ \cos t \\ 3 \end{pmatrix}$$

Show that the speed of the particle is 1 m s^{-1}.

Find the power of the force acting on the particle and show that the work done over the period $0 \le t \le \frac{\pi}{2}$ is zero.

Describe the motion.

5 A force is given by $\mathbf{F} = \lambda \begin{pmatrix} 1 \\ 2 \\ 3 \end{pmatrix}$.

Find λ if the force does 14 joules of work in moving a unit mass from $(1, 1, 1)$ to $(7, 6, 5)$.

Solutions to Activity 8.1

► Creating a required modulus

1 $\mathbf{F} = n \begin{pmatrix} 3 \\ 4 \\ 12 \end{pmatrix}$ with n taking a value so that the modulus is 39,

the required magnitude.

$\begin{pmatrix} 3 \\ 4 \\ 12 \end{pmatrix}$ gives us the direction but not necessarily the right size.

So the problem is to find n.

$\begin{pmatrix} 3 \\ 4 \\ 12 \end{pmatrix}$ has modulus $\sqrt{3^2 + 4^2 + 12^2} = 13$.

We want a modules of 39 $\quad \therefore \quad n = 3$

i.e. $\mathbf{F} = 3 \begin{pmatrix} 3 \\ 4 \\ 12 \end{pmatrix}$ or $\begin{pmatrix} 9 \\ 12 \\ 36 \end{pmatrix}$

2 (a) $\mathbf{r} = (t^2\mathbf{i} + 2t\mathbf{j} - t\mathbf{k}) \quad \therefore \quad \mathbf{v} = \dfrac{d\mathbf{r}}{dt} = (2t\mathbf{i} + 2\mathbf{j} - \mathbf{k})$

► Power
► Work done

(b) Power $= \mathbf{F} \cdot \mathbf{v} = (t\mathbf{i} + 2t\mathbf{j} + \mathbf{k}) \cdot (2t\mathbf{i} + 2\mathbf{j} - \mathbf{k})$
$$= 2t^2 + 4t - 1 \text{ watts}$$

► Work done $= \int \text{power } dt$

(c) Work done $= \displaystyle\int_1^3 \mathbf{F} \cdot \mathbf{v} \, dt$

$$= \int_1^3 (2t^2 + 4t - 1) dt$$

$$= \left[\frac{2}{3} t^3 + 2t^2 - 1 \right]_1^3$$

$$= 31\frac{1}{3} \text{ J}$$

3 $\mathbf{a} = \begin{pmatrix} 1 \\ 2t \\ -1 \end{pmatrix} \Rightarrow \mathbf{v} = \int \mathbf{a} dt = \begin{pmatrix} b + A \\ t^2 + B \\ -t + C \end{pmatrix}$

When $t = 0$, $\mathbf{v} = \begin{pmatrix} 1 \\ 0 \\ 0 \end{pmatrix} \Rightarrow A = 1, B = 0, C = 0$

$\therefore \quad \mathbf{v} = \begin{pmatrix} t + 1 \\ t^2 \\ -t \end{pmatrix}$ m s^{-1}

Power $= \mathbf{F} \cdot \mathbf{v}$

We know $\mathbf{v}$, we need $\mathbf{F}$, so use NL2.

$\mathbf{F} = m\mathbf{a}$

$\therefore \quad \mathbf{F} = m \begin{pmatrix} 1 \\ 2t \\ -1 \end{pmatrix}$ N

and then power $= \mathbf{F} \cdot \mathbf{v} = m \begin{pmatrix} 1 \\ 2t \\ -1 \end{pmatrix} \cdot \begin{pmatrix} t + 1 \\ t^2 \\ -t \end{pmatrix}$

$\therefore \quad$ power $= m(t + 1 + 2t^3 + t) = m(2t^3 + 2t + 1)$ W

Change in energy = work done on particle

$= \int_0^3 \mathbf{F} \cdot \mathbf{v} \, dt$

$= m\int_0^3 (2t^3 + 2t + 1)dt$

$= m\left[\frac{1}{2}t^4 + t^2 + t \right]_0^3$

$= \frac{105}{2}$ joules

$\mathbf{r} = \int \mathbf{v} dt = \int \begin{pmatrix} t + 1 \\ t^2 \\ -t \end{pmatrix} dt = \begin{pmatrix} \frac{1}{2}t^2 + t + D \\ \frac{1}{3}t^3 + E \\ -\frac{1}{2}t^2 + F \end{pmatrix}$

When $t = 0$, $\mathbf{r} = \begin{pmatrix} 0 \\ 0 \\ 0 \end{pmatrix} \quad \therefore \quad D = E = F = 0$

After 5 seconds $\mathbf{r} = \begin{pmatrix} \frac{35}{2} \\ \frac{125}{3} \\ \frac{25}{2} \end{pmatrix}$

i.e. at the point $(\frac{35}{2}, \frac{125}{3}, \frac{-25}{2})$

▶ Vectors are often given in trigonometric form.

4 $\mathbf{r} = \begin{pmatrix} \sin t \\ \cos t \\ 3 \end{pmatrix}$

$\mathbf{v} = \dfrac{d\mathbf{r}}{dt} = \begin{pmatrix} \cos t \\ -\sin t \\ 0 \end{pmatrix}$ $\therefore$ speed $= \sqrt{\cos^2 t + (-\sin t)^2} = 1 \text{ m s}^{-1}$

$\mathbf{P} = \mathbf{F} \bullet \mathbf{v} = m\mathbf{a} \bullet \mathbf{v} = m\begin{pmatrix} -\sin t \\ -\cos t \\ 0 \end{pmatrix} \bullet \begin{pmatrix} \cos t \\ -\sin t \\ 0 \end{pmatrix}$

$\therefore$ $P = m(-\sin t \cos t + \cos t \sin t + 0) = 0$

Work done $= \displaystyle\int_0^{\frac{\pi}{2}} P dt = \left[A\right]_0^{\frac{\pi}{2}} = 0$

The particle is describing a circle, $x = \sin t$, $y = \cos t$, radius 1, centre $(0, 0, 3)$ at constant speed. Hence the energy is constant and no work is done.

5 The vector displacement from $(1, 1, 1)$ to $(7, 6, 5)$ is

$\begin{pmatrix} 7 - 1 \\ 6 - 1 \\ 5 - 1 \end{pmatrix} = \begin{pmatrix} 6 \\ 5 \\ 4 \end{pmatrix}$

Work done $= \mathbf{F} \bullet \mathbf{s}$ $\Rightarrow$ $14 = \lambda\begin{pmatrix} 1 \\ 2 \\ 3 \end{pmatrix} \bullet \begin{pmatrix} 6 \\ 5 \\ 4 \end{pmatrix}$

$14 = 28\lambda$

$\Rightarrow$ $\lambda = \frac{1}{2}$

9 · Relative Velocity

► Chapter 2

Chapter outline

Reminders

▌ Relative velocity

▌ Resolving and resultants

▌ Compass bearings

▌ Maxima and minima by differentiation

New theory in this chapter

▌ Relative velocity in any direction

▌ Question technique

Pure mathematics needed

▌ Maxima and minima by differentiation

▌ Sine rule

▌ Compound angles

RELATIVE VELOCITIES IN DIFFERENT DIRECTIONS

In Chapter 2 on impacts we met relative velocity in almost every question, but also in every case we compared velocities in the same direction. What happens when the velocities are in different directions? That is the subject of this chapter.

We have previously met the idea of the object we are working 'relative to' being made 'stationary' and that remains a dominant principle in the questions which follow.

Diagram drawing is important and adherence to the mathematics and the mechanics is vital. This may appear to be a statement of the obvious: it is. And it is surprising how many students ignore the statement and give way to their imaginations which, in this topic, plays costly tricks.

► In some of the work we have to make assumptions, as we have seen, and we veer away from reality. In this work the situations are real and the results to the problems are just as real.

(ACT) *Activity 9.1*

► Solutions on page 191

1 A particle A has velocity in vector form of $3\mathbf{i} - \mathbf{j}$, whilst particle B has velocity of $5\mathbf{i} + 4\mathbf{j}$. Find the velocity of B relative to A.

2 The pedal cranks on a bicycle are 7 inches long i.e. the pedals go round in a circle of diameter 14 inches. The cyclist is

► Mountain bike, low gears and all that!

pedalling furiously at 198 rpm to achieve a speed of $8\frac{1}{4}$ mph. Find the speed of her foot relative to the ground

(a) when it is at its lowest point

(b) when it is at its highest point.

► A popular type of question

3 The diagram shows two ships, A and B, 5 km apart. A is going north at 15 kmph and B is going east at 12 kmph. Find the shortest distance between them.

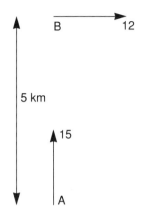

4 Picture the scene:

You are cycling great!

Starts raining grumble!!

Rains harder more grumble!!!
      Stop to put on cape.

Funny, hardly seems to be raining.

► If you are not a cyclist you will have to take our word for it!

How often has this happened to you? Many times if you are a cyclist!

Explain this phenomenon, that it seems to rain harder when we are pedalling than when we are walking, in mechanics terms.

► Similar to question 3

5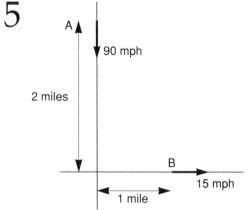

The diagram shows a light plane A travelling south at 90 mph, and a balloon B travelling east at 15 mph and it shows their positions relative to each other. A photographer in the balloon takes a photo of the plane when it is closest. Given that the diagram shows the positions at first sighting, how long does he wait before taking the photo?

6 A swimmer is at point A on one bank of a river. Directly across the river, which is 100 m wide, is the point B. The river is flowing at 4 kmph and his velocity relative to the water is 3 kmph. Find the direction he must swim relative to the water so that his distance from B is a minimum when he reaches the other side, and find what this minimum distance is.

7 A ship is sailing on a bearing of 290° at 12 knots relative to the water. The water is flowing at 5 knots in direction 020°. Five miles north and 35 miles west of the ship a hovercraft is travelling eastwards at 60 knots. Find out whether the ship passes behind the hovercraft or vice versa.

8 A Jumbo Jet and a Tornado are flying at the same height. The Jumbo is going at 250 mph in direction 100° and the Tornado at 400 mph in direction 050°. The Jumbo is 12 miles north of the Tornado.

An official 'near miss' occurs if they get within two miles of each other. Does a 'near miss' occur?

Solutions to Activity 9.1

1

Making A stationary ⇒   Apply the same velocities to B

▶ The basic routine for most relative velocity questions. Remember: the one you are working **relative to** is the one you make stationary.

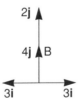

i.e. a velocity of   has been imposed on the whole system.

This makes A stationary and effectively the centre of operations.

Hence we have

and the velocity of B relative to A is $2\mathbf{i} + 6\mathbf{j}$.

2 Firstly we need to find the speed of the feet relative to the bike.

If u is the speed of the foot

$u = 14\pi \times 198$ inches per minute

$\quad = 14\pi \times 198 \times 60$ inches per hour

$\quad = \dfrac{14\pi \times 198 \times 60}{12 \times 3 \times 1760}$ miles per hour (mph)

$\therefore \quad u = 8.25$ mph

Hence the velocity of the foot relative to the bike is

8.25 mph backwards at the lowest point and

8.25 mph fowards at the highest point.

(a) Velocity relative to the ground at the lowest point is $8.25 - 8.25 = 0$

(b) Velocity relative to the ground at the highest point is $8.25 + 8.25 = 16.5$ mph

This means that at the lowest point her foot is not moving but at the highest point it is going twice as fast as the bike. Hard to believe – but true!

3

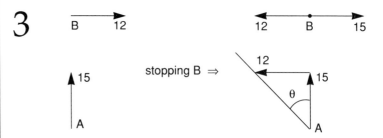

> ► 12 inches (in) = 1 foot (ft)
> 3 ft = 1 yard (yd)
> 1760 yd = 1 mile

> ► You can extend this problem by considering the wheels on a car, bike, anything.

Hence the problem becomes

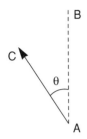

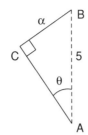

Velocity diagram
B is stationary
A is travelling in the
direction AC

Distance diagram
d is the shortest distance
from B to the path of A and
this is the required distance

$\tan\theta = \dfrac{12}{15}$

$\Rightarrow \quad \theta = 38.7° \quad \Rightarrow \quad d = 5\sin\theta$

$\therefore \quad d = 5\sin 38.7° = 3.1$ km

4 When we assess how hard it is raining we are using what we feel as a guide. What we feel is the rain hitting us when its momentum is destroyed. So we could take the rain's momentum destroyed as a measure of rainfall.

If rain falls with velocity u and you are walking with velocity v

i.e. the momentum of the rain relative to you is

$m\sqrt{v^2 + u^2}$ at $\theta = \tan^{-1}\dfrac{v}{u}$ to the vertical

and this is the momentum you destroy.

$\Rightarrow \quad$ impulse on you is $m\sqrt{v^2 + u^2}$

Now, when cycling, assuming a velocity three times walking velocity,

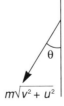

▶ During the course of the book we have considered

● whether rain falls in straight lines
● the impulse when it hits the ground
● the feel of the rain in different situations

This serves to remind you of the omnipresence of mechanics and that there is more to rainfall than weeds and lost umbrellas.

i.e. momentum of rain (same mass)
is now

$m\sqrt{9v^2 + u^2}$ at $\theta = \tan^{-1}\dfrac{3v}{u}$

Hence the impulse on you is

$m\sqrt{9v^2 + u^2}$

so it seems to be raining harder.

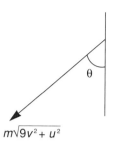

$m\sqrt{9v^2 + u^2}$

5 Stopping the balloon $\Rightarrow$
Velocity diagram

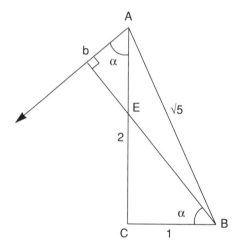

Distance diagram

The photograph should be taken when the plane is at D.
The velocity of the plane relative to the balloon is
$\sqrt{90^2 + 15^2} = 91.2$ mph
in direction AD where $\alpha = \tan^{-1}\dfrac{1}{6} = 9.5°$
In $\triangle$BCE   CE $= \tan\alpha = 0.16$ mile
$\therefore$ AE $= 2 - 0.16 = 1.84$ miles
$\therefore$ AD $= 1.84\cos\alpha = 1.8$ miles

Time taken to reach D $= \dfrac{1.8}{91.2}$ hours $= \dfrac{1.8 \times 60 \times 60}{91.2}$ seconds
i.e. $t = 71$ seconds
The photographer should wait 71 seconds for the best shot.

► Time to pause and reflect on how the problem is transformed by the technique of stopping one and working on the other – a cornerstone of your work on relative velocity.

6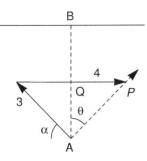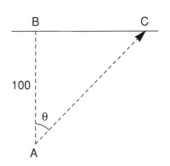

Velocity diagram

Distance diagram
For BC to be a minimum
θ must be a minimum

$\Rightarrow$ find equation for θ: $\tan\theta = \dfrac{PQ}{QA}$

$\therefore$ $\tan\theta = \dfrac{4 - 3\cos\alpha}{3\sin\alpha}$

Since, for $0 < \theta < 90°$, $\tan\theta$ is increasing
the minimum θ also gives a minimum $\tan\theta$.

▶ A useful equation because it introduces α which is what we want.

$\dfrac{\mathrm{d}}{\mathrm{d}\alpha}(\tan\theta) = \dfrac{3\sin\alpha \times 3\sin\alpha - 3\cos\alpha(4 - 3\cos\alpha)}{9\sin^2\alpha}$

For a minimum: $9\sin^2\alpha - 12\cos\alpha + 9\cos^2\alpha = 0$ $\Rightarrow$ $\cos\alpha = \dfrac{3}{4}$

$\therefore$ he swims at $\arccos\dfrac{3}{4}$ with the bank.

$BC = 100\tan\theta = \dfrac{100\left(4 - \frac{3 \times 3}{4}\right)}{\frac{3\sqrt{7}}{4}} = \dfrac{100 \times 7}{3\sqrt{3}}$

$\therefore$ minimum value of BC = 88.2 miles

7 Put the information in the question on the diagram.

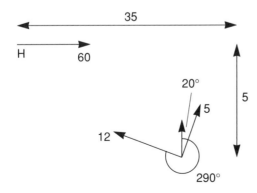

Stop the hovercraft by applying 60 knots due west, and consider the ship:

Velocity diagram

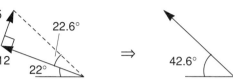

Distance diagram

► AB is shown > HB but could be < HB.

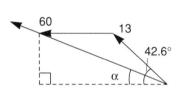
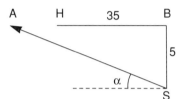

To find AB, we need α.

To find α

$$\tan\alpha = \frac{13\sin 42.6°}{60 + 13\cos42.6°}$$

$\Rightarrow \quad \alpha = 7.2°$

$\Rightarrow \quad AB = \dfrac{5}{\tan\alpha}$

$\qquad = 39.6$ miles

Therefore the ship passes behind the hovercraft.

► A seemingly complicated question solved by a series of fairly simple steps but, above all, illustrating the use of good diagrams.

8 Stop the Tornado!

Velocity diagrams

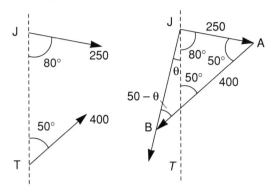

Distance diagram

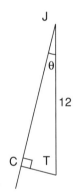

TC is the minimum distance.
We need θ.

Therefore find θ from $\triangle AJB$.

Using the sine rule

$$\frac{400}{\sin(\theta + 80°)} = \frac{250}{\sin(50° - \theta)}$$

$\Rightarrow$ $8(\sin50°\cos\theta - \cos50°\sin\theta) = 5(\sin\theta \cos80° + \sin80°\cos\theta)$

Divide by $\cos\theta$

$\Rightarrow$ $8\sin50° - 5\sin80° = (5\cos50° + 8\cos50°)\tan\theta$

$\Rightarrow$ $\tan\theta = \dfrac{8\sin50° - 5\sin80°}{5\cos50° + 8\cos50°}$

$\Rightarrow$ $\theta = 11.3°$

$\Rightarrow$ $TC = 12\sin\theta = 2.35$ miles

A 'near miss' does not occur.

Circular Motion

► See page 8

► See page 15

► See pages 30 and 37

► See page 53

► See page 108

Chapter outline

Reminders

▮ Resolution

▮ Acceleration

▮ Newton's second law (NL2)

▮ Energy conservation

▮ Conservation of momentum

New theory in this chapter

▮ None: it is an application of known theory to a specific type of problem

Pure mathematics needed

▮ Simultaneous equations

▮ Simple trigonometry

▮ Simple differentiation

CIRCULAR MOTION

On page 47 we considered the fact that when something is going round in a circle, even at constant speed, acceleration is taking place because the velocity vector is constantly changing direction.

In question 6 on page 128 we did a problem in which a mass was going round in a horizontal circle and we found the force acting on it was towards the centre of the circle. Newton's second law tells us that if there is a force there is an acceleration and since the force is towards the centre of the circle so is the acceleration.

This force can easily be felt if you get the block, clear the desk and set the block going round in a circle on the desk with your hand at the middle.

► **Centripetal and centrifugal forces**
T_1 is centrifugal force, acting away from the centre
T_2 is centripetal force, acting towards the centre
Don't bother unduly about these words.

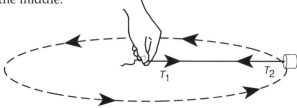

You feel the force T_1 pulling on your hand: it is equal to the force T_2 pulling on the block.

What would happen to your block if the string suddenly snapped?

Now we have accepted that this acceleration exists we will quantify it.

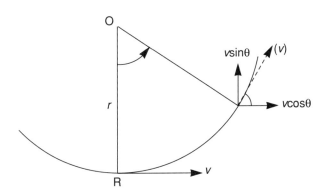

The diagram shows a particle moving on a circle radius r, centre O with constant speed v. At B the speed is shown dotted and it is replaced by components shown, parallel to AO and perpendicular to AO.

Now consider θ to be very small, i.e. B is the adjacent point to A.

The time taken from A to B is $\dfrac{\text{distance}}{\text{speed}} = \dfrac{r\theta}{v}$ θ in radians.

Change in velocity parallel to AO: $v\sin\theta - 0 = v\sin\theta$

Therefore acceleration = change in velocity in unit time

$$= \frac{v\sin\theta}{r\theta/v} = \frac{v^2\sin\theta}{r\theta}$$

For very small angles $\sin\theta = \theta$

$\therefore$ acceleration $//$ AO $= \dfrac{v^2\theta}{r\theta} = \dfrac{v^2}{r}$

i.e.   the acceleration towards the centre of the circle is $\dfrac{v^2}{r}$.

Digest this result: you will use it often.

(**ACT**) *Activity 10.1*

In each question, decide on the forces acting towards the centre and write down the equation which follows from applying Newton's second law.

1 The situation already described in the text – a block going round in a circle on the desk.

2 A small mass m sliding down the outside of a cylindrical pipe of large diameter lying on a horizontal floor.

▶ Our concentration on forces and acceleration towards the centre of the circle continues with the next activity.

▶ Solutions on page 200

3   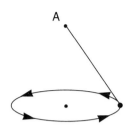   The block going round in a horizontal circle but with your hand above the circle at A.

4   A ring of mass m threaded on a smooth vertical circular wire sets off from

(a) the top **(b)** the bottom.

Consider each case when the radius to the ring has turned through θ, $\theta < 20°$.

5   A ball bearing rolling about on the inside of a hemispherical bowl.

Solutions to Activity 10.1

1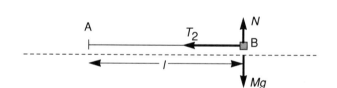

The only force on B towards the centre is T_2.

$$\text{NL2} \quad \Rightarrow \quad T_2 = M \times \frac{v^2}{l}$$
$$\qquad\qquad\quad \uparrow \quad\ \uparrow \quad\ \uparrow$$
$$\qquad\quad \text{force}\ \ \text{mass}\ \ \text{acceleration}$$

2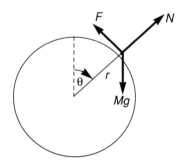

N = normal reaction by cylinder on mass

F = force of friction

The question does not specify 'smooth' so we must assume F acts.

Forces towards centre: $mg\cos\theta - N$

Acceleration towards centre: $\dfrac{v^2}{r}$

$$\therefore \quad mg\cos\theta - N = \frac{mv^2}{r}$$

3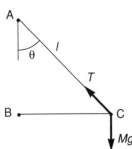

B is the centre of the circle.
Force towards B is $T\sin\theta$

NL2: $T\sin\theta = \dfrac{Mv^2}{l\sin\theta}$

because BC is the radius of the circle and BC = $l\sin\theta$. An arrangement of this sort is called a **conical pendulum**.

► Conical pendulum

4 **(a)**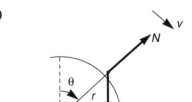

Forces towards centre:
$mg\cos\theta - N$

Acceleration towards the centre:

$\dfrac{v^2}{r}$

$\therefore \ mg\cos\theta - N = \dfrac{mv^2}{r}$

(b)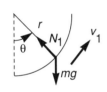

Forces: $N_1 - mg\cos\theta$

Acceleration towards the centre:

$\dfrac{v_1^2}{r}$

$\therefore \ N_1 - mg\cos\theta = \dfrac{mv_1^2}{r}$

5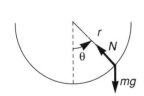

$$N - mg\cos\theta = \dfrac{mv^2}{r}$$

Referring to the question on page 198: What would happen if the string snapped? The block would go outwards radially? *Wrong.* It feels as if this would happen because of the pull on the hand.

The block would carry on in straight line along the tangent? *Correct.*

When the string snaps there are no horizontal forces on the block and hence by Newton's first law it continues in a straight line in the direction it is already going – along the tangent at that point.

If the surface is rough and friction acts the block still goes in a straight line along the tangent, but slows down.

Go back over these five questions and make sure that you understand why the forces are acting as shown and you understand the application of Newton's second law.

► Notation: $\dot{\theta} = \dfrac{d\theta}{dt}$

$\ddot{\theta} = \dfrac{d^2\theta}{dt^2}$

An alternative to $\dfrac{v^2}{r}$

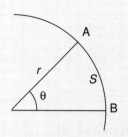

s is the length of the arc AB

$s = r\theta$ provided θ is in radians

Differentiating with respect to (wrt) t:

$$\frac{ds}{dt} = r\frac{d\theta}{dt}$$

i.e. $v = r\dot{\theta}$

v is the velocity along the tangent

$\dot{\theta}$ is the angular speed

► $\dot{\theta}$ is often replaced by ω – the Greek letter omega.

Differentiating again wrt t: $\dfrac{dv}{dt} = r\dfrac{d^2\theta}{dt^2}$

i.e. $a = r\ddot{\theta}$

a is the acceleration along the tangent

$\ddot{\theta}$ is the angular acceleration

for $v = r\dot{\theta}$

The acceleration $\dfrac{v^2}{r}$ may then be written $\dfrac{(r\omega)^2}{r} = r\omega^2$,

and this form is quite often used.

Drawing $\dfrac{mv^2}{r}$ on diagrams or not, as the case should be

► Important – a point of confusion concerning $\dfrac{mv^2}{r}$ – you must get this quite clear.

Probably the greatest cause of confusion in problems based on the circle is the drawing on the force diagram of a force $\dfrac{mv^2}{r}$. The remedy is simple – *don't*: it should not be there. Your force diagram should show all the separate forces which are there because of weight, tension in string, reaction of wire etc. It is the sum total of these which is equal to mass × acceleration and this is where $m \times \dfrac{v^2}{r}$ comes in.

For question 5 in the last Activity:

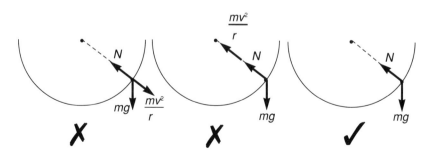

Horizontal circles

As we shall see, horizontal and vertical circles present quite different problems. At this point we concentrate on horizontal circles.

▶ Horizontal circles – they are less complicated than vertical circles.

Refer back to Activity 10.1, question 1.

We already have the equation $T_2 = \dfrac{Mv^2}{l}$

Are there any other equations?

Vertically: $N = Mg$

▶ Because in the vertical direction the block is in equilibrium.

Or using NL2: $N - Mg = M \times 0$ (zero acceleration) $\Rightarrow N = Mg$

And now for question 3 from the same activity:

Towards the centre: $T\sin\theta = \dfrac{Mv^2}{l\sin\theta}$ already established

Vertically: $T\cos\theta = Mg$ vertical equilibrium

(ACT) *Activity 10.2*

▶ Solutions on page 204

1 A girl of mass 50 kg in riding on a roundabout which has a diameter of 12 m and is rotating at 40 rpm. What is the horizontal force acting on her?

2 A mass on the end of a piece of string is describing a conical pendulum. If the string is inclined at 60° to the vertical show that

$\omega = \sqrt{\dfrac{2g}{l}}$, where l is the length of the string.

3 A particle is making horizontal circles on the inside of a hemispherical smooth bowl. If the plane of the circles is at a distance h below the centre of the bowl find h in terms of g and ω, the angular velocity of the particle.

4 Whirl your block above your head in a horizontal circle. Is this possible with the point where you grip the string at the centre of the circle?

5 The diagram (right) shows a mass m at C attached by two strings, AC and BC, to two fixed points A and B. C is describing horizontal circles with BC and AC taut. Find the minimum value of the speed of C for this motion to be possible. Lengths are as shown.

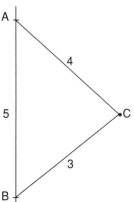

Solutions to Activity 10.2

1

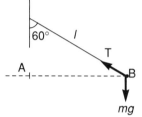

Applying NL2 along the radius: $F = 50 \times 6 \times \omega^2$

40 rpm = $40 \times 2\pi$ radians per minute

$= 40 \times \frac{2\pi}{60}$ radians per second

$= \omega$

$\therefore\ F = 50 \times 6 \times \left(\dfrac{40 \times 2\pi}{60}\right)^2 = 5263.8$ N

NB   5263.8 N = weight of $\dfrac{5263.8}{9.81}$ kg = 536 kg $\approx \dfrac{1}{2}$ tonne

▶ At this point you have applied all the mechanics principles you can. The result you require comes from manipulating the equations you have got.

2

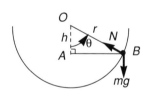

Mass B is describing a horizontal circle with A as centre.

Applying NL2 // BA:

$T\sin 60° = m \times l\sin 60° \times \omega^2$

$\Rightarrow\ T = ml\omega^2$ **(1)**

Resolving vertically for B:

$T\cos 60° = mg \ \Rightarrow\ \dfrac{T}{2} = mg$ **(2)**

T, m not required, therefore **(1)** can be divided by **(2)**:

$2 = \dfrac{l\omega^2}{g} \ \Rightarrow\ \omega = \sqrt{\dfrac{2g}{2}}$

3

Applying NL2 // BA:

$N\sin\theta = mr\sin\theta\omega^2$

$\Rightarrow\ N = mr\omega^2$ **(1)**

Resolving vertically for B:

$N\cos\theta = mg \ \Rightarrow\ \dfrac{Nh}{r} = mg$ **(2)**

(1) divided by **(2)** $\Rightarrow\ \dfrac{r}{h} = \dfrac{r\omega^2}{g} \ \Rightarrow\ h = \dfrac{g}{\omega^2}$

▶ Although these questions describe different situations they boil down to horizontal circles to which we apply
● NL2 along the radius
● consideration of vertical motion.

4

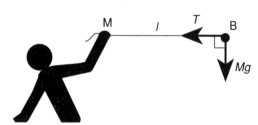

Applying NL2 // BH: $T = \dfrac{mv^2}{l}$

Resolving vertically for B: $0 = Mg$

$\therefore$ motion is possible only if $M = 0$ or $g = 0$

i.e. it is impossible except in Space where $g = 0$.

5   What if the mass is moving too slowly? BC becomes slack, so there will be no tension in BC.

Hence a solution may be possible by investigating tension.

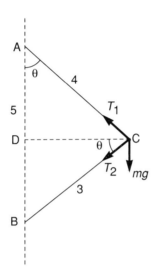

Applying NL2 // CD: $T_1\sin\theta + T_2\cos\theta = \dfrac{mv^2}{r}$

$\Rightarrow$ $T_1 \times \dfrac{3}{5} + T_2 \times \dfrac{4}{5} = \dfrac{mv^2}{4 \times \frac{3}{5}}$ $\Rightarrow$ $36T_1 + 48T_2 = 25mv^2$ **(1)**

Resolving vertically for the mass:

$T_1\cos\theta = T_2\sin\theta + mg$ $\Rightarrow$ $4T_1 - 3T_2 = 5mg$ **(2)**

Eliminating T_1 from **(1)** and **(2)** (and thereby investigating T_2):

$75T_2 = 25mv^2 - 45mg$

The required condition is that $T_2 > 0$

$\Rightarrow$ $25mv^2 - 45mg > 0$

$\Rightarrow$ $v > \sqrt{\dfrac{9g}{5}}$

Vertical circles

So much for horizontal circles for the time being; we shall now look at vertical circles.

Consider question 4 in Activity 10.1, page 200.

► Planning: significance of 'minimum speed' and 'motion to be possible'?

► Try it!

► Notice also that all the information given is numerical, which implies numerical solutions are possible.

► Vertical circles

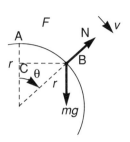

We have already seen that

$$mg\cos\theta - N = \frac{mv^2}{r} \tag{1}$$

Now the mass is sliding down the wire freely and the principle of conservation of energy applies.

As it falls PE is lost and KE is gained and PE lost = KE gained

$$\Rightarrow \quad mg \times AC = \frac{1}{2}mv^2 - \frac{1}{2}mu^2 \text{ where } u \text{ is the velocity at A}$$

If $u = 0 \quad \Rightarrow \quad mg(r - r\cos\theta) = \frac{1}{2}mv^2 \tag{2}$

Note here that we have a second equation with the term mv^2 in it and hence a much used link between (1) and (2).

e.g. eliminating mv^2 between (1) and (2):

$$\Rightarrow \quad r(mg\cos\theta - N) = 2mgr(1 - \cos\theta) - \text{an equation connecting the}$$
force exerted by the wire with the position of the ring.

If $N = 0 \quad \cos\theta = 2 - 2\cos\theta \quad \Rightarrow \quad 0 = \arccos\frac{2}{3}$

i.e. when $\theta = 48.2°$ no force is exerted on the ring by the wire.

What about when $\theta > 48.2°$?

▶ Think about it

▶ Solutions on page 207

(ACT) *Activity 10.3*

1 A small ring of mass m is threaded on a smooth wire in the form of a vertical circles of radius r. If it has velocity u when at the lowest point find u in terms of r and g if the ring reaches the top of the wire.

2 The same small ring is attached to a piece of string of length r and is made to move in a vertical circle. If it has velocity u at its lowest point, find u in terms of r and g.

3 A string of length l has its end A fixed and it is held horizontally with a particle of mass $2m$ at the other end, B. B is released. When B reaches its lowest point it collides and coalesces with a mass C of value m.

Find how far, in terms of l, the combined mass rises and find the tension in the string in terms of m and g at that point.

4 A particle, mass m, slides down the outside of a smooth circular cylinder, radius r, set with its axis horizontal. Find the angle the radius to the particle makes with the vertical when the particle leaves the cylinder, assuming that it sets off from rest at the top of the cylinder.

5 One end of a light rod is hinged to a fixed point at A and the other end carries a mass, m. The system just manages to complete vertical circles. Find the ratio of the stresses in the rod in the two positions when the mass is at its lowest point and at its highest point.

6 A ring of mass m is threaded on a smooth wire in the form of a vertical circle, radius r. It is gently displaced from the highest point on the wire. When it reaches the bottom it collides with a similar ring of mass $2m$, coefficient of restitution $\frac{1}{2}$. Find the height to which the second ring rises and find the force exerted on it by the wire at that point.

7 A light rod is smoothly hinged at one end A. At the other end, B, is a mass m. The rod is held in a horizontal position and then released. After it has turned through θ, where $\theta < 90°$, find the horizontal and vertical components of the force exerted on the hinge by the rod.

8 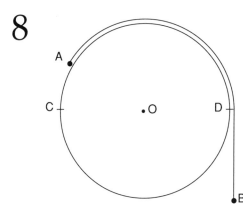 A cylindrical pipe is arranged with its axis horizontal. A string of length πr, where r is the radius of the pipe, passes over the pipe and has at its ends two masses, A of mass m and B of mass $2m$. Initially A is at C and B is at D where CD is the horizontal diameter. The system is released from rest.

Find the tension in the string in terms of m, g and θ where $\angle AOC = \theta$.

Solutions to Activity 10.3

1 The ring can only move on the wire i.e. it must remain on the circular path.

The ring must have enough KE at the bottom to change to the PE it must have at the top.

$$\frac{1}{2}mu^2 \geq mg \times 2r$$

$$\Rightarrow \quad u \geq 2\sqrt{gr}$$

► Is the result the same as in question 1? Many students think so. Are they right?

2

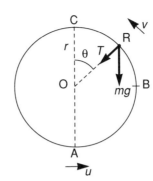

If the ring does not reach the level of B before it stops it will remain on the circular path.

If it does not have sufficient velocity between B and C the string will slacken and the ring will leave the circular path.

Applying NL2 // RO:

$$T + mg\cos\theta = \frac{mv^2}{r}$$

Applying conservation of energy:

$$\frac{1}{2}mu^2 = \frac{1}{2}mv^2 + mgr(1 + \cos\theta)$$

Eliminating mv^2: $T + mg\cos\theta = \frac{mu^2}{r} - 2mg(1 + \cos\theta)$

Condition for a full circle is $T > 0$ when $\theta = 0$

► The velocity required to reach the top of a circle – often asked for!

$$\Rightarrow \quad \frac{mu^2}{r} - 2mg\,(1 + 1) - mg \times 1 > 0$$

$$\Rightarrow \quad u \geq \sqrt{5gr}$$

i.e. a greater value than in question 1.

3

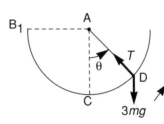

The mass falls from B_1 with impact at C. D is the position of the combined mass when it is rising.

From B_1 to C:
Applying conservation of energy:

$$2mgl = \frac{1}{2} \times 2mu^2 \quad \Rightarrow \quad u = \sqrt{2gl}$$

Impact at C:
Applying conservation of momentum:

$$2m\sqrt{2gl} = 3mv_1 \quad \Rightarrow \quad v_1 = \frac{2}{3}\sqrt{2gl}$$

From C to the highest point:

Applying conservation of energy: $\frac{1}{2} \times 3m \times \frac{4}{9} \times 2gl = 3\,m \times g \times h$

$$\Rightarrow \quad h = \frac{4l}{9}$$

Applying NL2 // DA: $T - 3\,mg\cos\theta = \frac{mv^2}{l}$

At the highest point $v = 0$

$\therefore \quad T = 3mg\cos\theta$

At the highest point D is $\frac{4}{9}l$ above C $\quad\Rightarrow\quad \cos\theta = \frac{5}{9}$

$\Rightarrow \quad T = \frac{5}{3}mg$ at the highest point.

4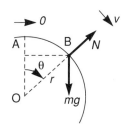

B represents any point where the particle is still in contact.

Applying NL2 // BO:

$$mg\cos\theta - N = \frac{mv^2}{r}$$

Applying conservation of energy:

$$\frac{1}{2}mv^2 = mgr(1 - \cos\theta)$$

Eliminating $\frac{mv^2}{r}$ $\quad\Rightarrow\quad mg\cos\theta - N = 2mg(1 - \cos\theta)$

When the particle leaves the cylinder $N = 0$

$\Rightarrow \quad \cos\theta = \frac{2}{3} \quad\Rightarrow\quad \theta = 48.2°$

▶ Particle leaving a circular surface – another popular topic!

5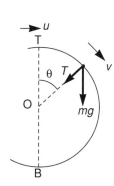

The rod is shown in a general position.

Applying NL2 along the rod:

$$mg\cos\theta - T = \frac{mv^2}{r} \qquad\qquad \textbf{(1)}$$

Applying conservation of energy:

$$\tfrac{1}{2}mv^2 - \tfrac{1}{2}mu^2 = mgr(1 - \cos\theta) \qquad \textbf{(2)}$$

Eliminating mv^2 from **(1)** and **(2)**:

$$r(mg\cos\theta - T) - mu^2 = 2mgr(1 - \cos\theta)$$

The particle just manages to complete circles $\quad\Rightarrow\quad u = 0$

$\therefore \quad mg\cos\theta - T = 2mg(1 - \cos\theta)$

$\Rightarrow \quad T = mg(3\cos\theta - 2)$

At the top $\theta = 0$ $\qquad\qquad T_T = mg$

At the bottom $\theta = 180°$ $\quad T_B = -5mg$

Ratio of stresses $= T_B : T_T = 5mg : mg = 5 : 1$

▶ **NB** The negative result for T_B means that T is acting in the opposite sense to that shown on the diagram.

At the top: $T = mg$

forces in rod pushing outwards

The rod is then acting as a strut.

► Strut defined

At the bottom: $T = 5mg$

forces in rod pulling inwards

The rod is then acting as a tie.

► Tie defined

6

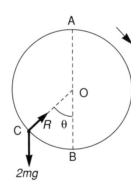

$2mg$

The ring is displaced from A.

Impact occurs at B.

C is the position of the second ring in subsequent motion.

For the first ring A → B, applying conservation of energy:

$\frac{1}{2}mv^2 = mg \times 2r \implies v = 2\sqrt{rg}$

For the impact, applying conservation of momentum:

$m \times 2\sqrt{rg} = mw + 2mu$

where w and u are the velocities of the two particles after collision

$\implies 2\sqrt{rg} = w + 2u$ **(1)**

Applying NEL: $\frac{1}{2}2\sqrt{rg} = u - w$ **(2)**

From **(1)** and **(2)**: $3u = 3\sqrt{rg}$ i.e. $u = \sqrt{rg}$

For the second ring, applying conservation of energy:

$\frac{1}{2} \times 2mu^2 - \frac{1}{2} \times 2mv^2 = 2mgh$ **(3)**

Applying NL2: $R - 2mg\cos\theta = \dfrac{2mv^2}{r}$ **(4)**

From **(3)**: at the highest point h, $v = 0$

$\therefore \quad \dfrac{1}{2}rg = gh \ \Rightarrow \ h = \dfrac{r}{2}$

$h = r - r\cos\theta = r(1 - \cos\theta) \ \Rightarrow \ 1 - \cos\theta = \dfrac{1}{2} \ \Rightarrow \ \theta = 60°$

Substituting in **(4)**: $\theta = 60°$ and $v = 0$ $R - mg = 0 \ \Rightarrow \ R = mg$

$\therefore$ the second ring rises to a height of $\dfrac{1}{2}r$ above B and then
$R = mg$

 7

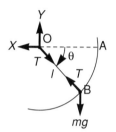

The rod falls from OA to OB.

Applying conservation of energy:

$\dfrac{1}{2}mv^2 = mgl\sin\theta$ **(1)**

Applying NL2 // BO for B:

$T - mg\sin\theta = \dfrac{mv^2}{l}$ **(2)**

From **(1)** and **(2)**:

$T - mg\sin\theta = 2mg\sin\theta$

$\Rightarrow \quad T = 3mg\sin\theta$

The hinge is in equilibrium.

$\therefore$ resolving horizontally: $X = T\cos\theta = 3\,mg\sin\theta\cos\theta$

and resolving vertically: $Y = T\sin\theta = 3mg\sin^2\theta$

► The same story is being repeated throughout each of these 'vertical circle' questions:

● NL2 along radius
● energy equation.

Occasionally there is also a variation, such as COM in question 6.

 8

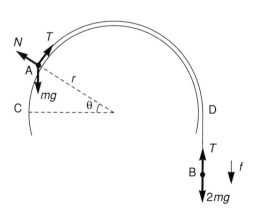

The system has acceleration f as shown.

► Differentiating the energy equation.

► Not the better method in this case, but it introduces an interesting point.

► DB = AC = $r\theta$

► $\dot{\theta}$ cancels out.

Applying NL2 for B: $2mg - T = 2mf$ **(1)**

Applying NL2 along the tangent for A: $T - mg\cos\theta = mf$ **(2)**

From **(1)** and **(2)**: $T = \dfrac{2}{3}mg(1 + \cos\theta)$

Alternative method

Using conservation of energy:

gain in PE of A + gain in KE of A and B = loss in PE of B

$$mgr\sin\theta + \frac{1}{2} \times 3mv^2 = 2mgr\theta$$

$$\Rightarrow\quad gr\sin\theta + \frac{3}{2}r^2\dot{\theta}^2 = 2gr\theta$$

*Differentiating wrt t $\Rightarrow$ $gr\sin\theta\dot{\theta} + 3r\dot{\theta}\ddot{\theta} = 2g\dot{\theta}$

$$\Rightarrow\quad r\ddot{\theta} = \frac{g}{3}(2 - \cos\theta)$$

Applying NL2 for A: $T - mg\cos\theta = mr\ddot{\theta}$

$$\Rightarrow\quad T = \frac{2}{3}mg(1 + \cos\theta)$$

As we said not the better method in this case but the step at * of differentiating the energy equation invariably leads to $\dot{\theta}$ cancelling out and leaving an expression for $\ddot{\theta}$. It is a technique used quite often.

Simple Harmonic Motion and Similar

INTRODUCTION

Before we have a look at the next round of problems there are two points to make.

• In this work NL2 and hence acceleration feature prominently and:

$$\text{acceleration} = \frac{dv}{dt} \qquad \text{the } v, t \text{ form}$$

$$= \frac{d^2x}{dt^2} \qquad \text{the } x, t \text{ form}$$

$$= \frac{dv}{dx} \cdot \frac{dx}{dt} = v\frac{dv}{dx} \qquad \text{the } v, x \text{ form}$$

► Three ways of expressing acceleration

Hence another version of the triangle we had on page 40.

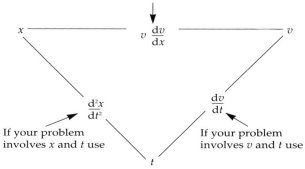

If your problem involves v and x use

x ——————— $v\frac{dv}{dx}$ ——————— v

$\frac{d^2x}{dt^2}$ $\frac{dv}{dt}$

If your problem involves x and t use   If your problem involves v and t use

t

► Another version of a well-known triangle

This will become clearer when we start using it.

*   Your integration needs to be in good order.

► Solutions on page 215

(ACT) *Activity 11.1*

1 A body of mass m is falling in a medium which offers a resistance of kv^2, where v is its velocity. Initially the mass has velocity u and it has terminal velocity w.

(a) Find k in terms of m, g and w.

(b) Find x, the distance moved, in terms of m, g, k, u and v.

(c) Express v in terms of mg, k, u and x.

2 An engine is working at constant power P and it is driving a vehicle with resistance to motion which is constant and equal to R. Initially $v = 1$. If the mass of the engine is M find an expression for t in terms of M, R, P and v in the period during which the vehicle is accelerating.

3 A particle of mass m experiences a force F in its direction of motion and a resistance R to that motion. $R = mx$, $F = ma$ where a is a constant, and maximum R occurs when $x = a$, x being the distance travelled from a point O where the velocity is zero. Find

(a) the value of x when the velocity becomes constant

(b) v in terms of x

(c) u in terms of a where u is the final velocity.

4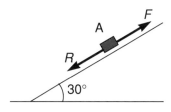

The diagram shows a cart A of mass M on a plane inclined at 30° to the horizontal. It is acted on by forces F and R as shown.
$F = Mg(1 + 2t)$ for $0 \le t \le 3$ and for $t > 3$, $F = Mg$.
$$R = \frac{Mg}{2}.$$

The initial velocity is u, and when $t = 0$, x (distance travelled) $= 0$.

Find the terminal velocity and the distance travelled to attain it in terms of u and g.

5 A particle is moving in a straight line. When it is at a distance x from a fixed point O the only force acting on the particle is mk^2x, where m is the mass of the particle and k is a constant, acting in the direction towards O. Given that $v = 0$ when $x = a$ and $x = 0$ when $t = 0$ find

(a) v in terms of a, k and x

(b) x in terms of a, k and t

Solutions to Activity 11.1

1

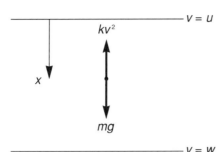

▶ The diagram shows the forces and also identifies different variables and constants.

Applying NL2: $mg - kv^2 = ma$

The question is concerned with velocity and distance, v and x, therefore use

$$a = v\frac{dv}{dx}$$

$$mg - kv^2 = mv\frac{dv}{dx}$$

(a) Terminal velocity means when the particle has stopped accelerating i.e. acceleration is zero.

$$\therefore \quad mg - kw^2 = 0 \quad \Rightarrow \quad k = \frac{mg}{w^2}$$

(b) $mg - kv^2 = mv\dfrac{dv}{dx}$

$$\int dx = \int \frac{mv}{mg - kv^2} \ dv$$

▶ Separating the variables

Integrating $\Rightarrow \quad x = -\dfrac{1}{2k} \ln(mg - kv^2) + A$

When $x = 0$, $v = u$ $\Rightarrow \quad 0 = \dfrac{1}{2k} \ln(mg - ku^2) + A$

Substituting for A: $x = \dfrac{1}{2k} \ln(mg - ku^2) - \dfrac{1}{2k} \ln(mg - kv^2)$

$$= \frac{1}{2k} \ln\left\{\frac{mg - ku^2}{mg - kv^2}\right\}$$

$$\Rightarrow \quad mg - kv^2 = (mg - ku^2)e^{-2kx}$$

$$\Rightarrow \quad v^2 = \frac{1}{k}\left(mg - e^{-2kx}(mg - ku^2)\right)$$

$$\Rightarrow \quad v = \frac{1}{\sqrt{k}}(mg - e^{-2kx}(mg - ku^2))^{1/2}$$

▶ Some will say, 'Why are we doing this? Why not use, because of *v* and *x*, $v^2 = u^2 + 2ax$?'

Why not indeed? Countless students, every year, have thought exactly the same, and proceeded to use $v^2 = u^2 + 2ax$, and thereby have managed to score zero marks.

The equations established on pages 38-9 are for uniform acceleration.

We are now dealing with variable acceleration, a very different game.

We have moved from the soccer pitch to the rugby pitch: more complicated, more challenging,

▶ **General notes on these questions**
• In these questions you must expect a good deal of algebraic manipulation.
• Much pure mathematics following a modest amount of mechanics. In this question we had one line of mechanics, the application of NL2, and much pure, variables separable, integration, log and exponential, algebraic manipulation.
• Complicated answers occur frequently.

► Using $\dfrac{dv}{dt}$ because the question is about v and t

2

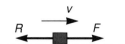

Power $= Fv \Rightarrow F = \dfrac{P}{v}$

Applying NL2: $F - R = Ma$

i.e. $\dfrac{P}{v} - R = M\dfrac{dv}{dt}$

Separating variables:

$$\int dt = \int \dfrac{Mv}{P - Rv}\,dv$$

► You must be prepared to go back to your Pure Mathematics for this work.

Integrating: $t + A = -\dfrac{Mv}{R} - \dfrac{MP}{R^2} \times \ln(P - Rv)$

Integration of RHS:

method 1 – divide and integrate $-\dfrac{M}{R} + \dfrac{MP}{R(P - Rv)}$

method 2 – substitution: let $u = P - Rv$

We used method 1.

When $t = 0, v = 1 \Rightarrow A = -\dfrac{M}{R} - \dfrac{MP}{R^2}\ln(P - Rv)$

Substituting for A: $\Rightarrow t = \dfrac{M}{R}(1 - v) + \dfrac{MP}{R^2}\ln\left(\dfrac{P - R}{P - Rv}\right)$

► $\ddot{x} = \dfrac{d^2x}{dt^2}$

$\ddot{x}$ is read as 'x double dot'

3

O   R   F

x

i.e. $x = a$ for constant velocity

► Using $v\dfrac{dv}{dx}$ form because the question is about v and x

Applying NL2: $F - R = m\ddot{x}$

(a) When v is constant, acceleration $= 0$

i.e. $F - R = 0$

$\Rightarrow ma - mx = 0$

(b) $F - R = m\ddot{x}$

$\Rightarrow ma - mx = m\ddot{x}$

$\Rightarrow a - x = v\dfrac{dv}{dx}$

Separating variables: $\int(a - x)dx = \int v\,dv$

$\Rightarrow ax - \dfrac{x^2}{2} = \dfrac{v^2}{2} + A$

When $x = 0, v = 0 \Rightarrow A = 0$

$\therefore v = \sqrt{2ax - x^2}$

(c)   The final velocity is when the acceleration = 0

i.e. when $x = a$ from **(a)**

and then $u = \sqrt{2a^2 - a^2}$

$\therefore \quad u = a$

4

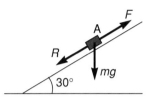

Applying NL2 along the plane: $F - R - Mg\sin30° = Ma$

$\Rightarrow \quad Mg(1 + 2t) - \dfrac{Mg}{2} - \dfrac{Mg}{2} = Ma$

$\therefore \quad 2gt = \dfrac{dv}{dt}$

► Using $\frac{dv}{dt}$ form because the question is about v and t

Integrating: $gt^2 + A = v$

When $t = 0, v = u \quad \Rightarrow \quad v = u + gt^2$

Terminal velocity is reached when $a = 0$

Now if $t > 3$ then $F = Mg \quad \Rightarrow \quad a = 0$

Therefore maximum velocity is reached at $t = 3$ because $v = u + gt^2$ is an increasing function.

$\therefore \quad$ terminal velocity $v = u + 9g$

To bring in x, the distance, we have $v = \dfrac{dx}{dt}$

$\Rightarrow \quad \dfrac{dx}{dt} = u + gt^2$

Integrating: $x = ut + \frac{1}{3}gt^3 + B$

When $t = 0, x = 0 \quad \Rightarrow \quad x = ut + \frac{1}{3}gt^3$

When $t = 3 \quad x = 3u + 9g$

5

Applying NL2: $F = -m\ddot{x}$

$\Rightarrow mk^2x = -m\ddot{x} \Rightarrow \ddot{x} = -k^2x$

For v, x use $v\dfrac{dv}{dx} = \ddot{x}$

$\Rightarrow \quad v\dfrac{dv}{dx} = -k^2x$

Separating variables: $\displaystyle\int v\,dv = -\int k^2x\,dx$

$\Rightarrow \quad \dfrac{v^2}{2} = -\dfrac{1}{2}k^2x^2 + A$

When $v = 0, x = a \quad \Rightarrow \quad A = \frac{1}{2}k^2a^2$

$\Rightarrow v^2 = k^2(a^2 - x^2) \quad \Rightarrow \quad v = k\sqrt{a^2 - x^2}$

► – the v, x equation

For x, t use $v = \dfrac{dx}{dt}$

$$\Rightarrow \quad \frac{dx}{dt} = k\sqrt{a^2 - x^2}$$

Separating variables: $\displaystyle\int \frac{dx}{\sqrt{a^2 - x^2}} = \int k\,dt$

$$\Rightarrow \quad \sin^{-1}\frac{x}{a} = kt + B$$

When $x = 0$, $t = 0$ $\Rightarrow$ $B = 0$

► – the x, t equation

$$\therefore \quad \frac{x}{a} = \sin kt \quad \Rightarrow \quad x = a\sin kt$$

At this point we have answered the question as asked but this example leads us into a particular area of work which we shall now develop.

Simple harmonic motion

► The word 'simple' distinguishes this work from 'Compound harmonic motion' which is more complicated and which we don't do on this course.

In doing the last question in Activity 11.1, we have covered the bulk of the theory we need; there are just one or two trimmings and explanations to add.

► Definition of SHM

> ### The definition of simple harmonic motion, SHM
>
> Simple harmonic motion is defined as motion in which the acceleration is proportional to the displacement from a fixed point (the k^2x bit) and directed towards that point (the – sign).
>
> In equation form: $\ddot{x} = -cx$

► SHM equation

As we have already seen, it is algebraically convenient to write c as a square; we used k^2. Most often ω (omega) is used so we have $\ddot{x} = -\omega^2 x$

► – the v, x equation

The velocity-distance equation is then $v = \omega\sqrt{a^2 - x^2}$

The maximum value of v is when $x = 0$

► v_{max}

and then $v_{max} = \omega a$

► – the x, t equation

The distance-time equation is then $x = a\sin\omega t$

The maximum value of x is when $\sin\omega t = 1$

and then $x_{max} = a$

► Amplitude

a is the **amplitude**.

From this equation we can sort out the actual motion.

As t goes from 0 to $\dfrac{\pi}{2\omega}$ we have

as t goes from $\dfrac{\pi}{2\omega}$ to $\dfrac{\pi}{\omega}$ we have

as t goes from $\dfrac{\pi}{\omega}$ to $\dfrac{3\pi}{2\omega}$ we have

as t goes from $\dfrac{3\pi}{2\omega}$ to $\dfrac{2\pi}{\omega}$ we have

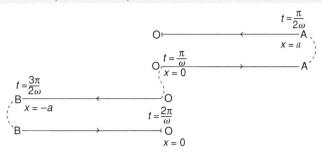

The particle has now done a full cycle and the total time taken is $\dfrac{2\pi}{\omega}$; this is known as the **period**.

▶ $T = \dfrac{2\pi}{\omega}$ the period

When we arrived at $x = a\sin\omega t$ an alternative solution would have been $x = a\cos\omega t$ given the initial condition $x = a$ when $t = 0$.

i.e. $x = a\sin\omega t$ is used when $t = 0$ with particle at O

   $x = a\cos\omega t$ is used when $t = 0$ with particle at A.

In both cases x is measured from O. A popular pitfall is to measure x from A when using $x = a\cos\omega t$.

For $x = a\cos\omega t$ the cycle diagram is:

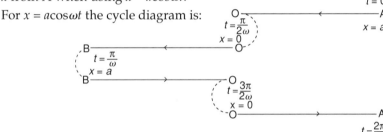

The velocity-time equations

These are obtained by differentiating the x, t equations.

Hence $v = a\omega\cos\omega t$

   or $v = -a\omega\sin\omega t$

In both cases we have maximum speed when $\cos\omega t$ or $\sin\omega t = 1$ and $v_{\max} = a\omega$.

In summary, using the x, v, t triangle:

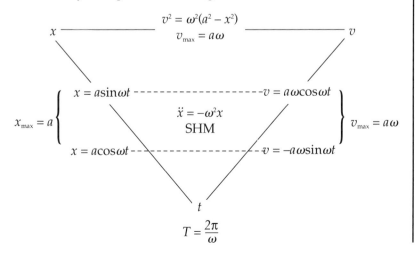

▶ Yet another version of that triangle!

Two situations which produce simple harmonic motion

Situation one

The diagram represents a spring AB on a smooth horizontal table with the end A fixed. A particle of mass m is attached at B which is then stretched to D. The particle is released and some time later it is at C.

The only force on C in the direction of motion is T, the tension in the spring.

Applying NL2 for C: $T = -m\ddot{x}$

This – sign is because T is in direction CB
while x is in direction BC.

How about T?

► Hooke's law

There is a simple law, which you can easily prove practically for yourself, known as **Hooke's law** which states (obviously for elastic springs and strings) that tension is proportional to extension.

$$T \propto x$$
$$\Rightarrow \quad T = cx$$

a constant

in mathematics

► C, the spring constant

$$c = \frac{\lambda}{l}$$

in physics

c is known as the
spring constant

► λ, the modulus

where λ is a constant known as the modulus and l is the natural, unstretched length of the spring.

So the equation of motion becomes

$$\frac{\lambda x}{l} = -m\ddot{x}$$

$$\ddot{x} = -\frac{\lambda}{ml}x \quad \longleftarrow \quad \text{which is SHM because}$$

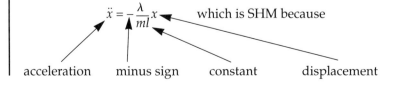

acceleration   minus sign   constant   displacement

Situation two

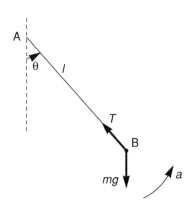

The diagram shows a string of length l fixed at A and carrying a mass m at the other end B. T is the tension in the string.

Applying NL2 along the tangent at B: $mg\sin\theta = -ma$

► – sign because a is in the opposite direction to $mg\sin\theta$

But $a = l\ddot{\theta}$

∴ $g\sin\theta = -l\ddot{\theta}$

► Simple pendulum

If θ is small $\sin\theta = \theta$

Hence $g\theta = -l\theta$

$\ddot{\theta} = -\dfrac{g}{l}\,\theta$ which is SHM.

This arrangement is known as a **simple pendulum** (to distinguish it from the compound pendulum which is not in this course).

 Activity 11.2

► Solutions on page 222

1 A particle is performing SHM with equation of motion $\ddot{x} = -9x$ and the amplitude is $2m$. Find the period, the maximum velocity and the velocity 1 m from the mean position.

► Questions 1–4(b) use standard SHM formulae. In 4(c) expect to introduce a principle that you know well.

2 A cork is bobbing up and down on the waves on a lake and in a vertical sense it is thought to be doing SHM. The waves are passing at one every three seconds and it moves 25 cm vertically from trough to peak. Find the maximum vertical velocity of the cork and the time it spends on the top third of the wave.

3 A particle is performing SHM horizontally between two points A and B where AB = 10. The period of the motion is 4. Find the ratio of the time taken to travel from A to C to the time to travel from C to B where AC = 7.

4 A simple pendulum consists of a mass m on the end of a string of length l. Its maximum angular displacement is β.

  (a) Find the period in terms of l and g.

  (b) Find the maximum angular velocity.

  (c) Show that $\beta^2 = 2(1 - \cos\beta)$.

5 A particle is performing SHM of amplitude $3a$ and period T. Show that the time spent in the middle third of the motion is approximately $\dfrac{T}{5}$.

6 Using a bit of Blu-Tak, set a match vertically near the edge of the turntable on your record player. Switch on the player so that the turntable revolves. Now go across the room (4 yards or so) and sit so that the record player is at eye-level. Watch the match. Are you watching SHM? Justify your answer.

Solutions to Activity 11.2

► Most – if not all – of the SHM formulae are on examination reference leaflets but don't let this mean that you don't need to know them. It is **essential** that you know all your formulae, SHM included. You cannot hope to achieve fluency and efficiency if you do not know them.

1 $\ddot{x} = -9x = -\omega^2 x$

Amplitude $a = 2$

(a) $T = \dfrac{2\pi}{\omega} \implies T = \dfrac{2\pi}{3}$ seconds

(b) $v_{max} = a\omega \implies v_{max} = 2 \times 3 = 6$ m s^{-1}

(c) Using the v, x equation; $v^2 = \omega^2(a^2 - x^2) \implies v^2 = 9(4 - 1) = 27$

$\implies v = 3\sqrt{3}$ m s^{-1}

2

B ─ $x = 12.5$ cm

A ─ $x = \dfrac{2}{3} \times 12.5$

O ─ mean position

Amplitude $a = 0.25$ m

Time $T = 3$ seconds

$v_{max} = a\omega = a \times \dfrac{2\pi}{T}$

$\implies v_{max} = 0.25 \times \dfrac{2\pi}{3} = 0.5$ m s^{-1}

Use x, t equation: $x = a\cos\omega t$ because we require the time from B to A.

$\dfrac{2}{3} \times 0.125 = 0.125\cos\dfrac{2\pi}{3}t$

$\implies t = 0.4$ seconds

∴ time spent on top third of wave $= 2 \times 0.4 = 0.8$ seconds.

3

A ─────── O ── C ── B
       5   2   3

$\dfrac{t_{AC}}{t_{CB}} = \dfrac{t_{AO} + t_{OC}}{t_{OB} - t_{OC}} = \dfrac{1 + t_{OC}}{1 - t_{OC}}$

because $t_{AO} = \dfrac{T}{4} = 1$

To find t_{OC}:

$x = a\sin\omega t \implies 2 = 5\sin\dfrac{\pi}{2}t$ because $T = \dfrac{2\pi}{\omega} \implies \omega = \dfrac{\pi}{2}$

∴ $t = 0.26$

∴ $\dfrac{t_{AC}}{t_{CB}} = \dfrac{1.26}{0.24} = 1.7$

4 Equation of motion: $\ddot{\theta} = -\dfrac{g}{l}\theta$

(a) $T = \dfrac{2\pi}{\omega} \implies T = 2\pi\sqrt{\dfrac{l}{g}}$

(b) $v_{max} = a\omega \implies \dot{\theta}_m = \beta\sqrt{\dfrac{g}{l}}$

(c) Applying conservation of energy: gain in KE = loss in PE

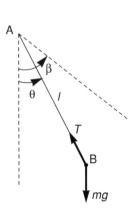

$$\frac{1}{2} ml^2 \dot{\theta}_m^2 = mgl(1 - \cos\beta)$$

Substituting for $\dot{\theta}$m $\Rightarrow$ $\frac{1}{2} l\beta^2 \times \frac{g}{l} = g (1 - \cos\beta)$

$\therefore$ $\beta^2 = 2(1 - \cos\beta)$

5

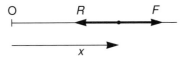

To find the time taken to travel from O to C, $t_{\rm OC}$:

$x = a\sin\omega t$ $\Rightarrow$ $a = 3a\sin\omega t_{\rm OC}$ $\Rightarrow$ $t_{\rm OC} = \dfrac{0.3T}{2\pi}$

Time for middle third $= 4 \times t_{\rm OC}$ $(O \rightarrow C \rightarrow O \rightarrow D \rightarrow O)$

$= 4 \times \dfrac{0.3T}{2\pi}$

$= 0.19T \approx \dfrac{T}{5}$

6

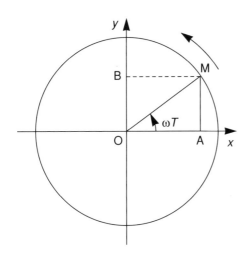

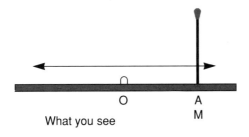

What you see

M is the match going round at constant speed. Let the speed be ω radians per second (rad s^{-1}) $\angle$MOA $= \omega t$ where t is time.

$OA = r\cos\omega t$

> ► **NB**   Where did the idea to use conservation of energy come from?
> Partially from the result; β^2 on one side and $(1 - \cos\beta)$ on the other looked at bit like kinetic and potential energy: and partially from being awake to all principles which apply in a given situation; energy is clearly one in this case.

> ► OA is known as the projection of OM on Ox; and similarly for OB on Oy.

Therefore $x = r\cos\omega t$

Looks like SHM.

$\dot{x} = -r\omega\sin\omega t$

$\ddot{x} = -r\omega^2\cos\omega t$

$\ddot{x} = -\omega^2 x$ SHM

And the same thing is happening for the point B along Oy.

Energy and springs

As we saw on page 220 an ordinary spring can produce simple harmonic motion, but there is another mechanics principle involved at which we should look. This is the energy involved.

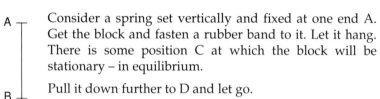

Consider a spring set vertically and fixed at one end A. Get the block and fasten a rubber band to it. Let it hang. There is some position C at which the block will be stationary – in equilibrium.

Pull it down further to D and let go.

What happens? It bobs up and down between B and D.

At B the block has potential energy.

As it falls to C, it loses potential energy and gains kinetic energy.

Near D it is still losing potential energy, but it is also losing kinetic energy because it is slowing down.

At D it has lost its potential energy *and* it has lost its kinetic energy.

Where has all this energy gone?

The block then starts to rise.

Moving from D to C it gains potential energy and kinetic energy.

Where does it come from?

▶ Remember the energy ⟷ work done equation: the elastic is doing work on the block as it rises; it is giving it energy and the falling block did work on the elastic as it fell; it gave the elastic energy.

It must come from the spring or the elastic.

Now we need to look at the energy of a spring.

Potential energy of a spring

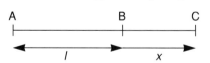

ABC represents a spring, fixed at the end A.

It is stretched out to C.

Thus AB is the unstretched length l and BC is the extension x.

Now energy = work done

and work done = force × distance

So where is the problem?

Think for a minute about the force needed to stretch a spring: the greater the stretch, the greater the force needed; i.e. the force varies.

Our force × distance rule only holds for a force which does not vary.

So what do we do?

Consider the section BC.

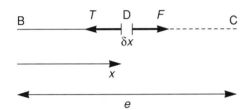

Consider a small element of extension δx at D.

F is the force doing the work and $F = T$

► *F is considered constant because δx is so small.*

Work done over $\delta x = F \times \delta x$

Total work done in stretching from B to C = $\displaystyle\sum_{x=0}^{e} F\delta x$

As $\delta x \to 0$ Work done = $\displaystyle\int_{0}^{e} T\mathrm{d}x$

$\qquad = \displaystyle\int_{0}^{e} \frac{\lambda x}{l}\, \mathrm{d}x \qquad$ because $T = \dfrac{\lambda x}{l}$

$\qquad = \dfrac{\lambda e^2}{2l}$

Work done stretching spring = energy given to it

∴   PE of spring is $\dfrac{\lambda x^2}{2l}$

► *x is the letter usually used for extension*

Why is it called potential energy?

> **Potential energy** is the energy a body has because of its position or state: when a spring is stretched it is in a state where it can do work – it has potential energy.

► *Potential energy*

(ACT) *Activity 11.3*

► *Solutions on page 226*

1 An elastic string of modules $2mg$ and natural length l is vertical with its upper end fixed and a mass m attached to its lower end. The string is in equilibrium. Find the extension.

The mass m is then pulled down a further distance a and released. Show that the mass then performs simple harmonic motion and find the period.

► Think carefully: done correctly, this is an easy question.

2 The end A of an elastic string of length l, modulus $4mg$, is fixed and a mass m is attached to the other end, B. B is held on a level with A and then allowed to fall. Find the maximum extension of the string.

3

A   C   M   D   B   AB is an elastic string
├──────┼──────────┤   of modulus $2mg$ and
natural length $2l$.

It is stretched horizontally and the ends A and B are fixed. $AC = CM = MD = DB = l$. A particle of mass m is attached to the string at M and M is then pulled until it is at D. The particle is then released. Find the period of the subsequent motion and the speed of the particle as it passes through M. Also find the time taken to reach a point halfway between M and C.

4 An elastic string of natural length a is fixed vertically. The upper end is fixed and the lower end carries two masses, one of $3m$ and the other of m. It is in equilibrium, then the mass of m falls off. If the modulus of the string is $2mg$ find, by energy consideration, the maximum height reached in the ensuing motion.

5 With reference to question 2, find

(a) the maximum height reached by the mass after leaving B, the lowest point

(b) the time it takes to get there.

Solutions to Activity 11.3

1

The diagram is not to scale.

At C, the equilibrium position:

Resolving vertically for mass: $T = mg$

$\therefore \quad \dfrac{\lambda e}{l} = mg$

$\therefore \quad \dfrac{2mge}{l} = mg$

$\Rightarrow \quad e = \tfrac{1}{2}$

The mass is now pulled down to E and released.

At D:

Applying NL2 for mass: $mg - T = m\ddot{x}$

$\Rightarrow \quad mg - \dfrac{\lambda(e + x)}{l} = m\ddot{x}$

$\Rightarrow \quad mg - \dfrac{2mg}{l} \times \dfrac{l}{2} - \dfrac{2mgx}{l} = m\ddot{x}$

$\Rightarrow \quad \dfrac{-2g}{l} x = \ddot{x}$

which is SHM.

$T = \dfrac{2\pi}{\omega} = 2\pi \sqrt{\dfrac{l}{2g}}$

> ► Show on the diagram any position D at a distance *x* from the equilibrium position C, not from B: this makes the algebra easier because the mass oscillates about C, not B, and for SHM displacement is measured from the centre of oscillation.

> ► Looks complicated at this stage...

> ► but invariably simplifies to something like this.

The pattern of this question is one you can expect to meet again:

• finding the equilibrium position

• applying Newton's second law

• SHM equation

• use of SHM results.

2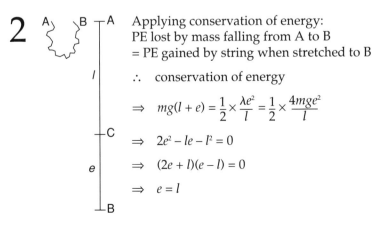

A Applying conservation of energy:
PE lost by mass falling from A to B
= PE gained by string when stretched to B

$\therefore$ conservation of energy

$\Rightarrow \quad mg(l + e) = \dfrac{1}{2} \times \dfrac{\lambda e^2}{l} = \dfrac{1}{2} \times \dfrac{4mge^2}{l}$

$\Rightarrow \quad 2e^2 - le - l^2 = 0$

$\Rightarrow \quad (2e + l)(e - l) = 0$

$\Rightarrow \quad e = l$

> ► KE is zero both initially and at full stretch.

> ► Another favourite in examinations

3

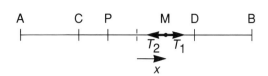

The problem resolves into a particle M attached to two strings AM and BM.

Applying NL2: $\quad T_1 - T_2 = m\ddot{x}$

$$\Rightarrow \quad \frac{\lambda(l-x)}{l} - \frac{\lambda(l+x)}{l} = m\ddot{x}$$

$$\Rightarrow \quad \frac{-2\lambda x}{l} = m\ddot{x}$$

$\lambda = 2mg \quad \Rightarrow \quad \frac{-2gx}{l} = \ddot{x} \quad$ i.e. SHM

$$T = \frac{2\pi}{\omega} \quad \Rightarrow \quad T = 2\pi\sqrt{\frac{l}{2g}}$$

$v_{max} = a\omega \quad \Rightarrow \quad v_{max} = l\sqrt{\frac{2g}{l}} = \sqrt{2gl}$

Time to reach P = time to reach M (t_1) + time from M to P (t_2)

$$= \frac{T}{4} + t_2$$

M $\to$ P, $x = 0$ when $t = 0 \quad \Rightarrow \quad x = a\sin\omega t$

$$\Rightarrow \quad \frac{l}{2} = l\sin\sqrt{\frac{2g}{l}}\, t_2$$

$$\Rightarrow \quad \frac{\pi}{6} = \sqrt{\frac{2g}{l}}\, t_2$$

$$\Rightarrow \quad t_2 = \frac{\pi}{6} = \sqrt{\frac{l}{2g}}$$

$\therefore \quad$ time taken D $\to$ P $= \frac{\pi}{2}\sqrt{\frac{l}{2g}} + \frac{\pi}{6}\sqrt{\frac{l}{2g}} = \frac{2\pi}{3}\sqrt{\frac{l}{2g}}$

Fine but it can be done much more neatly.

Considering the motion from D to P in one step:

When $t = 0, x = 1 \quad \therefore \quad x = a\cos\omega t$

At P, $x = -\frac{l}{2} \quad \therefore \quad -\frac{l}{2} = l\cos\omega t$

$$\Rightarrow \quad \omega t = \cos^{-1}\left(-\frac{1}{2}\right) = \frac{2\pi}{3}$$

$$\Rightarrow \quad t = \frac{2\pi}{3}\sqrt{\frac{l}{2g}}$$

► A much better method!

4

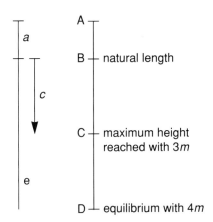

With $4m$:

Applying Hooke's law: $4mg = \dfrac{2mge}{a}$

$\therefore \quad e = 2a$

Applying conservation of energy:

energy at D = energy at C

$$\frac{1}{2} \times \frac{\lambda e^2}{a} = \frac{1}{2} \times \frac{\lambda c^2}{a} + 3mg(e - c)$$

PE of string   PE of string   PE gained
stretched to D stretched to C by mass 3m

$\therefore \quad 2mg \times 4a^2 = 2mgc^2 + 6mga(2a - c)$

$\Rightarrow \quad 4a^2 = c^2 + 6a^2 - 3ac$

$\Rightarrow \quad 2a^2 - 3ac + c^2 = 0$

$\Rightarrow \quad c = 2a$ or $c = a$

$\therefore \quad 3m$ mass rises a distance $e - c = 2a - a = a$
in the ensuing motion.

► **NB** The other value obtained for c, i.e. 2a, is the initial position and it is the other position where the energy equation quoted is satisfied.

5 By conservation of energy, the mass will rise to A. To find e:

At D the mass is in equilibrium.

$\therefore \quad mg = \dfrac{4mge}{l}$

$\Rightarrow \quad e = \dfrac{l}{4}$

For the mass at a distance x below D:

Applying NL2:

$mg - T = m\ddot{x}$

$mg - \dfrac{4mg(e + x)}{l} = m\ddot{x}$

$\Rightarrow \quad -\dfrac{4gx}{l} = \ddot{x}$ i.e. SHM

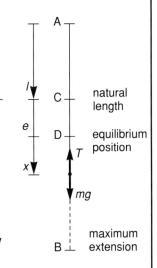

So what have we got?   SHM from B to C

At C string slackens, no longer SHM   Free particle from C
to A

For SHM B to C, amplitude = BD $= \dfrac{3l}{4}$ and $t = 0$ when $x = \dfrac{3l}{4}$

Hence $x = a\cos\omega t \Rightarrow -\dfrac{l}{4} = \dfrac{3l}{4}\cos2\sqrt{\dfrac{g}{l}}\,t$

$\Rightarrow \quad t = 1.9 \times \dfrac{1}{2}\sqrt{\dfrac{l}{g}} = 0.95\sqrt{\dfrac{l}{g}}$

Now for C to A, uniform acceleration, we use $v, t \quad \Rightarrow \quad v = u + at$

We don't know u therefore back to SHM section to find v at C.

$v^2 = \omega^2(a^2 - x^2) \quad \Rightarrow \quad v^2 = \dfrac{4g}{l}\left(\dfrac{9l^2}{16} - \dfrac{l^2}{16}\right) = 2gl$

$v = u + at \quad \Rightarrow \quad 0 = \sqrt{2gl} - gt \quad \Rightarrow \quad t = \sqrt{\dfrac{2l}{g}} = 1.4\sqrt{\dfrac{l}{g}}$

$\therefore$ total time from B to A is $0.95\sqrt{\dfrac{l}{g}} + 1.4\sqrt{\dfrac{l}{g}} = 2.35\sqrt{\dfrac{l}{g}}$

Worksheet 7

► Solutions on page 232

1 A and B are two balls of the same size which are moving towards each other with speeds of 3 m s⁻¹ and 4 m s⁻¹ respectively. Ball A has mass $2m$ and ball B has mass m. The impact between them is direct. Find their speeds after the impact. The coefficient of restitution is $\frac{2}{3}$.

2

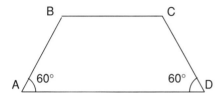

AB, BC and CD are three equal uniform rods of weight W and length $2a$, smoothly jointed at B and C and arranged in a vertical plane as shown. A and D are joined by a light string and the whole lot stands on a level table. Find the force exerted by BC on CD at C.

3 A particle of mass m is describing vertical circles on the end of a piece of string of length 2 m. Its speed at the highest point of the circle is 5 m s⁻¹. Show that the tension in the string is greatest when the particle is at the lowest point and find the tension.

4

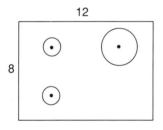

The diagram shows a rectangular lamina with holes cut in it. The centres of the holes are at the centre of the quarter of the lamina they are in. The lamina measures 12×8 and the holes have diameters of 1, 1 and 2. Find the centre of gravity of the lamina.

5 A projectile is fired at 50 m s⁻¹ at an angle of 50°. Find whether or not it will hit a target 95 m away horizontally and 70 m above the level of projection.

6 A particle is pulled by a constant force P against a resistance which is equal to kv, where v is the velocity. When $v = w$ the acceleration is zero.

Show that $k = \dfrac{P}{w}$ and that the time taken to reach a velocity v

is $\dfrac{mw}{P} \ln \dfrac{w - u}{w - v}$ where u is the initial velocity.

▶ A bearing of 070° means the aeroplane is flying directly 70° east of north. Bearings are measured clockwise from north.

7 Aeroplane A is travelling at 350 mph on a bearing of 070° and aeroplane B is travelling at 270 mph on a bearing of 330°. Find the velocity of A relative to B.

8 Find λ if the work done by a force $\mathbf{F} = \lambda \begin{pmatrix} 1 \\ 2 \\ 3 \end{pmatrix}$,

in moving a unit mass from A, position vector $\begin{pmatrix} -8 \\ 2 \\ 18 \end{pmatrix}$, to B,

position vector, $\begin{pmatrix} 8 \\ 50 \\ 30 \end{pmatrix}$ is 370 joules.

9 A particle of mass m is attached to one end of an elastic string. The other end is fixed to a point on a horizontal smooth table. The string, of natural length l and modulus λ, is now stretched until the extension is a. The particle is released.

Find how long it takes before the particle comes to instantaneous rest in terms of l, a, m, λ and π.

10 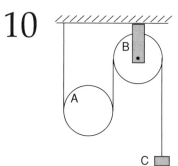 B is a fixed smooth pulley.

A piece of string is attached to a fixed point, D, passes under a free smooth pulley A of mass $2m$, over B and carries C, a mass of $5m$, at the other end.

Find the acceleration of A and the tension in the string.

Solutions to Worksheet 7

▶ Impact: COM, NEL

1

	A	B
→+	$2m$	m
Velocity before	3	–4
Velocity after	u	v

Conservation of momentum:

$2m \times 3 + m \times -4 = 2mu + mv \quad \Rightarrow \quad 2 = 2u + v$

NEL: $\quad -\dfrac{2}{3}(-4 - 3) = v - u \quad \Rightarrow \quad 14 = 3v - 3u$

Solving $\quad \Rightarrow \quad u = -\dfrac{8}{9}, v = \dfrac{34}{9}$

2

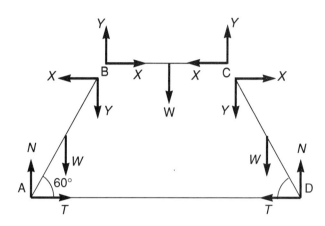

► Reactions at joints

Resolving vertically for the whole: $N + N_1 = 3W$

But $N = N_1$, by symmetry, $\therefore$ $N = \dfrac{3W}{2}$

Resolving vertically for CD: $N = Y + W$ $\Rightarrow$ $Y = \dfrac{W}{2}$

Taking moments about D for CD:

$X \times 2a\sin60° = \dfrac{W}{2} \times 2a\cos60° + W \times a\cos60°$

$\Rightarrow$ $X = \dfrac{2Wa\cos60°}{2a\sin60°} = \dfrac{W}{\sqrt{3}}$

Force exerted $= W\sqrt{\left(\dfrac{1}{2}\right)^2 + \left(\dfrac{1}{\sqrt{3}}\right)^2} = W\sqrt{\dfrac{7}{12}} = 0.76W$

in direction $\tan^{-1}\left(\dfrac{\frac{1}{2}}{\frac{1}{\sqrt{3}}}\right) = 40.9°$ below horizontal

3

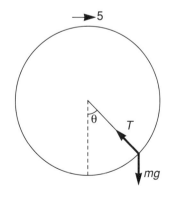

NL2 along radius:

$$T - mg\cos\theta = \dfrac{mv^2}{r}$$

► Circular motion – vertical

Conservation of energy: $\underbrace{\tfrac{1}{2}mv^2 - \tfrac{1}{2}m \times 5^2}_{\text{gain in KE}} = \underbrace{mgr(1 + \cos\theta)}_{\text{loss in PE}}$

Eliminating $\dfrac{mv^2}{r}$: $T = mg\cos\theta + 2mg(1 + \cos\theta) + \dfrac{m5^2}{r}$

► When finding maximum and minimum values of trigonometric functions think of values of sin/cos before starting a differentiation method.

$$\therefore \quad T = \underbrace{2mg + \frac{25m}{r}}_{\text{constant}} + \underbrace{3mg\cos\theta}_{\substack{\text{variable and} \\ \text{maximum when } \theta = 0}}$$

Therefore T is maximum when the mass is at the lowest point and then $T = 61.5$ m.

► Centre of gravity

► **Use of $\bar{x}$ and $\bar{y}$**

Don't worry about using $\bar{x}$ and $\bar{y}$ when x and y have not been defined in this question. Their use is standard in this situation.

4

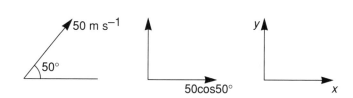

Taking moments about AB:

$(12 \times 8 - 2\pi \times (\frac{1}{2})^2 - \pi \times 12)\bar{x}$
$= 12 \times 8 \times 6 - 2\pi \times (\frac{1}{2})^2 \times 3 - \pi \times 12 \times 9 \quad \Rightarrow \quad \bar{x} = 5.9$

Taking moments about BC:

$(12 \times 8 - 2\pi \times (\frac{1}{2})^2 - \pi \times 1^2)\bar{y}$
$= 12 \times 8 \times 4 - \pi \times (\frac{1}{2})^2 \times 2 - \pi \times (\frac{1}{2})^2 \times 6 - \pi \times 1^2 \times 6$
$\Rightarrow \quad \bar{y} = 1.2$

Therefore the centre of gravity is 5.9 from AB and 1.2 from BC.

► Projectiles

5

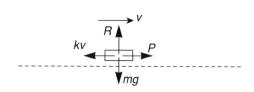

► The common factor horizontally and vertically is time, t.

Horizontally, when $x = 95$ $95 = 50\cos50° \times t \quad \Rightarrow \quad t = 2.956$ s

Vertically: $s = ut + \frac{1}{2}at^2$

$\Rightarrow \quad y = 50\sin50° \times 2.956 - \frac{9.81}{2} \times 2.956^2$

► Just misses!

$\Rightarrow \quad y = 70.36$ m

► Variable acceleration

6

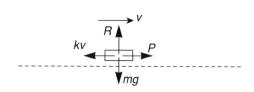

Applying NL2: $P - kv = ma$

$a = 0$ when $v = w \quad \Rightarrow \quad P = kw \quad \Rightarrow \quad k = \dfrac{P}{w}$

Need v, t therefore use $a = \dfrac{dv}{dt} \quad \Rightarrow \quad P - kv = m\dfrac{dv}{dt}$

Separating variables: $\int dt = \int \dfrac{m\,dv}{P - kv}$

Integrating: $t = -\dfrac{m}{k}\ln(P - kv) + A$

Initial velocity is u $\therefore$ $A = \dfrac{m}{k}\ln(P - ku)$

$\Rightarrow$ $t = \dfrac{m}{k}\ln(P - ku) - \dfrac{m}{k}\ln(P - kv)$

$\therefore$ $t = \dfrac{m}{k}\ln\left(\dfrac{P - ku}{P - kv}\right) = \dfrac{mw}{P}\ln\left(\dfrac{w - u}{w - v}\right)$

7

► Relative velocity

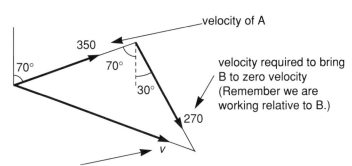

the velocity of A relative to B

From the diagram, use the cosine rule:

$v^2 = 350^2 + 270^2 - 2 \times 350 \times 270 \times \cos 100°$

$\Rightarrow$ $v = 477.7$ mph

Now using the sine rule:

$\dfrac{477.7}{\sin 100°} = \dfrac{270}{\sin\theta}$

$\therefore$ $\theta = 33.8°$

$\therefore$ the bearing of A relative to B is $70° + 33.8° = 103.8°$

► The velocity of A relative to B is the velocity of A − the velocity of B.

8

Work done = force × distance

When the force is not in the same direction as the distance:

work done = $F\cos\theta \times d$

where θ is the angle between the force and the distance.

► Work done using vector forms

$\therefore$ work done $= \mathbf{F} \cdot \mathbf{d}$

In this case $\mathbf{F} \cdot \mathbf{d} = \lambda \begin{pmatrix} 1 \\ 2 \\ 3 \end{pmatrix} \cdot \begin{pmatrix} 8 - -8 \\ 50 - 2 \\ 30 - 18 \end{pmatrix} = \lambda(16 + 96 + 36) = 370$

$\therefore \quad \lambda = \dfrac{5}{2}$

► Simple harmonic motion

9

Consider the article at some point D.

NL2: $\Rightarrow \quad T = -m\ddot{x}$

► SHM = simple harmonic motion

But $T = \dfrac{\lambda x}{l} \quad \therefore \quad \dfrac{\lambda x}{l} = -m\ddot{x}$ i.e. $\ddot{x} = -\dfrac{\lambda}{ml} x$ which is SHM

At B, $T = 0$ therefore $\ddot{x} = 0$

Therefore the particle is at maximum speed, with which it continues for a distance of $2l$ when the string again becomes taut. The particle then slows to a stop after a further distance a.

Hence the motion consists of a half SHM cycle with a constant speed section in the middle.

Time for SHM part: $t_1 = \dfrac{\pi}{\omega} = \pi \sqrt{\dfrac{ml}{\lambda}}$

Time for constant velocity part: $t_2 = \dfrac{2l}{v_m} = \dfrac{2l}{a\omega} = \dfrac{2l}{a} \sqrt{\dfrac{ml}{\lambda}}$

$\therefore \quad$ time to next stop $= t_1 + t_2 = \left(\pi + \dfrac{2l}{a} \right) \sqrt{\dfrac{ml}{\lambda}}$

► NL2

10

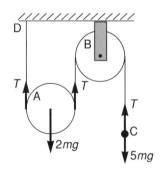

Acceleration of A is $\dfrac{a}{2}$ given the acceleration of C is a.

NL2 for C: $5mg - T = 5ma$

NL2 for A:

$2T - 2mg = 2m\dfrac{a}{2}$

$\Rightarrow 8mg = 11ma \Rightarrow a = \dfrac{8g}{11}$

$\therefore \quad$ acceleration of A is $\dfrac{4g}{11}$

and $T = 5mg - 5ma = 5m \left(g - \dfrac{8g}{11} \right) = \dfrac{15mg}{11}$

Worksheet 8

▶ Solutions on page 238

1 A rectangular block is in equilibrium on a rough sloping plane. Draw a force diagram showing exactly where the forces act on the block.

2 A particle is in equilibrium on the inside of a rough hemi-spherical bowl. If $\mu = \frac{1}{2}$ find the minimum distance, in terms of r, below the centre of the bowl at which equilibrium is possible.

3 A cyclist, A, sets off from rest and has uniform acceleration a. T seconds later a second cyclist, B, follows the some route with uniform velocity, u. Show that $u > 2aT$ for B to overtake A.

▶ You will need your quadratic theory in the latter part of this solution.

4 A projectile is launched at 250 m s^{-1} at an angle of 30° from the top of a 100 m cliff. Find where it lands in the sea.

5 A mass A of 5 kg is on a rough horizontal table 2 m from the edge. It is connected by a light string passing over a smooth pulley at the edge of the table to a mass, B, of 1 kg hanging freely. The system just moves.

B is now increased to 1.5 kg; find how long it takes A to reach the edge of the table.

6 A particle doing SHM covers 90 oscillations per minute. The maximum acceleration is 2 m s^{-2}. Find the maximum velocity and the amplitude.

7 Find the centre of gravity of a uniform semicircular lamina.

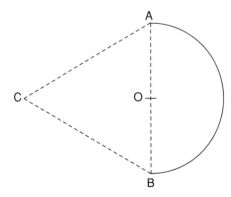

The lamina is joined to an isosceles triangle as shown, CA = CB. If the centre of gravity of the whole is at O find h, the height of the triangle, in terms of r.

8 Three equal uniform rods of length $2a$ are joined to form an equilateral triangle ABC. The triangle is suspended from A. Find the force exerted on BC by AB in terms of W, the weight of the rod.

9 A uniform beam is 2 m long. It rests on two supports, 30 cm apart, so that it is horizontal. The mass of the beam is 10 kg and the forces exerted by the supports differ by $2g$ N. Where are the supports?

10 A gun of mass M fires a bullet of mass m. In the process kinetic energy K is generated. Show that the velocity of the bullet is $\left(\dfrac{2MK}{m(M + m)}\right)^{\frac{1}{2}}$

Solutions to Worksheet 8

► Three-force problem

1 R acts through A because the block is in equilibrium.
It is under three forces which are concurrent.
F and W meet at A.

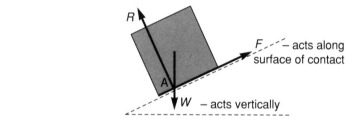

R

F — acts along surface of contact

W — acts vertically

► Friction

2

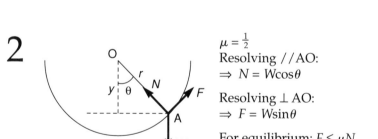

$\mu = \frac{1}{2}$
Resolving $//$ AO:
$\Rightarrow N = W\cos\theta$

Resolving $\perp$ AO:
$\Rightarrow F = W\sin\theta$

For equilibrium: $F \le \mu N$
$\Rightarrow \quad W\sin\theta \le \frac{1}{2} W\cos\theta$

i.e. $\tan\theta \le \frac{1}{2} \quad \Rightarrow \quad \theta \le 26.6°$

When θ is a maximum y is a minimum.
Then $y = r\cos\theta = r \times \dfrac{2}{\sqrt{5}} = 0.89r$

3 Need s, t therefore use $s = ut + \frac{1}{2}at^2$

For A: $s = \frac{1}{2}at^2$

For B: $s = u(t - T)$

At the overtaking point s is the same for both.

$\therefore$ $\frac{1}{2}at^2 = u(t - T)$

$\frac{1}{2}at^2 - ut + uT = 0$

For real solutions $b^2 \geq 4ac$ $\Rightarrow$ $u^2 \geq 4 \times \frac{1}{2}a \times uT$

$\Rightarrow$ $u \geq 2aT$

$u = 2aT$ $\Rightarrow$ equal roots
$\Rightarrow$ B catches up with A but they then ride together.

$u > 2aT$ $\Rightarrow$ two different roots
$\Rightarrow$ B overtakes A, who then later overtakes B.

$\therefore$ for overtaking $u > 2aT$

▶ Uniform acceleration

▶ This is a quadratic in t and solving it will give times when overtaking occurs.

▶ Aesthetically this is a good example of applied mathematics: using principles of mechanics to form an equation to which pure principles are applied to form conclusions.

4

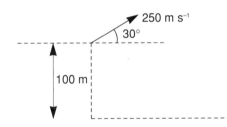

Horizontally: $x = 250\cos 30° \times t$

$\therefore$ need to know t

Vertically: $s = ut + \frac{1}{2}at^2$ $\Rightarrow$ $-100 = 250\sin 30° \times t - \frac{1}{2}gt^2$

$\Rightarrow$ $9.81t^2 - 250t - 100 = 0$

$\Rightarrow$ $t = 25.9$ or $t = -0.39$

And then $x = 250\cos 30° \times 25.9 = 5608$ m

▶ Projectile

▶ What is the significance of the negative value of t?
    You have to remember that at the stage of solving the quadratic in t you are solving a pure quadratic equation. The other value of t is the other time when the curve in question would have ordinate of −100: it is the time back to where the starting point would have been if the projectile had been fired from sea level.
    So, although the negative time has no value in this question in a practical sense, it does have mathematical significance.

5

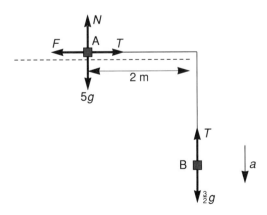

Mass just moves $\Rightarrow$ $F = \mu N, a = 0$

▶ NL2, uniform acceleration

Initially B = 1 kg

Resolving for the whole system: $g - F = 0$ and $N = 5g$

$\Rightarrow \quad g = 5\mu g$

$\Rightarrow \quad \mu = \frac{1}{5}$

When B = 1.5 kg

Resolving for the whole system:

$\frac{3}{2}g - \mu N = \frac{13}{2}a$

$\Rightarrow \quad \frac{3}{2}g - g = \frac{13}{2}a$

$\Rightarrow \quad g = 13a \quad \Rightarrow \quad a = \frac{g}{13}$ m s^{-2}

For A: s, t equation $\Rightarrow \quad s = ut + \frac{1}{2}at^2$

$2 = \frac{1}{2} \times \frac{g}{13} \times t^2$

$\Rightarrow \quad t = 2.3$ s

▶ Simple harmonic motion – use of standard formulae

6

90 oscillations per minute $\quad \Rightarrow \quad T = \frac{2}{3}$ s

$\therefore \quad \frac{2\pi}{\omega} = \frac{2}{3} \quad \Rightarrow \quad \omega = 3\pi$

$\therefore \quad$ the equation of motion is $\ddot{x} = -9\pi^2 x$

Maximum acceleration is when $x = a \quad \Rightarrow \quad 2 = -9\pi^2 x$

$\therefore \quad$ amplitude, $a = \frac{2}{9\pi^2}$ m

$v_{max} = a\omega$

$= \frac{2}{9\pi^2} \times 3\pi = \frac{2}{3\pi}$ m s^{-1}

▶ Centre of gravity

7

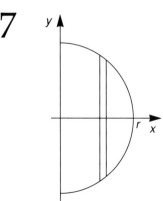

Moment of sum = sum of moments

$\frac{1}{2}\pi r^2 \bar{x} = \sum_{x=0}^{r} 2y\delta x \times x$

$\therefore \quad \frac{1}{2}\pi r^2 \bar{x} = \int_0^r 2x\sqrt{r^2 - x^2}\, dx$

$= \left[-\frac{2}{3}(r^2 - x^2)^{3/2} \right]_0^r$

$\Rightarrow \quad \frac{1}{2}\pi r^2 \bar{x} = \frac{2}{3}r^3$

$\Rightarrow \quad \bar{x} = \frac{4r}{3\pi}$

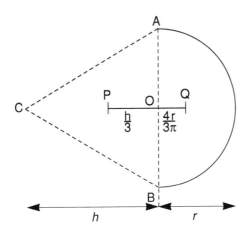

P is the centre of gravity of ΔOAB.

Q is the centre of gravity of the semicircle.

Taking moments about AB:

$$rh \times \frac{h}{3} = \frac{1}{2}\pi r^2 \times \frac{4r}{3\pi}$$

because the moment of the whole is zero.

$$\Rightarrow \quad h^2 = 2r^2$$

$$h = r\sqrt{2}$$

 8

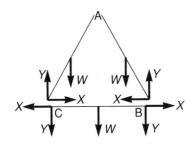

By symmetry the forces at joints B and C are the same.

We are required to find X and Y.

Resolving vertically for BC:

$$2Y + W = 0 \quad \Rightarrow \quad Y = -\frac{W}{2}$$

► Reactions at joints

Taking moments about A for AB:

$$Wa\cos 60° + 2aX\sin 60° = 2aY\cos 60°$$

$$\Rightarrow \quad W + 2X\tan 60° = 2Y$$

$$\Rightarrow \quad 2\sqrt{3}X = -2W$$

$$\Rightarrow \quad X = -\frac{W}{\sqrt{3}}$$

force on BC is at B and is $\sqrt{X^2 + Y^2} = W\dfrac{\sqrt{7}}{12}$

at $\tan^{-1}\dfrac{\sqrt{3}}{2}$ to the horizontal.

9

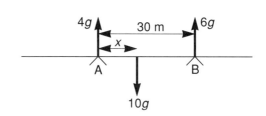

Using NL2, reactions at the supports are $4g$ and $6g$ N.

Taking moments about A for the beam:

$10g \times x = 6g \times 30$

$\Rightarrow \quad x = 18$ cm

i.e. one support is 82 cm from one end of the beam and the other support is 88 cm from the other end.

▶ Quite a frightening looking question at first glance!

▶ COM, energy

10

	Gun	**Bullet**
	M	m
Velocity before	0	0
Velocity after	V	v

COM: $0 = MV + mv$ **(1)**

Energy: $K = \dfrac{1}{2}MV^2 + \dfrac{1}{2}mv^2$ **(2)**

From **(1)**: $V = -\dfrac{mv}{M}$

Substituting in **(2)**: $K = \dfrac{1}{2}M\left(-\dfrac{mv}{M}\right)^2 + \dfrac{1}{2}mv^2$

$\Rightarrow \quad v = \left\{ \dfrac{2MK}{m(M+m)} \right\}^{\frac{1}{2}}$

▶ **NB** The gun and the bullet are assumed free to move and hence COM applies. Before the shot there is no momentum: after the shot the bullet has momentum one way and the gun the other (the recoil or 'kick' that can be felt).

▶ Solutions on page 244

Worksheet 9

1   A body is moving with uniform acceleration. It covers 29 m in the fifth second and 47 m in the eighth second of its motion. Find how far it has gone after 10 seconds.

2

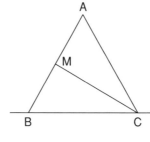

AB and AC are two uniform rods of length $2l$ smoothly joined at A.

AB has weight W and AC has weight w. MC is a taut string joining C to the midpoint of AB. The whole stands on smooth level ground at B and C where BC = $2a$. Find the tension in the string.

3 Two balls of the same size are in direct impact. Find the conditions which must apply if they exchange velocities.

4 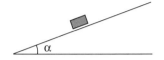 The diagram shows the cross-section of a car on a banked track going in a horizontal circle at 54 kmph. The radius of the circle is 100 m. Find the angle of the banking, α, if there is no force of friction acting across the wheels.

5 A conical pendulum of length l is describing circles of radius r at a constant angular speed of ω.

Show that $\dfrac{r^2}{l^2} = 1 - \dfrac{g^2}{l^2 w^4}$

6 Ships A and B are on straight courses which converge with an angle of 60° between them. A is 12 miles from the point of intersection and sailing at 16 knots while B is 8 miles away sailing at 10 knots. Find the shortest distance between them.

7 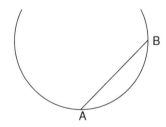 The diagram shows part of a spherical bowl with a rod of weight W inside it. The radius of the bowl is r and the length of the rod is $r\sqrt{2}$.

A is the lowest point of the bowl and the rod is in limiting equilibrium. Find the coefficient of friction.

8 A solid is formed by rotating the curve $y^2 = 4x$ between $x = 0$ and $x = 1$ about the x-axis. Find the position of the centre of gravity of the solid.

9 An elastic string of natural length l and modulus mg has one end fixed and carries a mass m at the other end. The string is hanging vertically. The mass is pulled down until the extension is $\frac{3}{2}l$ and then released.

Show that the subsequent motion is simple harmonic. Find the period and the time taken to reach the point where the extension of the string is $\frac{3}{4}l$.

10 A particle A of mass $2m$ is displaced from rest at the top of a smooth vertical circular wire of radius r, on which it is threaded. When it reaches the lowest point it collides with bead B, of mass m, going in the opposite direction with velocity $3\sqrt{rg}$. The coefficient of restitution is $\frac{2}{3}$.

Find the height to which B rises and find the reaction of the wire on B at that point.

Solutions to Worksheet 9

▶ Uniform acceleration

1 The problem involves s and t, so use $s = ut + \frac{1}{2}at^2$

We need to find u and a before the question can be answered.

After 5 s: $s_5 = 5u + \frac{1}{2}a \times 5^2$

After 4 s: $s_4 = 4u + \frac{1}{2}a \times 4^2$

In the fifth second $s_5 - s_4 = 29 = u + \frac{1}{2}a \times 9$

Similarly in the eighth second $47 = u + \frac{1}{2}a \times 15$

Solving simultaneously: $18 = 6 \times \frac{1}{2}a \implies a = 6 \text{ m s}^{-2}$

and $u = 2 \text{ m s}^{-1}$

After 10 s $s = 10 \times 2 + \frac{1}{2} \times 6 \times 10^2 = 320 \text{ m}$

▶ *X* and *Y* are not wanted, which suggests A as the point to take moments about.

▶ Reaction at joints

2

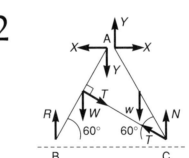

Taking moments about A for AB:

$R \times 2l\cos60°$

$= W \times l\cos60° + T \times l$

$\implies R = \frac{1}{2}W + T$ **(1)**

We need to find R.

Taking moments about C for the whole system:

$R \times 4l\cos60° = W \times 3l\cos60° + w \times l\cos60°$

$R = \frac{1}{4}(3W + w)$ **(2)**

Substituting for R in **(1)** $\implies T = \dfrac{W + w}{4}$

▶ Impact

3

	A	B
	M	m
Before	u	v
After	v	u

COM: $Mu + mv = Mv + mu$

$$\Rightarrow \quad M(u - v) = m(u - v)$$

$$\Rightarrow \quad M = m$$

NEL: $u - v = -e(v - u)$

$$\Rightarrow \quad u - v = e(u - v) \quad \Rightarrow \quad e = 1$$

Therefore the conditions are $e = 1$ and $M = m$.

4

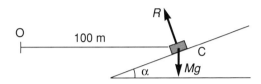

► Circular motion – horizontal

No friction along the slope of the plane.

The only forces are as shown where $R \perp$ track.

NL2 along radius CO: $R\sin\alpha = \dfrac{Mv^2}{r}$

$$\Rightarrow \quad R\sin\alpha = \frac{Mv^2}{100} \tag{1}$$

Vertically: $R\cos\alpha = Mg$ **(2)**

(1) divided by **(2)**: $\Rightarrow \quad \tan\alpha = \dfrac{v^2}{100g} = \dfrac{15 \times 15}{100 \times 9.81}$

because $54\ \text{kmh}^{-1} = 15\ \text{m s}^{-1}$

$$\Rightarrow \quad \alpha = 12.9°$$

5 Unbelievable: such a simple description with such a heavy looking result on the end. However, at least we can draw a diagram.

► Conical pendulum
► Looking at the required result:
$\dfrac{r}{l} = \sin\theta$

$\Rightarrow \dfrac{r^2}{l^2} = 1 - \left(\dfrac{g}{l\omega^2}\right)^2$

looking suspiciously like
$\sin^2 = 1 - \cos^2 \dots$
possibly an idea to work on.

► Done with one eye on the diagram!

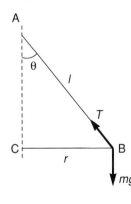

The mechanics: NL2 along the radius: $T\sin\theta = mr\omega^2$

Vertically: $T\cos\theta = mg$

Dividing: $\tan\theta = \dfrac{r\omega^2}{g} = \dfrac{r}{g/\omega^2}$

i.e. $AC = \dfrac{g}{\omega^2}$

Going back to the original idea i.e.
$\sin^2\theta = 1 - \cos^2\theta$

$$\Rightarrow \frac{r^2}{l^2} = 1 - \frac{(g/\omega^2)^2}{l^2}$$

$$\Rightarrow \frac{r^2}{l^2} = 1 - \frac{g^2}{l^2\omega^4}$$

► Not too bad in the end!

► Relative velocity

6 Velocity diagrams

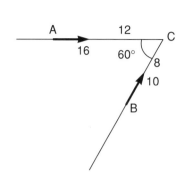

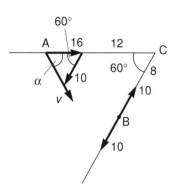

Distance diagram

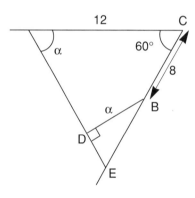

Aim: to find d

Need: BE and $\angle$DBE

Firstly, find the angles from the velocity diagram.

Cosine rule:
$v^2 = 16^2 + 10^2 - 2 \times 16 \times 10\cos60° \Rightarrow v = 14$

Sine rule:
$$\frac{10}{\sin\alpha} = \frac{14}{\sin60°}$$

$$\Rightarrow \alpha = 38.2°$$

Transferring to the distance diagram:

$\alpha = 38.2°$ and $\angle$BED $= 81.8°$

Sine rule: $\dfrac{CE}{\sin38.2} = \dfrac{12}{\sin81.8°} \Rightarrow CE = 7.50$

$d =$ BEsin$\angle$BED

$= 0.5\sin81.8° = 0.49$

$\therefore$ nearest distance is 0.49 miles.

► Our drawing shows CE > CB i.e. 7.5 > 8 – Not to worry! It is now obvious where we should have drawn AE but the final working out is the same.

► Friction

7

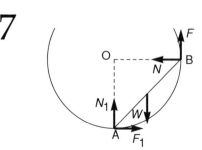

Since AB $= r\sqrt{2}$

ΔOAB is right-angled and isosceles.
Limiting equilibrium
$\Rightarrow F = \mu N$
and $F_1 = \mu N_1$

Taking moments about A for AB:

$\Rightarrow W = 2N + 2F$ **(1)**

Taking moments about B for AB: $\Rightarrow$ $W + 2F_1 = 2N_1$ **(2)**

Equation **(1)** $\Rightarrow$ $W = 2N(1 + \mu) = 2\mu N_1(1 + \mu)$ because $F_1 = N$

Equation **(2)** $\Rightarrow$ $W = 2N_1(1 - \mu)$

Dividing: $1 = \dfrac{\mu(1 + \mu)}{(1 - \mu)}$

$\Rightarrow$ $\mu^2 + 2\mu - 1 = 0$ $\Rightarrow$ $\mu = 0.4$ (by formula).

8

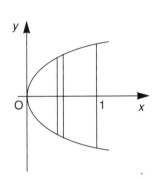

Moments of sum = sum of moments

$$\pi \int_0^1 y^2 dx \times \bar{x} = \pi \int_0^1 y^2 x \, dx$$

$$\int_0^1 4x \, dx \times \bar{x} = \int_0^1 4x^2 \, dx$$

$\Rightarrow$ $2\bar{x} = \frac{4}{3}$ $\Rightarrow$ $\bar{x} = \frac{2}{3}$

$\therefore$ centre of gravity is at $(\frac{2}{3}, 0)$
($\bar{y} = 0$ by symmetry)

▶ Centre of gravity

9

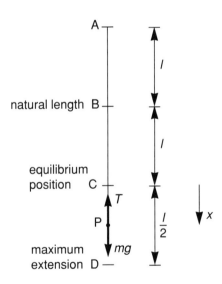

▶ Simple harmonic motion

The system is in equilibrium: $\Rightarrow$ $mg = T$

$mg = \dfrac{mge}{l}$ $\Rightarrow$ $e = l$

For the mass at P:

NL2: $mg - T = m\ddot{x}$

$\Rightarrow$ $mg - \dfrac{mg(l + x)}{l} = m\ddot{x}$

$\Rightarrow$ $\ddot{x} = -\dfrac{g}{l} x$ i.e. SHM

▶ Firstly find the equilibrium position – usually the first move.

$$T = \frac{2\pi}{\omega} = 2\pi\sqrt{\frac{l}{g}}$$

At the point where the extension is $\frac{3l}{4}$, $x = -\frac{l}{4}$

Because motion starts at the extremity, we use $x = a\cos\omega t$

$$\Rightarrow \quad -\frac{l}{4} = \frac{l}{2}\cos\sqrt{\frac{g}{l}}\,t$$

$$\Rightarrow \quad t = \frac{2\pi}{3}\sqrt{\frac{l}{g}}$$

► Circular motion
► Impact

10

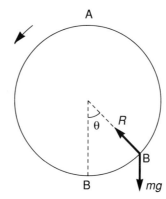

At the impact:

$2m$	m
$2\sqrt{rg}$	$-3\sqrt{rg}$
u	v

COM: $2m \times 2\sqrt{rg} - 3m\sqrt{rg} = 2mu + mv$

$$\Rightarrow \quad \sqrt{rg} = 2u + v \tag{1}$$

NEL: $-\frac{2}{5}(-3\sqrt{rg} - 2\sqrt{rg}) = v - u$

$$\Rightarrow \quad 2\sqrt{rg} = v - u \tag{2}$$

From **(1)** and **(2)**: $5\sqrt{rg} = 3v$

$v = \frac{5}{3}\sqrt{rg}$

COE for $2m$:

$\frac{1}{2} \times 2m \times v^2 = 2mg \times 2r$

$$\Rightarrow \quad v = 2\sqrt{rg}$$

COE for B: $\frac{1}{2}m \times \frac{25}{9}rg = mgh$

$h = \frac{25r}{18}$

NL2 for B: $R - mg\cos\theta = \frac{mv^2}{r}$

At the highest point $v = 0$ $R = mg\cos\theta$

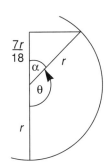

From the diagram $\cos\alpha = \dfrac{7}{18}$

$\Rightarrow \quad \cos\theta = \dfrac{7}{18}$

$\therefore \quad R = -\dfrac{7mg}{18}$

R has magnitude $\dfrac{7mg}{18}$

acting away from the centre of the circle.

Worksheet 10

▶ Solutions on page 250

1 A ball falls from a height of 80 cm onto a solid level plane. The sum of the maximum heights after the first and second bounces is 105 cm. Find the coefficient of restitution.

2 A particle of mass m is on the end of a string of length l hanging vertically, the upper end of the string being fixed. The particle is given a horizontal velocity, u, and the string subsequently becomes slack when it makes an angle of 60° with the upward vertical. Find u in terms of l and g.

3 An elastic string of natural length l extends a distance e when a mass m is attached and the whole system is allowed to hang vertically with the upper end fixed.
   A second mass m is added to the first and gently released. Find the period of the motion and the maximum extension.

4 A cyclist covers 175 m in 40 seconds. For the first $\frac{1}{14}$ of the distance he accelerates uniformly and for the last $\frac{1}{14}$ he retards uniformly at the same rate. Find his uniform speed.

5 A heavy uniform beam is resting in limiting equilibrium against a rough vertical wall and on rough horizontal ground. The coefficient of friction is the same at both contacts. Show that the total reactions at the ends of the beam are perpendicular to each other.

6 The acceleration of a particle is given by $\frac{1}{4}(v - v^2)$ where v is the velocity. Given that $v = \frac{1}{2}$ when $t = 0$ find t in terms of v, and v in terms of t.

7 Find the centre of gravity of semicircular piece of wire, of radius r. The ends of this piece are joined by a straight wire of the same mass per unit length and the whole shape is then suspended from one end of the diameter. Find the angle the diameter makes with the vertical.

8 The position vector of a particle of mass m is given by

$$\mathbf{r} = \begin{pmatrix} a\sin\omega t \\ b\cos\omega t \\ c\omega t \end{pmatrix}$$

Find v and a. If $\mathbf{F}$ is the force acting on the particle, find the power.

9 The sides of a triangle taken in order represent completely three forces. Show that the forces constitute a couple and show that the moment of the couple is equal in magnitude to twice the area of the triangle.

10 A projectile is fired with velocity 4.9 m s^{-1} at angle θ to hit a target distant a horizontally and b vertically. Show that there are two possible angles of projection provided a condition relating a and b is met, and find the condition.

Solutions to Worksheet 10

► Uniform acceleration

► Impact

► See page 120

1 When the ball falls a distance h and hits the plane with velocity v we have $v^2 = 2gh$

It leaves the plane with velocity ev and rises to h_1 and then

$$0 = e^2v^2 - 2hg_1$$

$$\Rightarrow \quad h_1 = e^2h$$

$\therefore$ in this question first rebound height $= e^2 \times 80$

second rebound height $= e^4 \times 80$

Hence $80e^4 + 80e^2 = 105$

$$16e^4 + 16e^2 - 21 = 0$$

$$(4e^2 - 3)(4e^2 + 7) = 0$$

$$\Rightarrow \quad e^2 = \frac{3}{4} \text{ or } e = \frac{\sqrt{3}}{2}$$

2

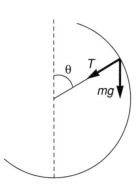

Always show, and consider, some general position, θ, as shown. It is not a good idea to consider only special positions; in this case $\theta = 60°$.

▶ Circular motion – vertical

NL2 along the radius:

$$T + mg\cos\theta = \frac{mv^2}{l}$$

COE:

$$\frac{1}{2}\,mu^2 = \frac{1}{2}\,mv^2 + mgl\,(1 + \cos\theta)$$

Eliminating v^2 $\Rightarrow$ $T + mg\cos\theta = \frac{mu^2}{l} - 2mg(1 + \cos\theta)$

Now use special values   i.e. $T = 0$ when $\theta = 60°$

$\Rightarrow$ $\dfrac{g}{2} = \dfrac{u^2}{l} - 2g \times \dfrac{3}{2}$

$\Rightarrow$ $u = \sqrt{\dfrac{7gl}{2}}$

3

▶ Simple harmonic motion

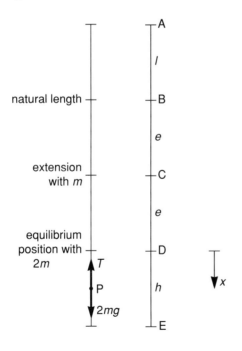

At C: $mg = \dfrac{\lambda e}{l}$ $\therefore$ $\lambda = \dfrac{mgl}{e}$

$2 \times$ load $= 2 \times$ extension

▶ Hooke's law

$\Rightarrow$ new equilibrium position is at D.

NL2 for P: $2mg - T = 2m\ddot{x}$

$$2mg - \frac{\lambda(2e + x)}{l} = 2m\ddot{x}$$

$$\Rightarrow \quad \ddot{x} = \frac{-g}{2e} x \text{ i.e. SHM}$$

$$\text{Period, } T = \frac{2\pi}{\omega} = 2\pi\sqrt{\frac{2e}{g}}$$

When falling from C to E the mass loses PE and the string gains PE. KE is zero at both places.

Therefore COE:

$$\Rightarrow \quad 2m(e + h) = \frac{1}{2} \times \frac{mgl}{e} \times \frac{(2e + h)^2}{l} - \frac{1}{2} \times \frac{mgl}{e} \times \frac{e^2}{l}$$

loss in PE of masses   PE of string at E   PE of string at C

$$\Rightarrow \quad h = e$$

$$\therefore \quad \text{maximum extension is } 2e + h = 3e$$

► Uniform acceleration

4

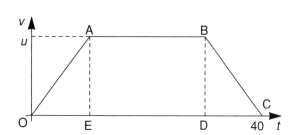

$$\frac{1}{14} \times 175 = 12.5 \qquad \text{therefore 12.5 whilst accelerating and 12.5 m whilst retarding.}$$

If t is time of acceleration $\frac{1}{2} \times t \times u = 12.5$

i.e. $tu = 25$

For ABDE:

$$(40 - 2t) \times u = 150$$

$$\Rightarrow \quad 40u - 2tu = 150$$

$$\Rightarrow \quad u = 5 \text{ m s}^{-1}$$

► See page 139

5

► Friction
► Angle of friction

In limiting equilibrium the total reaction makes angle λ (angle of friction) with the normal.
   Since μ is the same at both ends reactions make equal angles with normals to two perpendicular walls. Hence they are perpendicular to each other.

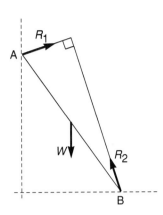

R_1, R_2 and W are concurrent, because they are in equilibrium under three forces. R_1, R_2 and W meet on the semicircle with AB as diameter (angle in semicircle = 90°).

6 $\quad \dfrac{dv}{dt} = \dfrac{1}{4}(v - v^2)$

► Variable acceleration

Separating variables: $\displaystyle\int \dfrac{dv}{v - v^2} = \dfrac{1}{4}\int dt$

$\Rightarrow \displaystyle\int \dfrac{1}{v} - \dfrac{1}{1-v}\, dv = \dfrac{1}{4}\int dt \quad \Rightarrow \quad \ln v - \ln(1 - v) = \dfrac{t}{4} + A$

$\Rightarrow \quad \ln\left(\dfrac{v}{1-v}\right) = \dfrac{t}{4} + A$

When $t = 0$, $v = \dfrac{1}{2} \quad \Rightarrow \quad A = 0 \quad \therefore \quad t = 4\ln\left(\dfrac{v}{1-v}\right)$

Rearranging: $e^{t/4} = \dfrac{v}{1-v} \quad (1 - v)e^{t/4} = v \quad \Rightarrow \quad v = \dfrac{e^{t/4}}{1 + e^{t/4}}$

7

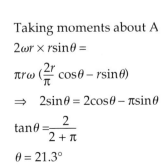

Moment of an element about Oy is $r\delta\theta \times r\cos\theta$

$\therefore \quad \pi r \bar{x} = \displaystyle\int_{-\frac{\pi}{2}}^{\frac{\pi}{2}} r^2 \cos\theta\, d\theta$

$\pi r \bar{x} = 2r^2$

$\bar{x} = \dfrac{2r}{\pi}$

► Centre of gravity

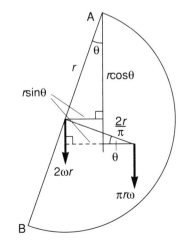

Taking moments about A

$2\omega r \times r\sin\theta =$

$\pi r \omega \left(\dfrac{2r}{\pi} \cos\theta - r\sin\theta\right)$

$\Rightarrow \quad 2\sin\theta = 2\cos\theta - \pi\sin\theta$

$\tan\theta = \dfrac{2}{2 + \pi}$

$\theta = 21.3°$

▶ Vectors

8
$$\mathbf{r} = \begin{pmatrix} a\sin\omega t \\ b\cos\omega t \\ c\omega t \end{pmatrix}$$

$$\mathbf{v} = \frac{d\mathbf{r}}{dt} = \begin{pmatrix} a\omega\cos\omega t \\ -b\omega\sin\omega t \\ c\omega \end{pmatrix}$$

$$\mathbf{a} = \frac{d\mathbf{v}}{dt} = \begin{pmatrix} -a\omega^2\sin\omega t \\ -b\omega^2\cos\omega t \\ 0 \end{pmatrix}$$

▶ Power

Power $= \mathbf{F.v} = m\mathbf{a.v}$

$$= m\begin{pmatrix} a\omega\cos t \\ -b\omega\sin\omega t \\ c \end{pmatrix}.\begin{pmatrix} -a\omega^2\sin\omega t \\ -b\omega^2\cos\omega t \\ 0 \end{pmatrix}$$

$$= m\omega^3(-a^2\cos\omega t\sin\omega t + b^2\sin\omega t\cos\omega t)$$

$$= m\omega^3(b^2 - a^2)\sin\omega t\cos\omega t$$

▶ Couple

9

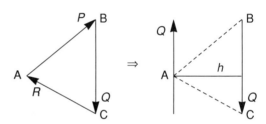

The resultant of P and R is a force of magnitude Q acting through A (the intersection of R and P) as shown.

The two forces Q constitute a couple of moment Qh.

$Qh = BC \times h$ in magnitude
$= 2 \times$ area of $\triangle ABC$

▶ Projectiles

10

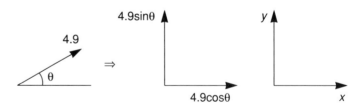

Horizontally: $x = 4.9\cos\theta \times t$

Vertically: $y = 4.9\sin\theta \times t - \frac{1}{2}gt^2$

Substituting for t: $y = \tan\theta \times x - \frac{1}{2}g \times \dfrac{x^2}{4.9^2 \cos^2\theta}$

Given that $x = a$, $y = b$

$$b = a\tan\theta - \frac{a^2}{4.9}(1 + \tan^2\theta)$$

$$\Rightarrow \quad a^2\tan^2\theta - 4.9a\tan\theta + a^2 + 4.9b = 0$$

This is a quadratic in $\tan\theta$ hence two solutions i.e. two angles of projection,

provided $4.9^2a^2 > 4a^2(a^2 + 4.9b)$

i.e. $4.9^2 > 4a^2 + 19.6b$

This latter part is what is meant by 'finding a condition'. It is a statement connecting the quantities concerned, in this case a and b.

► using $b^2 > 4ac$

► Finding a condition

Worksheet 11

► Solutions on page 257

1

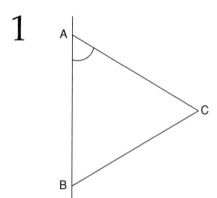

AC and BC are two uniform rods, of length $2a$ and weight W, rigidly jointed at C. They are held in a vertical plane by being smoothly hinged at A to a smooth wall and resting against the wall at B. Find the horizontal and vertical components of the reactions on the rods at A and B and find the moment of the restoring couple.

2 A force F propels a mass against negligible resistance. The acceleration produced is given by $9 + v^2$ m s^{-2}. Initially $x = 0$ and $v = 0$. Find the time taken to reach a velocity of 6 m s^{-1} and find the distance travelled in the process.

3

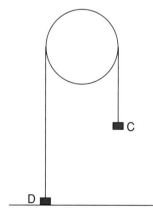

The diagram shows two masses D, $3m$, and C, $2m$, connected by a light inextensible string passing over a smooth fixed pulley.

The string is slack and C falls a distance h from rest before it becomes taut when D, resting on a table, is jerked into motion. Find

(a) the velocity of C after the impulse

(b) the impulse on D

(c) the time taken for C to stop.

4 A particle of mass m is sliding down a rough plane, with angle of inclination α. If the angle of friction is λ show that the acceleration is $a = \dfrac{g\sin(\alpha - \lambda)}{\cos\lambda}$.

5 A string AB of natural length l and modulus $6mg$ has end A fixed on a horizontal smooth table. At B a mass m is attached and the string is stretched to C where BC $= \frac{1}{2}l$. The mass is released.

Find the velocity of m when the string becomes slack and find how long it takes for the string to become taut again.

By using the theory of units verify the dimension of your answers.

6 Find the position of the centre of gravity of a semicircular lamina.

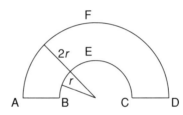

A lamina is formed by removing from the semicircle AFD a concentric semicircle BEC, radii as shown. If the lamina is suspended from A find the angle AD makes with the vertical.

7 A string of length $9a$ is attached to two fixed points A and B on a wall where A is above B and AB $= 3a$. A ring of mass m threaded on the string is made to do horizontal circles with B as centre and angular velocity ω.

Show that $\omega = \dfrac{1}{2}\sqrt{\dfrac{3g}{a}}$

8 Three equal spheres A, B and C of masses $2m$, m and $3m$, are at rest in a straight line on a horizontal table. A is given a velocity u in the direction AB and the coefficient of restitution is $\frac{1}{2}$. Find the velocities of A, B and C after two impacts and establish whether there is a third impact.

9 An elastic string of natural length $2a$ is stretched and fixed between two points A and D which are $4a$ apart vertically. The modulus is $2mg$. A particle of mass m is attached to the midpoint. Find the position of the particle when it is in equilibrium.

The particle is then pulled down a further distance $(< \frac{3}{4}a)$ and released. Show that it moves with SHM and find the period. Explain the condition $(< \frac{3}{4}a)$.

10

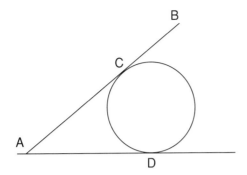

The diagram shows a uniform rod, of weight W, smoothly hinged to the floor at A and resting on a rough cylinder which in turn rests on the rough floor. $AC = \frac{5}{8} AB$. Equilibrium is limiting and $\mu = \frac{3}{4}$.

Show that the frictional forces on the cylinder are equal and find them.

Find the horizontal and vertical components. of the reaction at A on the rod.

Solutions to Worksheet 11

1

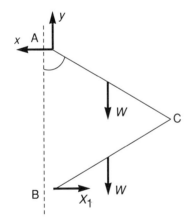

Taking moments about B for the whole:

$X \times 4a\cos\theta$
$= 2 \times W \times a\sin\theta$

$X = \dfrac{W}{2}\tan\theta$

Resolving vertically for the whole:

$Y = 2W$

Resolving horizontally for the whole:

$X_1 = X = \dfrac{W}{2}\tan\theta$

► This problem shows the value of always thinking very carefully before you begin a solution. There is a tendency here to treat this as a full 'reactions at joints' problem and arrive at a solution, quite correctly, by finding the reactions at joint C along the way. There is a more efficient solution.

► Couples

X and X_1 constitute the restoring couple which has moment

$L = \dfrac{W}{2}\tan\theta \times 4a\cos\theta = 2Wa\sin\theta$

► This result can be verified by taking moments about A for the whole.

2 $\dfrac{\mathrm{d}v}{\mathrm{d}t} = 9 + v^2$

► Variable acceleration

Separating variables: $\displaystyle\int \frac{\mathrm{d}v}{9 + v^2} = \int \mathrm{d}t$

$\Rightarrow \quad \dfrac{1}{3}\tan^{-1}\dfrac{v}{3} = t + A$

When $t = 0$, $v = 0$ $\Rightarrow$ $A = 0$

$v = 6$ $\Rightarrow$ $t = \frac{1}{3}\tan^{-1} 2 = 0.37$ s

Concerned with x and v $\Rightarrow$ $v\dfrac{\mathrm{d}v}{\mathrm{d}x} = 9 + v^2$

$$\int \frac{v\,\mathrm{d}v}{9 + v^2} = \int \mathrm{d}x$$

$$\frac{1}{2}\ln(9 + v^2) = x + B$$

When $x = 0$, $v = 0$ $\Rightarrow$ $B = \frac{1}{2}\ln 9$

$$x = \frac{1}{2}\ln\frac{9 + v^2}{9}$$

$v = 6$ $\Rightarrow$ $x = \frac{1}{2}\ln 5 = 0.8$ m

► Impulse

3

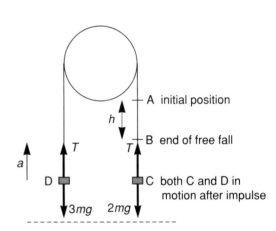

Mass $2m$ falls from A to B.

At B impulse occurs.

From B to C the string is taut, D and C are moving with acceleration a.

(a) A → B: need s, v $\Rightarrow$ $v^2 = u^2 + 2as$ $\Rightarrow$ $v^2 = 2gh$,
$v = \sqrt{2gh}$ m s^{-1}

At B impulse occurs and COM $\Rightarrow$ $2m\sqrt{2gh} = 5mw$

$\Rightarrow$ $w = \dfrac{2}{5}\sqrt{2gh}$ m s^{-1}

i.e. at B, after impulse, C has velocity $\frac{2}{5}\sqrt{2gh}$ downwards and D leaves the table with velocity $\frac{2}{5}\sqrt{2gh}$ at the same time.

(b) Impulse $J = 3m \times \dfrac{2}{5}\sqrt{2gh} = \dfrac{6m}{5}\sqrt{2gh}$

(c) Using the v, t equation, $v = u + at$ $\Rightarrow$ $0 = \dfrac{2}{5}\sqrt{2gh} + at$

It is necessary to find a, therefore:

NL2 for D: $T - 3mg = 3ma$

NL2 for C: $2mg - T = 2ma$

$\Rightarrow \quad a = -\dfrac{g}{5}$

Hence $0 = \dfrac{2}{5}\sqrt{2gh} - \dfrac{1}{5}gt \Rightarrow t = 2\sqrt{\dfrac{2h}{g}}$ s

4

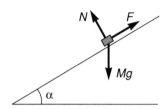

NL2 for the particle along the plane: $Mg\sin\alpha - F = Ma$

Since it is moving $F = \mu N$

and $N = Mg\cos\alpha$

$\therefore \quad F = \mu Mg\cos\alpha$

Also $\tan\lambda = \mu$

► NL2
► Angle of friction

$\therefore \quad F = Mg\cos\alpha\tan\lambda$

Hence $Mg\sin\alpha - Mg\cos\alpha\tan\lambda = Ma$

$\Rightarrow \quad a = \dfrac{g(\sin\alpha\cos\lambda - \cos\alpha\sin\lambda)}{\cos\lambda}$

$= \dfrac{g\,\sin(\alpha - \lambda)}{\cos\lambda}$

5

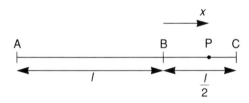

► COE

Another case for thinking carefully first.

At C the string has PE, P has none.

At B the string no PE, P has KE.

Hence by COE: $\dfrac{1}{2} \times \dfrac{\lambda}{l}(Y_2)^2 = \dfrac{1}{2}mv^2$

$\Rightarrow \quad \dfrac{6mgl}{4} = mv^2 \Rightarrow v = \dfrac{1}{2}\sqrt{6gl}$

From B to A and onwards P is moving freely.

Are there any forces in direction of motion? No.

String is taut after distance $2l$ and then

$2l = \dfrac{1}{2}\sqrt{6gl} \times t \Rightarrow t = \sqrt{\dfrac{8l}{3g}}$

$v = \dfrac{\sqrt{6}}{2}\{LT^{-2} \times L\}^{\frac{1}{2}} = \dfrac{\sqrt{6}}{2}\{L^2T^{-2}\}^{\frac{1}{2}} = \dfrac{\sqrt{6}}{2}\,LT^{-1}$ i.e. velocity

$t = \sqrt{\dfrac{8}{3}}\left\{\dfrac{L}{LT^{-2}}\right\}^{\frac{1}{2}} = \sqrt{\dfrac{8}{3}}\{T^2\}^{\frac{1}{2}} = \sqrt{\dfrac{8}{3}}\,T$ i.e. time

► Another SHM question – or is it?!

► Theory of units – expressing quantities in terms of [M], [L] and [T]

► Centre of gravity of a semicircle
  – see pages 177–8.

6

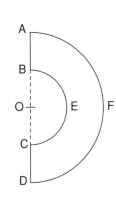

The centre of gravity of semicircle

BEC is $\dfrac{4r}{3\pi}$ from O.

The centre of gravity of semicircle

AFD is $\dfrac{8r}{3\pi}$ from O.

Taking moments about ABCD:

$$\frac{1}{2}(\pi 4r^2 - \pi r^2)\bar{x} = \frac{1}{2}\pi 4r^2 \times \frac{8r}{3\pi} - \frac{1}{2}\pi r^2 \times \frac{4r}{3\pi}$$

$$\Rightarrow \quad \bar{x} = \frac{28r}{9\pi}$$

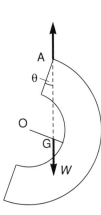

When the lamina is suspended from point A, the centre of gravity is vertically below A.

From the diagram $\tan\theta = \dfrac{OG}{AO}$

$$= \frac{28r}{9\pi} \times \frac{1}{2r} \quad \Rightarrow \quad \theta = 26.3°$$

► Circular motion – horizontal

7

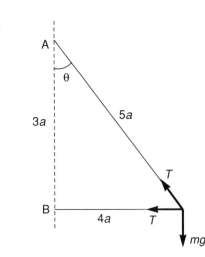

The smooth ring is threaded, not fixed, on the string hence tension is the same throughout the length of the string. NL2 along radius:

$$T + T\sin\theta = mr\omega^2$$

$$T + \tfrac{4}{5}T = m \times 4e\omega^2$$

$$\Rightarrow \quad \tfrac{9}{5}T = m \times 4\omega^2 a$$

Vertically for the ring:

$$T\cos\theta = mg \quad \Rightarrow \quad \tfrac{3}{5}T = mg$$

Eliminating T: $\quad \Rightarrow \quad 4m\omega^2 a = 3mg$

i.e. $\quad \omega = \dfrac{1}{2}\sqrt{\dfrac{3g}{a}}$

8

	A	B	C
$e = \frac{1}{2}$	$2m$	m	$3m$
	u	0	0
	u_1	v	0
	u_1	v_1	w

A, B impact:

$$\left.\begin{array}{ll} \text{COM:} & \Rightarrow \quad 2u = 2u_1 + v \\ \text{NEL:} & \Rightarrow \quad \dfrac{u}{2} = v - u \end{array}\right\} \Rightarrow \quad u_1 = \frac{u}{2} \text{ and } v = u$$

B, C impact:

$$\left.\begin{array}{ll} \text{COM:} & \Rightarrow \quad v = v_1 + 3w \\ \text{NEL:} & \Rightarrow \quad \dfrac{v}{2} = w - v_1 \end{array}\right\} \Rightarrow \quad w = \frac{3u}{8} \text{ and } v_1 = -\frac{u}{8}$$

Therefore velocities after two impacts are

$$\frac{u}{2}, -\frac{u}{8} \text{ and } \frac{3u}{8}$$

respectively and there is a third impact, between A and B.

9

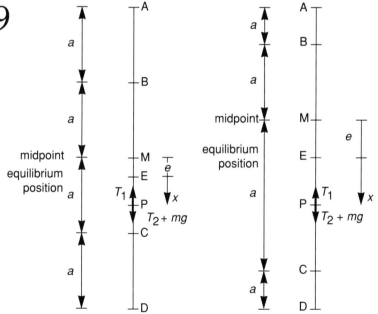

Diagram **(a)** bears some resemblance to a scale diagram and the part we shall be working with is compressed into a quarter of the diagram; three-quarters is wasted. Diagram **(b)** has no scale at all but it shows much more clearly the important parts and hence is a better diagram.

When at E, in equilibrium:

$T_2 + mg = T_1$

Now for T_1 and T_2: although AD is one string the fixing of a mass at the midpoint effectively makes two strings, AP and DP. The strings have the same modulus because the modulus is a constant for that particular string and it does not depend on the length of the string.

$$\therefore \quad \frac{2mg(a-e)}{a} + mg = \frac{2mg(a+x)}{a} \quad \Rightarrow \quad e = \frac{a}{4}$$

When at P: $\quad T_2 + mg - T_1 = m\ddot{x}$

$$\Rightarrow \quad \frac{2mg}{a}(a - \overline{e+x}) + mg - \frac{2mg}{a}(a+e+x) = m\ddot{x}$$

Substitute $e = \frac{a}{4} \quad \Rightarrow \quad \ddot{x} = -\frac{4g}{a}x$

i.e. SHM with $T = 2\pi\sqrt{\dfrac{a}{4g}} = \pi\sqrt{\dfrac{a}{g}}$

The condition $(< \frac{3}{4}a)$ is imposed so that both parts of the string remain taut.

► Friction

10

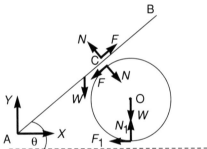

Taking moments about A for AB:

$$Wa\cos\theta = N \times \frac{5a}{8} \quad \Rightarrow \quad N = \frac{8W}{5}\cos\theta$$

where a is the length of the rod.

$\mu = \frac{3}{4}$ and the system is in limiting equilibrium.

$$\therefore \quad F = \frac{3}{4} \times \frac{8W}{5}\cos\theta = \frac{6W}{5}\cos\theta$$

Taking moments about O for the cylinder: $\quad F \times r = F_1 \times r$

$$\therefore \quad F_1 = F = \frac{6W}{5}\cos\theta$$

Resolving horizontally for AB:

$X + F\cos\theta = N\sin\theta$

$$\Rightarrow \quad X = \frac{W}{5}(8\cos\theta\sin\theta - 6\cos^2\theta)$$

$$= \frac{2W}{5}\cos\theta\,(4\sin\theta - 3\cos\theta)$$

Resolving vertically for AB:

$$Y = W - N\cos\theta - F\sin\theta$$

$$= W - \frac{8W}{5}\cos^2\theta - \frac{6W}{5}\cos\theta\sin\theta$$

$$= \frac{W}{5}(5 - 8\cos^2\theta - 6\cos\theta\sin\theta)$$

Worksheet 12

► Solutions on page 265

1 A force **F** given by $\begin{pmatrix} t \\ 2t^2 \\ 3 \end{pmatrix}$ N acts on a mass of 5 kg.

Find **a** and **v** given that initially the velocity is $\begin{pmatrix} 0 \\ 0 \\ 1 \end{pmatrix}$.

Find the momentum and the kinetic energy when $t = 6$

2

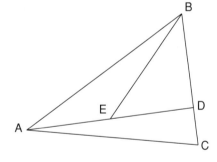

In the figure,

BD : DC = 2 : 1

AE = ED

AB = a, AC = b

Find **BE** in terms of **a** and **b**.

3 A force acting on a particle is given by $F = \dfrac{c}{(a + x^2)}$

where x is the distance from a fixed point towards which F acts and a and c are constants. Find the work done against F in moving the particle from the point where $x = 0$ to where $x = d$.

4 A particle travels in a straight line with uniform accelera-tion. After 2 seconds the distance covered is 26 m and after 8 seconds it is 176 m. What is the distance covered in the second second?

5

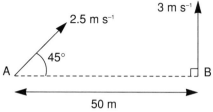

The diagram shows the positions and velocities of two boys. A wants to hit B with a snowball. His maximum range is 30 m. Does he have a chance?

6

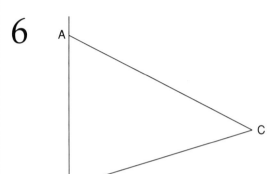

BC is a uniform rod smoothly jointed to a wall at B and supported by a string AC. Show that the line of action of the force on BC at B is along a median of △ABC.

7

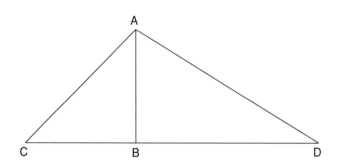

AB is a pole of negligible weight resting on rough ground at B. It is supported by two guy ropes AC and AD. Show that there is no horizontal force on the pole at B.

If the tension in AC is T_1 and in AD is T_2 show that

$$2T_1^2 = 3T_2^2$$

8

The initial velocity of a projectile from the origin is $u\mathbf{i} + v\mathbf{j}$, where $\mathbf{i}$ is horizontal and $\mathbf{j}$ vertically upwards. Show that the position vector $\mathbf{r}$ of the projectile is $ut\mathbf{i} + (vt - \frac{1}{2}gt^2)\mathbf{j}$.

Show that there are two times when the direction of motion is perpendicular to the line joining the particle to the origin provided that $v > u2\sqrt{2}$.

9

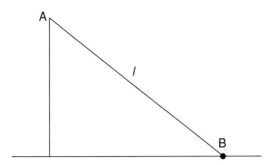

AB is a string of length l fixed at A. Attached at B is a particle of mass m which rests on a horizontal smooth table. The particle is made to describe circles on the table with velocity v. Show that the maximum value of v for the motion is $(gl\tan\theta\sec\theta)^{\frac{1}{2}}$.

10

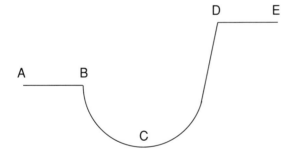

The diagram represents a track along which model cars are sent. The section A → B presents a resistance which causes a uniform retardation of 0.5 m s⁻². B → C → D → E is smooth; no resistance. AB = 1.5 m.

Find the minimum velocity to be given to the car at A so that it will arrive on the level section DE.

The vertical height of B above C is 75 cm and of D above C is 125 cm.

Solutions to Worksheet 12

1 NL2: $\mathbf{a} = \dfrac{\mathbf{F}}{m}$

► Vectors
► NL2

$$\Rightarrow \quad \mathbf{a} = \tfrac{1}{5}\begin{pmatrix} t \\ 2t^2 \\ 3 \end{pmatrix}$$

► Momentum

$$\mathbf{v} = \int \mathbf{a}\,dt = \tfrac{1}{5}\begin{pmatrix} \tfrac{1}{2}t^2 + A \\ \tfrac{2}{3}t^3 + B \\ 3t + C \end{pmatrix}$$

► Energy

When $t = 0$, $v = \begin{pmatrix} 0 \\ 0 \\ 1 \end{pmatrix}$ $\Rightarrow$ $A = 0, B = 0, C = 1$

$$\therefore \ v = \tfrac{1}{5} \begin{pmatrix} \tfrac{1}{2}t^2 \\ \tfrac{2}{3}t^3 \\ 3t + 1 \end{pmatrix}$$

► Remember momentum is a vector quantity, hence the answer given.

When $t = 6$, momentum, $m\mathbf{v} = 5 \times \tfrac{1}{5} \begin{pmatrix} \tfrac{1}{2} \times 6^2 \\ \tfrac{2}{3} \times 6^3 \\ 3 \times 6 + 1 \end{pmatrix} = \begin{pmatrix} 18 \\ 72 \\ 19 \end{pmatrix}$

► kJ = kilojoules
► 1 kJ = 1000 J

$KE = \tfrac{1}{2}mv^2 = \tfrac{1}{2} \times 5 \times \sqrt{18^2 + 72^2 + 19^2} = 14\ 672.5\ \text{J} = 14.7\ \text{kJ}$

► Vectors

2

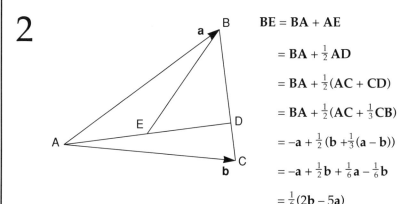

$\mathbf{BE} = \mathbf{BA} + \mathbf{AE}$

$= \mathbf{BA} + \tfrac{1}{2}\mathbf{AD}$

$= \mathbf{BA} + \tfrac{1}{2}(\mathbf{AC} + \mathbf{CD})$

$= \mathbf{BA} + \tfrac{1}{2}(\mathbf{AC} + \tfrac{1}{3}\mathbf{CB})$

$= -\mathbf{a} + \tfrac{1}{2}(\mathbf{b} + \tfrac{1}{3}(\mathbf{a} - \mathbf{b}))$

$= -\mathbf{a} + \tfrac{1}{2}\mathbf{b} + \tfrac{1}{6}\mathbf{a} - \tfrac{1}{6}\mathbf{b}$

$= \tfrac{1}{6}(2\mathbf{b} - 5\mathbf{a})$

► Work done

3 $F = \dfrac{c}{(a + x^2)}$

► This is known as the inverse square law (i.e. $\frac{1}{(\ )^2}$);
it features in gravitational forces.

Work done against F as x varies from 0 to d is

$$\int_0^d \frac{c}{a + x^2}\, dx \ = \left[-\frac{c}{a + x} \right]_0^d = -\frac{c}{a + d} + \frac{c}{a}$$

► See page ••.

$$= \frac{cd}{a(a + d)}$$

► Uniform acceleration

4

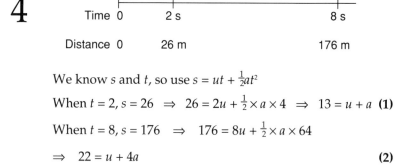

We know s and t, so use $s = ut + \tfrac{1}{2}at^2$

When $t = 2$, $s = 26$ $\Rightarrow$ $26 = 2u + \tfrac{1}{2} \times a \times 4$ $\Rightarrow$ $13 = u + a$ **(1)**

When $t = 8$, $s = 176$ $\Rightarrow$ $176 = 8u + \tfrac{1}{2} \times a \times 64$

$\Rightarrow$ $22 = u + 4a$ **(2)**

Solving **(1)** and **(2)**: $\Rightarrow$ $a = 3 \text{ m s}^{-2}, u = 10 \text{ m s}^{-1}$

Distance in 2nd second $= s_2 - s_1$

$$= 26 - (10 + \tfrac{3}{2} \times 1^2)$$

$$= 14.5 \text{ m}$$

5 **Velocity**

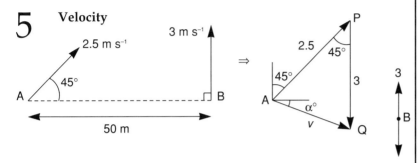

$\blacktriangleright$ Relative velocity

Distance

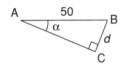

From $\triangle APQ$: $v^2 = 2.5^2 + 3^2 - 2 \times 2.5 \times 3\cos45°$

$\blacktriangleright$ All to find α so it can be transferred to the distance triangle.

$\Rightarrow$ $v = 2.15 \text{ m s}^{-1}$

In the same triangle: $\dfrac{\sin(45° + \alpha)}{3} = \dfrac{\sin45°}{2.15}$

$\Rightarrow$ $\alpha = 35.6°$

Now to $\triangle ABC$: $d = 50\sin\alpha$

$$= 29.1 \text{ m}$$

Since A can throw 30 m he does have a chance of hitting B (– but not much of one!).

6

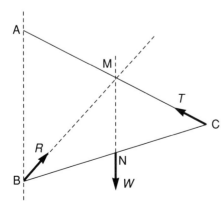

BC in is equilibrium under the action of three forces. Therefore they are concurrent.

The lines of action of W and T meet at M. Therefore the line of action of R is through M.

$\blacktriangleright$ Three-force problem

Now: MN//AB and N is the midpoint of BC.

► Midpoint theorem

Therefore M is the midpoint of AC.

Therefore R acts along the median.

7

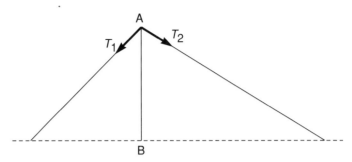

AB is in equilibrium under the action of three forces.

T_1 and T_2 meet at A therefore the reaction at B acts through A.

Therefore there is no horizontal component (friction) at B.

Resolving horizontally for the pole:

$T_1\cos45° = T_2\cos30°$

► An easy answer again to difficult looking question; often the case.

$T_1 \times \dfrac{1}{\sqrt{2}} = T_2 \times \dfrac{\sqrt{3}}{2} \quad \Rightarrow \quad 2T_1^2 = 3T_2^2$

8

► Projectile – vector form

$$\mathbf{a} = \begin{pmatrix} 0 \\ -g \end{pmatrix}$$

$$\mathbf{v} = \int \mathbf{a}\mathrm{d}t = \begin{pmatrix} A \\ -gt + B \end{pmatrix}$$

Velocity (initially)   Acceleration

$$\Rightarrow \begin{pmatrix} u \\ -gt + v \end{pmatrix}$$

$$\mathbf{r} = \int \mathbf{v}\mathrm{d}t = \begin{pmatrix} ut + C \\ -\frac{1}{2}gt^2 + vt + D \end{pmatrix}$$

$$\Rightarrow \begin{pmatrix} ut \\ vt - \frac{1}{2}gt^2 \end{pmatrix}$$

Direction of motion is perpendicular to the line joining the particle to the origin.

► Dot product

$\Rightarrow \quad \mathbf{v} \perp \mathbf{r} \quad \Rightarrow \quad \mathbf{v} \cdot \mathbf{r} = 0$

$\mathbf{v} \cdot \mathbf{r} = u^2t + (v - gt)(vt - \frac{1}{2}gt^2) = 0$

► Standard theory covered before but this time presented in vector form.

$\Rightarrow \quad u^2 + v^2 - \frac{3}{2}vgt + \frac{1}{2}g^2t^2 = 0$

This quadratic in t has two real roots if

$b^2 > 4ac \quad \Rightarrow \quad \frac{9}{4}v^2g^2 > 4(u^2 + v^2) \times \frac{1}{2}g^2$

$\Rightarrow \quad v > 2\sqrt{2}u$

9

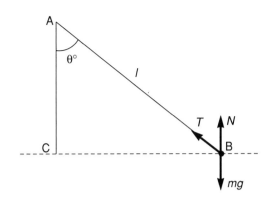

► Circular motion

The particle is moving in a circle centre C.

NL2 along radius: $T\sin\theta = \dfrac{mv^2}{l\sin\theta}$

Vertically: $T\cos\theta + N = mg$

While the particle remains on the table $N > 0$

$\Rightarrow$ $mg - T\cos\theta > 0$

$\Rightarrow$ $mg - \dfrac{mv^2\cos\theta}{l\sin^2\theta} > 0$

$\Rightarrow$ $v^2 < \dfrac{gl\sin^2\theta}{\cos\theta} = gl\tan\theta\sec\theta$

$\therefore$ maximum v is $(gl\tan\theta\sec\theta)^{\frac{1}{2}}$

10

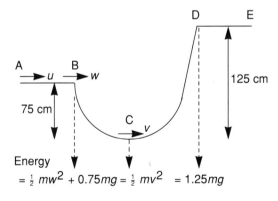

$$\text{Energy} = \tfrac{1}{2}mw^2 + 0.75mg = \tfrac{1}{2}mv^2 = 1.25mg$$

COE applies from $B \rightarrow C \rightarrow D \rightarrow E$

$(\tfrac{1}{2}mw^2 + mg \times 0.75) = \tfrac{1}{2}mv^2 = mg \times 1.25$

For AB: $w^2 = u^2 - 2 \times \tfrac{1}{2} \times 1.5$

$\Rightarrow$ $\tfrac{1}{2}m(u^2 - 1.5) + mg \times 0.75 = mg \times 1.25$

$u^2 - 1.5 + 14.7 = 24.5$

$\Rightarrow$ $u = 3.4$ m s^{-1}

► Conservation of energy

► Solutions on page 272

Worksheet 13

1   A solid hemisphere of radius r has its plane face fastened to the end of a cylinder of the same radius and made of the same material. The height of the cylinder is kr. When placed on its hemispherical surface on a smooth level plane the solid is always in equilibrium. Find the value of k.

2

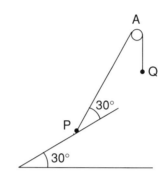

The diagram shows a particle P of weight W on a rough plane of inclination 30°, connected by a light string passing over a smooth peg at A and supporting at Q a mass of weight W. P is just moving up the plane.

Show that $\mu = \dfrac{W\sqrt{3} - w}{w\sqrt{3} - W}$

and show that if $w < W\sqrt{3}$ then $w > \dfrac{W}{\sqrt{3}}$

3   ABCD is a square of side l. Forces of 2, 8, 1 and 4 act along the sides AB, CB, DC and AD respectively. Find the direction and magnitude of the resultant and find the position of the point where its line of action cuts AB.

4   A projectile has a range of 25 m and an initial horizontal velocity of 5 m s⁻¹. Find

   (a)   the initial vertical component of velocity

   (b)   its direction after 3 seconds

   (c)   its distance from the start after 3 seconds.

   Use $g = 10$ m s⁻².

5   An engine is working at constant power, P, driving a car up a slope of inclination $\sin^{-1}\frac{1}{60}$ to the horizontal. The mass of the car is 600 kg. There is a resisting force of $\dfrac{K}{v}$. Show that, t seconds after the start of the motion and while it is still accelerating $t = 0.06 \ln \dfrac{P - K}{P - K - 100v} - 6v$.

6 In 18 seconds a particle accelerates uniformly from rest, travels at constant speed and decelerates uniformly to rest. The retardation is twice the acceleration and two-thirds of the distance is covered at constant speed. Find how much time is spend on each section.

7 A particle strikes a solid wall at angle α to the wall. If the coefficient of restitution is e and it leaves at β to the wall show that $\tan\beta = e\tan\alpha$.

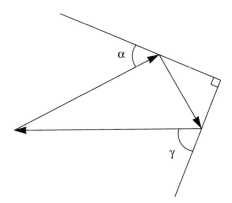

A ball starts from A, strikes two perpendicular walls and returns to A. e is the same at both impacts.
  Show that α and γ are complimentary.

8

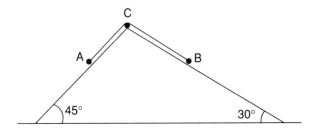

Particles A and B rest on two smooth planes as shown. They are connected by a light string passing over a smooth pulley at C. They are released from rest. Find the time it takes for A to travel 2 m.

9

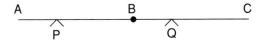

Two equal uniform heavy rods of length $6a$ are smoothly jointed at B. They are horizontal on supports at P and Q where AP = $2a$ and BQ = $2a$ and they are kept in equilibrium by the application of a couple of moment G to BC. Find the magnitude and direction of G.

10 A car of mass 1000 kg is being driven along a level road against a constant resistance of 1000 N. The engine is working at the rate of 60 kW. Find the acceleration when the velocity is 54 km h⁻¹.

Solutions to Worksheet 13

1

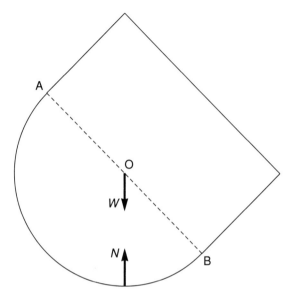

When the curved surface is placed on a plane, the reaction of the plane passes through O, centre of AB. This is true for all points of the curved surface. For equilibrium, the line of action of W is also through O; it is in line with N otherwise we would have a couple and not equilibrium.

The centre of gravity is also on the axis of symmetry of the solid hence we need to look at the position of the centre of gravity of the combined solid.

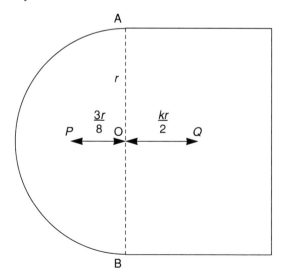

Positions of the centres of gravity of the hemisphere and cylinder are shown.

$$OP = \frac{3}{8} r$$

$$OQ = \frac{kr}{2}$$

► See page 178

Taking moments about AB for the whole:

$$(\pi r^2 \times kr + \frac{2}{3} \pi r^3)\bar{x} = \pi r^2 \times kr \times \frac{kr}{2} - \frac{2}{3} \pi r^3 \times \frac{3}{8} r$$

But $\bar{x} = 0$

$$\Rightarrow \quad 0 = \frac{1}{2} k^2 - \frac{1}{4} \quad \Rightarrow \quad k = \frac{1}{\sqrt{2}} = \frac{\sqrt{2}}{2}$$

2

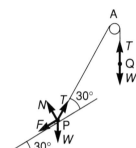

The system is in limiting equilibrium ∴ $F = \mu N$

► Friction
► Limiting equilibrium

Resolving vertically for Q:
$T = W$

Resolving // plane for P:
$T\cos 30° = F + w\sin 30°$ **(1)**

Resolving ⊥ plane for P:
$N + T\cos 60° = w\cos 30°$ **(2)**

Substituting for T and F in **(1)**: $W \frac{\sqrt{3}}{2} = \mu N + \frac{w}{2}$ **(3)**

Substituting for T and F in **(2)**: $N + \frac{W}{2} = w \frac{\sqrt{3}}{2}$ **(4)**

Eliminating N: $W \frac{\sqrt{3}}{2} = \mu \left(w \frac{\sqrt{3}}{2} - \frac{W}{2} \right) + \frac{w}{2}$

$$\Rightarrow \quad \mu = \frac{W\sqrt{3} - w}{w\sqrt{3} - W}$$

$\mu > 1$ and if $w < W\sqrt{3}$ then $W\sqrt{3} - w > 0$

$$\Rightarrow \quad w\sqrt{3} - W > 0 \text{ i.e. } w > \frac{W}{\sqrt{3}}$$

3

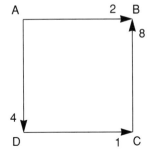
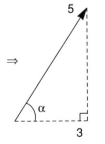

► Direction. magnitude and line of action of resultant.

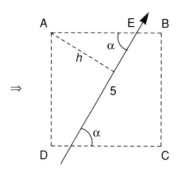

The diagrams explain the magnitude and direction of the resultant.

We need to find the position of E.

Taking moments about A:

$$8 \times l + 1 \times l = 5 \times h \quad \therefore \quad h = \frac{9l}{5}$$

By trigonometry:

$$AE = \frac{h}{\sin\alpha} = \frac{9l}{5} \times \frac{5}{4} = \frac{9l}{4}$$

i.e. the position of the resultant is:

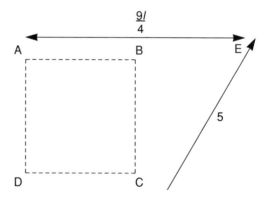

► Projectiles

4

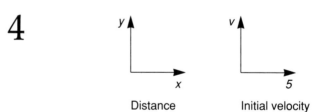

Range = 25 m

$\therefore$ time of flight = 5 s

Knowing s, t vertically $\Rightarrow$ $s = ut + \frac{1}{2}at^2$

$\Rightarrow$ $0 = v \times 5 - \frac{1}{2} \times 10 \times 5^2$

$\therefore$ $v = 25$ m s^{-1}

The direction of flight is obtained from the velocity.

After 3 seconds: $\dot{x} = 5$

$\dot{y} = 25 - 10 \times 3 = -5$

$\therefore$ 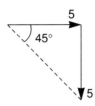 i.e. travelling in direction 45° below horizontal

After 3 seconds: $x = 5 \times 3 = 15$ m

$y = 25 \times 3 - \frac{1}{2} \times 10 \times 9 = 30$ m

Distance from start $= \sqrt{15^2 + 30^2} = 33.5$ m

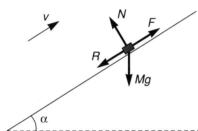 Applying NL2 along the plane:

$F - R - Mg\sin\alpha = Ma$

Power $= F \times v$

$\therefore \quad F = \dfrac{P}{v}$

► Once again don't let the frightening answers put you off: start from the principles you know.

► Power
► NL2
► Differential equations – with variables separable

Hence the equation is $\dfrac{P}{v} - \dfrac{K}{v} - 600 \times 10 \times \dfrac{1}{60} = 600a$

i.e. $\dfrac{P - K}{v} - 100 = 600\dfrac{dv}{dt}$

Letting $P - K = A$ and separating the variables:

$$\int dt = \int \frac{600v}{A - 100v}\, dv$$

$$t = 600 \int -\frac{1}{100} + \frac{A}{100(A - 100v)}\, dv = 6 \int -1 + \frac{A}{A - 100v}\, dv$$

► A bit of algebraic manipulation to get something that we can integrate

$$\therefore \quad t = 6\left[-v - \frac{1}{100} \ln(A - 100v)\right] + C$$

When $t = 0, v = 0 \;\Rightarrow\; C = \dfrac{6}{100} \ln A$

$$t = -6v - \frac{6}{100} \ln(A - 100v) + \frac{6}{100} \ln A$$

$$\therefore \quad t = -6v + \frac{6}{100} \ln \frac{P - K}{P - K - 100v}$$

$$\Rightarrow \quad t = 0.06 \ln \frac{P - K}{P - K - 100v} - 6v$$

► Uniform acceleration

6

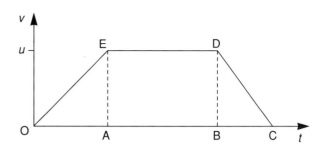

Let OA = 2*t*, then BC = *t* and AB = 18 – 3*t*

Area ABDE = 2 × (ΔOAE + ΔDBC)

∴ (18 – 3*t*)*u* = 2 × (*tu* + $\frac{1}{2}tu$)

⇒ *t* = 3   ∴   6 seconds accelerating

9 seconds constant speed

3 seconds decelerating.

7

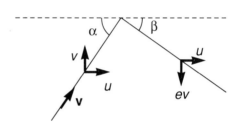

► Impacts

Normal rebound velocity is *e* × approach velocity.

$\tan\alpha = \dfrac{v}{u}$

$\tan\beta = \dfrac{ev}{u}$

∴ $\tan\beta = e\tan\alpha$

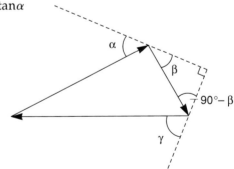

► A common story: the solution is based on good diagrams and using results already proved; no racing automatically into many equations based on momentum, etc.

$\tan\beta = e\tan\alpha$

and $\tan\gamma = e\tan(90° - \beta) = e\cot\beta = \dfrac{1}{\tan\alpha} = \cot\alpha$

∴ $\tan\gamma = \cot\alpha$

i.e. $\gamma + \alpha = 90°$

8

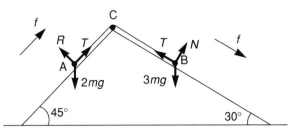

► NL2

► Uniform acceleration

The direction of f is a guess.

Applying NL2 for A: $T - 2mg\cos45° = 2mf$

Applying NL2 for B: $3mg\cos60° - T = 3mf$

$\Rightarrow \quad 3g \times \frac{1}{2} - 2g \times 1\frac{1}{\sqrt{2}} = 5f$

i.e. $1.5g - 1.41g = 5f \quad \Rightarrow \quad f = 0.017g$

For A to go 2 m, we need to look at $s, t \quad \therefore \quad s = ut + \frac{1}{2}at^2$

$2 = \frac{1}{2} \times 0.017g \times t^2 \quad \Rightarrow \quad t = 4.5$ s

9

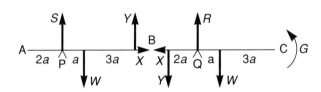

► Direction guessed correctly.

► Couple
► Reaction at joint

Taking moments about P for AB:

$Y \times 4a = W \times a \quad \Rightarrow \quad y = \frac{W}{4}$

Taking moments about Q for BC:

$Y \times 2a + G = Wa \quad \Rightarrow \quad G = Wa - \frac{W}{4} \times 2a$

$G = \frac{Wa}{2}$ anticlockwise

► They don't come much easier – once you have seen the solution. But how to start? The old story of a clear diagram and thinking simply, of basic principles, in this case 'moments'. The rest follows.

10

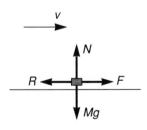

Applying NL2: $F - R = Ma$

$\Rightarrow \quad \frac{P}{v} - 1000 = 1000a$ because $P = Fv$

$\Rightarrow \quad \frac{60\ 000}{v} - 1000 = 1000a$ because 60 kW = 6000 W

$\Rightarrow \quad \frac{60}{v} - 1 = a$

$v = 54$ km h^{-1} = 15 m s$^{-1} \quad \Rightarrow \quad a = \frac{60}{15} - 1 = 3$ m s^{-2}

► Power
► NL2

► Solutions on page 280

Worksheet 14

1

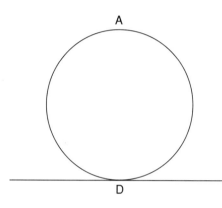

A projectile is fired vertically upwards from B. Simultaneously another is fired from A aimed at hitting B. Investigate the initial components of velocity of A if B is given velocity w.

2

The diagram shows a smooth cylinder set with its axis horizontal and lying on level ground. A particle is dislodged from A and it falls down the outside of the cylinder in a plane perpendicular to the axis. Find the angle the radius to the particle has turned through when the particle leaves the cylinder.

If the radius of the cylinder is 1 m find how far the particle is from D when it reaches ground level.

3

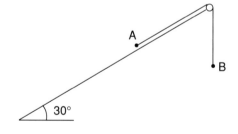

A and B, both mass m, are particles connected by a string passing over a smooth pulley, B. Pulley B is hanging vertically and A is on the smooth plane. A is given velocity $u = 3$ m s^{-1} down the plane. Find the velocity of B after it has travelled 50 cm.

4

A particle of mass m is sliding along a rough horizontal plane, coefficient of friction μ, against a resistance of mv. Given that when $t = 0$, $x = 0$ and $v = u$, express v and x in terms of μ, g, u and t.

5

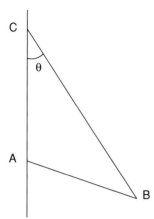

AB is a heavy uniform rod, length $2a$, resting against a rough wall at A. It is held in equilibrium by a string BC where AC = $2a$. If μ is the co-efficient of friction and BC makes angle θ with the wall as shown, show that $\mu \geqslant \tan\theta$.

6

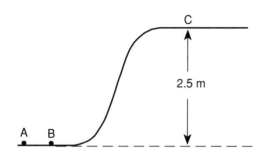

A is a marble of mass $3m$ which collides with an equally sized marble B of mass m. The track they are on is smooth. Given that the coefficient of restitution is $\frac{1}{2}$ determine whether or not B reaches C.

7

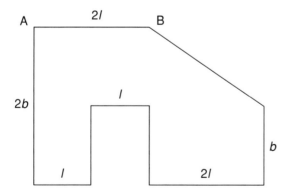

A lamina, mass m per unit area, is made from a rectangular plate and has the shape shown. Find the position of its centre of gravity.

It is in a vertical plane and hinged at A. It is held in the position shown (i.e. AB horizontal) by a couple. Find the moment of this couple and show its sense on the diagram.

8 The position of a mass of 4 kg is ($\sin\omega t\mathbf{i} + \cos\omega t\mathbf{j} + t\mathbf{k}$). The mass is acted on by a single force **F**. Find the magnitude of **F** and find the kinetic energy of the mass, showing that both are constant in value.

9

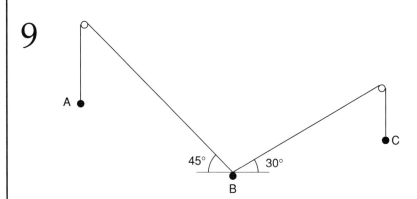

B is a weight W attached to two strings which pass over smooth pegs and carry masses M and m at A and C respectively. The system hangs in equilibrium, with the angles as shown. Show that $W = \frac{1}{2}g\,(\sqrt{2}M + m)$.

10 A particle is describing SHM at 240 oscillations per minute. The maximum acceleration is 3 m s⁻². Find the maximum velocity and the distance between the extremities.

Solutions to Worksheet 14

► Projectiles

1

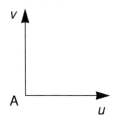 

Both projectiles cover the same height in the same time if they are to meet: hence $v = w$.

Additionally A has horizontal velocity so that it may cross the space A → B. Since A and B are at the same height throughout as soon as A travels horizontally to B they collide.

► Circular motion – vertical

► In greater detail on page 208

2 Refer to the diagram at the top of page 281.

Applying NL2 along the radius: $\quad mg\cos\theta - N = \dfrac{mv^2}{r}$

Applying COE: $\quad \frac{1}{2}mv^2 = mgr(1 - \cos\theta)$

Eliminating v and substituting $N = 0 \quad \Rightarrow \quad \cos\theta = \frac{2}{3}$

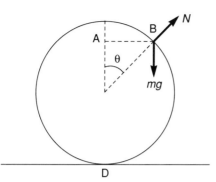

Now we have a projectile:

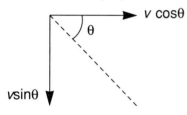

We can find the horizontal distance when we know t.

$\therefore$ use vertical motion to find t.

$$s = ut + \frac{1}{2}at^2$$

$$\Rightarrow \quad \frac{5r}{3} = v\frac{\sqrt{5}}{3}t + \frac{1}{2}gt^2$$

From the energy equation $v = \sqrt{\frac{2g}{3}}$ substituting $r = 1$, which was given.

$$\therefore \quad \frac{5}{3} = \frac{\sqrt{5}}{3} \times \sqrt{\frac{2g}{3}}t + \frac{1}{2}gt^2$$

$$\Rightarrow \quad 4.9t^2 + 1.8t - 1.7 = 0 \quad \Rightarrow \quad t = 0.43 \text{ s}$$

Horizontally: $\quad x = \sqrt{\frac{2g}{3}} \times \frac{2}{3} \times 0.43 = 0.73 \text{ m}$

But AB at point of leaving is $1 \times \frac{\sqrt{5}}{3} = 0.74 \text{ m}$

$\therefore$ distance from point of contact $= 1.47 \text{ m}$

3

▶ NL2

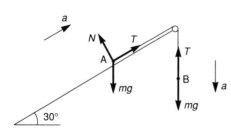

Applying NL2 for B: $\quad mg - T = ma$

Applying NL2 for A: $\quad T - mg\sin30° = ma$

Adding: $\quad \frac{g}{2} = 2a \quad \Rightarrow \quad a = \frac{g}{4}$

For B, after 50 cm, $v^2 = 9 - 2 \times \frac{g}{4} \times \frac{1}{2} \quad$ given $u = 3$

$\Rightarrow \quad v = 2.56 \text{ m s}^{-2}$

► Variable acceleration

4

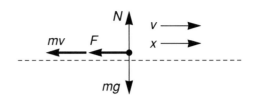

Applying NL2: $F + mv = -m\ddot{x}$

$\mu mg + mv = -m\ddot{x} = -m\dfrac{\mathrm{d}v}{\mathrm{d}t}$ because $F = \mu N = \mu mg$

Separating variables: $\displaystyle\int \mathrm{d}t = -\int \dfrac{\mathrm{d}v}{\mu g + v}$

Integrating: $t = -\ln(\mu g + v) + A$

When $t = 0, v = u$ $\Rightarrow$ $t = \ln\left(\dfrac{\mu g + u}{\mu g + v}\right)$

$\Rightarrow$ $(\mu g + v)\mathrm{e}^{t} = \mu g + u$

$\Rightarrow$ $v = (\mu g + u)\mathrm{e}^{-t} - \mu g$

$x = \displaystyle\int v\,\mathrm{d}t = \int (\mu g + u)\mathrm{e}^{-t} - \mu g\,\mathrm{d}t$

$\Rightarrow$ $x = -(\mu g + u)\mathrm{e}^{-t} - \mu gt + B$

When $t = 0, v = u$ $\Rightarrow$ $B = \mu g + u$

and then $x = (\mu g + u)(1 - \mathrm{e}^{-t}) - \mu gt$

► Moments
► Friction

5

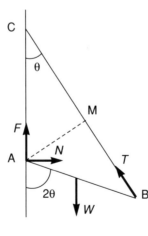

Taking moments about A for AB:

$T \times \text{AM} = W \times a\sin2\theta$

$\Rightarrow T \times 2a\sin\theta = W \times a \times 2\sin\theta\cos\theta$

$\Rightarrow$ $T = W\cos\theta$

Resolving horizontally for AB:

$T\sin\theta = N$ $\therefore$ $N = W\sin\theta\cos\theta$

Resolving vertically for AB:

$T\cos\theta + F = W$

$\therefore$ $F = W - W\cos^{2}\theta = W\sin^{2}\theta$

For equilibrium: $F \leqslant \mu N$

$W\sin^{2}\theta \leqslant \mu W\sin\theta\cos\theta$

$\Rightarrow$ $\mu \geqslant \tan\theta$

6

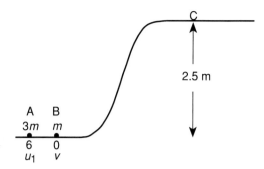

► Impacts

At the impact: COM: $\Rightarrow$ $3m \times 6 = 3\,mu_1 + mv$

$\Rightarrow$ $18 = 3u_1 + v$

NEL: $\Rightarrow$ $e \times 6 = v - u_1$ $\Rightarrow$ $3 = v - u_1$

Solving $\Rightarrow$ $27 = 4v$

If B reaches C, by COE: $\frac{1}{2}mv^2 \geqslant mgh$

$\therefore$ $\frac{1}{2} \times \left(\frac{27}{4}\right)^2 = 22.78$

$gh = 9.81 \times 2.5 = 24.5$

$\therefore$ B does not reach C.

7

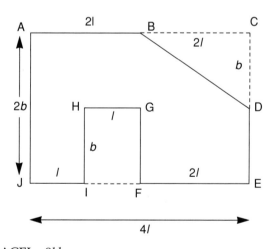

► Centre of gravity

Area ACEJ = $8bl$

Area BCD = bl

Area HGFI = bl

Area of remainder = $6bl$

Taking moments about AJ:

$6bl \times \bar{x} = 8bl \times 2l - bl \times \dfrac{3l}{2} - bl \times \dfrac{10}{3}l$

$\Rightarrow$ $\bar{x} = \dfrac{67}{36}l$

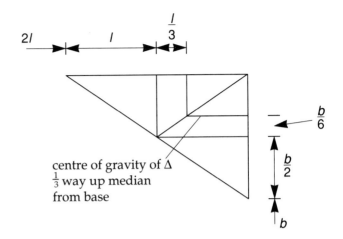

centre of gravity of Δ
$\frac{1}{3}$ way up median
from base

Taking moments about JE:

$$6bl \times \bar{y} = 8bl \times b - bl \times \frac{b}{2} - bl \times \frac{5}{3}b$$

$$\Rightarrow \quad \bar{y} = \frac{35}{36}b$$

The lamina is set vertically and hinged at A.

An anti-clockwise couple is required, of moment L.

Taking moments about A:

$$6mbl \times \frac{67}{36}l = L \quad \therefore \quad L = \frac{67}{6}mbl^2$$

► Vector form of NL2 and energy

8

$$\mathbf{r} = \begin{pmatrix} \sin\omega t \\ \cos\omega t \\ t \end{pmatrix} \qquad \mathbf{v} = \begin{pmatrix} \omega\cos\omega t \\ -\omega\sin\omega t \\ 1 \end{pmatrix} \qquad \mathbf{a} = \begin{pmatrix} -\omega^2\sin\omega t \\ -\omega^2\cos\omega t \\ 0 \end{pmatrix}$$

$$\mathbf{F} = m\mathbf{a} = -4\omega^2 \begin{pmatrix} \sin\omega t \\ \cos\omega t \\ 0 \end{pmatrix}$$

Magnitude of $\mathbf{F} = 4\omega^2\sqrt{\sin^2\omega t + \cos^2\omega t} = 4\omega^2$ a constant

$$\therefore \quad KE = 2(1 + \omega^2) \qquad a\ constant$$

$$KE = \frac{1}{2}mv^2$$

$$= \frac{1}{2} \times 4 \times \omega^2\cos^2\omega t + \omega^2\sin^2\omega t + 1$$

$$= 2 \times (\omega^2 + 1)$$

9

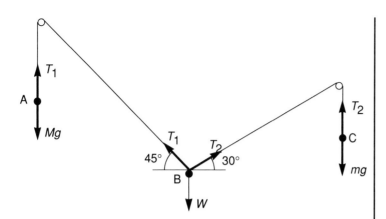

Resolving vertically for B: $T_1\cos45° + T_2\cos60° = W$

But $T_1 = Mg$ and $T_2 = mg$

∴ $Mg \times \dfrac{1}{\sqrt{2}} + mg \times \dfrac{1}{2} = W$

∴ $W = \dfrac{g}{2}(\sqrt{2M} + m)$

► Resolving

10 240 oscillations per minute

⇒   1 oscillation per $\dfrac{1}{240}$ minute   ⇒ $T = \dfrac{60}{240} = \dfrac{1}{4}$ s

$T = \dfrac{1}{4}$ ⇒ $\dfrac{2\pi}{\omega} = \dfrac{1}{4}$ i.e. $\omega = 8\pi$

Maximum acceleration when $x = a$ ⇒ $-3 = -\omega^2 a = -64\pi^2 a$

∴ $a = \dfrac{3}{64\pi^2}$ m

Maximum velocity $= a\omega = \dfrac{3}{64\pi^2} \times 8\pi = \dfrac{3}{8\pi}$ m s^{-1}

Distance between extremities $= 2 \times$ amplitude $= \dfrac{3}{32\pi^2}$ m

► Simple harmonic motion

Worksheet 15

► Solutions on page 287

1

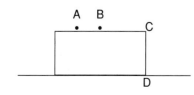

The diagram shows a table standing on level ground. A and B are equally sized marbles, of mass $4m$ and m respectively, at rest on a line perpendicular to

the edge of the table with BC = 1 m and CD = 0.8 m. A is given a velocity along AB of 3 m s^{-1} and the coefficient of restitution is $\frac{2}{3}$. Find

(a) how far from D the marble B hits the floor

(b) the direction in which it is going when it does so

(c) how long it takes from the time of impact.

2 Four masses of 5 kg each are attached by light strings 10 cm long to form a square. The system is set in motion, doing horizontal circles, with the centre of the square as the centre of the circle, at 480 rpm. Find the tension in the strings.

3 A light elastic string has end A fixed and at B carries a mass *m* in equilibrium. The natural length is 2*l* and the extension is *l*. The mass is then pulled down a distance $\frac{1}{2}l$ and released. Find

(a) the period

(b) the maximum velocity

(c) the minimum tension.

4 A bead of mass *m* is threaded on a smooth vertical circular wire of radius *r*. When the radius to the bead makes 60° with the upward vertical the bead is given a velocity $\sqrt{gr}$ along the downward tangent. Determine whether or not the bead will reach the top of the circle. Show that the ratio of the magnitudes of the reactions of the wire on the bead when it makes 45° and 135° with the upward vertical is $17 - 12\sqrt{2}$.

5 Two identical scale pans of mass 10 g are connected by a light string passing over a fixed smooth pulley. One pan carries a mass A of 40 g and the other a mass B of 50 g. The system is released. Find the forces exerted by the pans on A and B.

6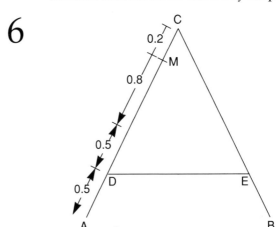

The diagram shows a pair of stepladders standing on level smooth ground. AB = AC. AB has mass 8 kg and BC has mass 2 kg. DE is a light cord under tension. At M is a man of mass 84 kg.

The rules say that the cord must have a breaking strain at least 40% higher then the anticipated strain. On the evidence given here, find the minimum breaking strain of the cord.

7 A particle is on a rough plane sloping at angle α. It is just moved up the plane by a force parallel to the plane equal to its own weight. Show that $\lambda = 45° - \frac{1}{2}\alpha$ where λ is the angle of friction.

8 A right circular cone of semi-vertical angle β is placed on a rough plane sloping to the horizontal at angle α. α is steadily increased. Show that, provided friction remains sufficiently strong, $\tan \leqslant 3\tan\beta$ for equilibrium.

9 **a** and **b** are vectors such that **a** + **b** is perpendicular to **b** and **a** + **2b** is perpendicular to **a**. Find the relationship between **a** and **b**.

10 A ball is projected, from A, with horizontal and vertical velocity components u and v. When it is at its highest point it strikes a wall, coefficient of restitution e. It strikes the ground at C, on the same horizontal level as A, after the rebound. If R is the range of the initial projection show that $AC = \dfrac{R}{2}(1 - e)$.

Solutions to Worksheet 15

► Impacts

1

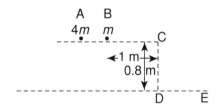

(a)   For the impact: **A**   **B**

$e = \frac{2}{3}$

A	B
$4m$	m
•	•
3	0
u	v

Applying COM:

$4m \times 3 = 4m \times u + m \times v \;\; \Rightarrow \;\; 12 = 4u + v$

and NEL: $\;\; -\frac{2}{3} \times -3 = v - u \;\; \Rightarrow \;\; 2 = v - u$

Solving $\;\; \Rightarrow \;\; v = 4 \; m \; s^{-1}$

From C, B is a projectile.

To find time to fall CD use $s = ut + \frac{1}{2}at^2$

$\Rightarrow \quad 0.8 = \frac{1}{2}gt^2 \quad \Rightarrow \quad t = 0.4$ s

Distance travelled horizontally $= 0.4 \times 4 = 1.6$ m

Therefore it lands at E 1.6 m from the foot of the table.

At E, vertically: $v = u + at \quad \Rightarrow \quad v = g \times 0.4 = 3.9$ m s^{-1}

(b) A strikes the ground at angle α where

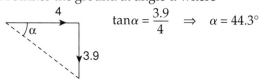

$\tan\alpha = \dfrac{3.9}{4} \quad \Rightarrow \quad \alpha = 44.3°$

(c) Time for B on the table: $t = \dfrac{BC}{4} = \dfrac{1}{4} = 0.25$ s

Therefore time to reach E $= 0.25 + 0.4 = 0.65$ s

► Circular motion – horizontal

2

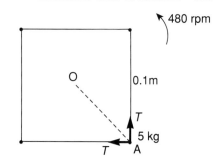

From symmetrical considerations the tensions are the same in all strings.

480 rpm = 8 rps
= $8 \times 2\pi$ radians s^{-1}

Applying   NL2 along AO for A:

$2 \times T\cos45° = mr\omega^2 = 5 \times 0.01 \times \sqrt{2} \times (16\pi)^2$

$\therefore \quad T = 126.3$ N

► Notice again no attempt is made at scale in the diagram.

The question does not ask you to establish SHM but the questions asked are dependent on SHM, hence it is good style firstly to develop the SHM equation.

► SHM established

3

When in equilibrium: $mg = \dfrac{\lambda l}{2l}$

$\therefore \quad \lambda = 2mg$

When at P, applying NL2:
$mg - T = m\ddot{x}$

$\Rightarrow \quad mg - \dfrac{2mg(l + x)}{2l} = m\ddot{x}$

$\ddot{x} = -gx$

(a) $T = \dfrac{2\pi}{\omega} = \dfrac{2\pi}{\sqrt{g}}$

(b) $v_{max} = a\omega = \frac{1}{2}l \times \sqrt{g} = \frac{1}{2}l\sqrt{g}$

(c) Minimum tension is when

$x = -\frac{1}{2}$ and then

$T = \dfrac{2mg}{l} \times \dfrac{l}{2} = mg$

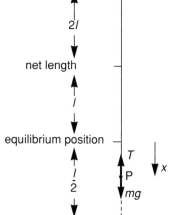

4

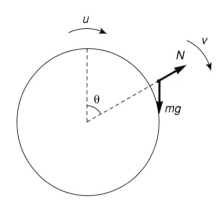

► Circular motion – vertical

We have different values of θ to consider but firstly we establish equations in terms of θ, i.e. equations which apply to any position. After that we will substitute values of θ as necessary.

► A reminder of the correct technique

Applying NL2 along the radius:

$$mg\cos\theta - N = \frac{mv^2}{r} \qquad (1)$$

and COE: $\quad mgr(1 - \cos\theta) = \frac{1}{2}mv^2 - \frac{1}{2}mu^2 \qquad (2)$

$\theta = 60°$, P is given velocity, $\sqrt{gr}$ along the downwards tangent.

By COE when P rises to $\theta = 60°$ it will have velocity $\sqrt{gr}$ along the upward tangent.

If it then gains height h before $v = 0$, by COE:

$$mgh = \frac{1}{2}mgr \quad \Rightarrow \quad h = \frac{1}{2}r$$

$\therefore$ just reaches the top of the wire, i.e. $u = 0$

Substituting $u = 0$ and eliminating v from **(1)** and **(2)**:

$$N = 3mg\cos\theta - 2mg = mg(3\cos\theta - 2)$$

When $\theta = 45°$ $\qquad N_1 = mg\left(\dfrac{3}{\sqrt{2}} - 2\right)$

When $\theta = 135°$ $\qquad N_2 = mg\left(-\dfrac{3}{\sqrt{2}} - 2\right)$

$$\frac{N_1}{N_2} = \frac{3 - 2\sqrt{2}}{3 + 2\sqrt{2}}$$

$$= \frac{3 - 2\sqrt{2}}{3 + } \frac{3 - 2\sqrt{2}}{3 + 2\sqrt{2}}$$

$$= 17 - 12\sqrt{2}$$

► Once again a frightening looking result obtained by starting with the basic mechanics principles to form equations and then manipulating the algebra.

► NL2

► The technique of considering parts of a complex system in isolation.

► The stumbling block for many in this question would be in failing to isolate the masses and consider them individually.

► i.e. an increase in weight

► i.e. a decrease in weight

► Moments

5

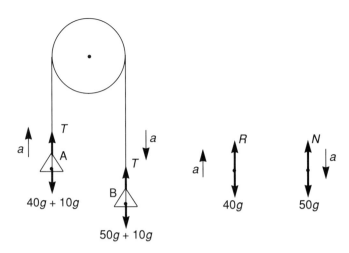

The masses have been drawn separately. This is to emphasize that we are being asked to find R and N, the forces exerted on the masses by the pans.

We shall need to know a, the acceleration, and for that we use the main diagram.

Applying NL2 for B: $60g - T = 60a$

Applying NL2 for A: $T - 50g = 50a$

$$\Rightarrow \quad a = \frac{g}{11}$$

For the 40 g mass: $R - 40g = \dfrac{40g}{11} \quad \Rightarrow \quad R = \dfrac{12}{11} \times 40g = 43.6g$

For the 50 g mass: $50g - N = \dfrac{50g}{11} \quad \therefore \quad N = \dfrac{10}{11} \times 50g = 45.5g$

6

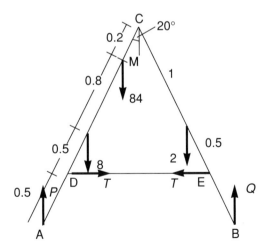

► Kilogram weight = the weight of one kilogram
1 kg wt = $1 \times g$ $\Rightarrow$ g newtons
Weights are shown in kg wt – not newtons and provided we use these throughout our results will be in kg wt.

Taking moments about A for the whole:

$Q \times 4 = 2 \times 3 + 84 \times 1.8 + 8 \times 1$

$\Rightarrow \quad Q = 41.3$ and $P = 84 + 8 + 2 - 41.3 = 52.7$

Taking moments about C for CB:

$$Q \times 2\cos70° = 2 \times 1\cos70° + T \times 1.5\cos20°$$

$$\therefore \quad T = (41.3 \times 2 \times \cos70° - 2 \times \cos 70°) \times \frac{1}{1.5\cos20°}$$

$$\Rightarrow \quad T = 19.6 \text{ kg wt}$$

A 40% increase $\Rightarrow$ a tension of 27.4 kg wt

i.e. the cord must have a breaking strain of at least 27.4 kg wt.

7   **Method 1**

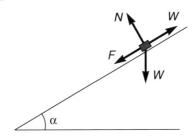

► Friction – method is important in this question.

Resolving // plane: $W = F + W\sin\alpha$

Resolving $\perp$ plane: $N = \quad \cos\alpha$

Just moving $\therefore \quad F = \mu N$

$$\Rightarrow \quad W - W\sin\alpha = \mu W\cos\alpha$$

$$\mu = \frac{1 - \sin\alpha}{\cos\alpha}$$

$$\therefore \quad \tan\lambda = \frac{1 - \sin\alpha}{\cos\alpha} = \frac{\sin90° - \sin\alpha}{\cos90° + \cos\alpha}$$

► Technique of adding in to an expression, not easy to recognize and requires very good insight.

$$= \frac{2\cos\frac{1}{2}(90° + \alpha)\sin\frac{1}{2}(90° - \alpha)}{2\cos\frac{1}{2}(90° + \alpha)\cos\frac{1}{2}(90° - \alpha)}$$

$$\tan\lambda = \tan\tfrac{1}{2}(90° - \alpha)$$

$$\therefore \quad \lambda = \tfrac{1}{2}(90° - \alpha) = 45° - \tfrac{1}{2}\alpha$$

Method 2

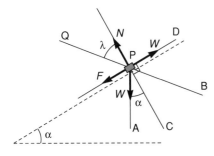

The resultant of W and W is along PB where PB bisects $\angle$APD.

The resultant of F and N is along PQ: limiting therefore λ as shown.

$$\angle\text{BPA} = 90° + \frac{\alpha}{2}$$

$$\angle\text{BPC} = \frac{90° + \alpha}{2} - \alpha$$

$$= \frac{90° - \alpha}{2}$$

$$\therefore \quad \lambda = \frac{90° - \alpha}{2} = 45° - \frac{1}{2}\alpha$$

► The power of a geometrical solution is well illustrated here.

► Vertically opposite angles

► Equilibrium

8

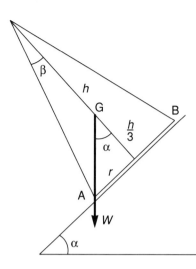

If friction is strong enough equilibrium will be broken by toppling.

The cone is about to topple when it is in the position shown.

Any increase in α will cause the line of action of W to be outside AB and the cone will topple.

From the diagram $\tan\beta = \dfrac{r}{h}$

and $\tan\alpha = \dfrac{r}{h/3} = \dfrac{3r}{h}$

$\therefore \quad \tan\alpha = 3\tan\beta$

► Vectors
► This is one of an infinity of possibilities for **a** and **b** but it serves to define **a** and **b** for this solution.

9

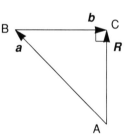

R is the resultant of **a** and **b**.

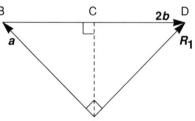

$\mathbf{R}_1$ is the resultant of **a** + 2**b**.

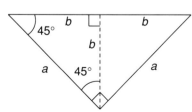

Combining the triangles above we get this triangle from which
$a^2 = b^2 + b^2$

$\Rightarrow \quad \mathbf{a} = \mathbf{b}\sqrt{2}$

10

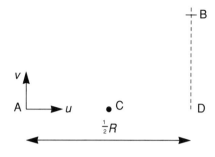

The velocity of the ball on impact is u because it is going horizontally at the highest point.

The velocity of rebound is eu.

The time of flight T from A to B is the same as from B to C (from considering vertical motion).

► Projectiles
► Impacts

$$\therefore \quad \frac{R}{2} = uT$$

and $DC = euT$

$$\Rightarrow \quad DC = \frac{eR}{2}$$

$$\therefore \quad AC = \frac{R}{2} - \frac{eR}{2}$$

$$= \frac{R}{2}(1 - e)$$

Worksheet 16

Solutions on page 295

1

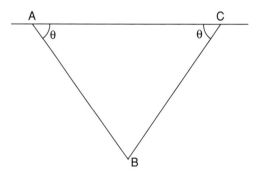

AC is a rough horizontal rod. AB is a uniform rod, weight W, smoothly hinged at A. C is a ring threaded on AC and joined to B by a light string. Show that, for equilibrium, $5\mu \geq \cot\theta$.

2

Two particles A, mass $2m$ and B, mass $3m$, are connected by a light string 2 m long. B is also connected by a light string to C, a mass of m. A and B are touching 3 m from the edge of a smooth level table. C is hanging over the edge of the table with the string BC taut. The system is released from rest. Find the velocity with which A starts to move and find the impulse on A.

3   A mass of 2 kg on the end of a 1 m piece of string is describing horizontal circles at the rate of 3 revolutions per second (rps). Find the difference in level between the ends of the piece of string.

4   A sphere A, mass $3m$, travelling with velocity u, collides directly with an equally sized sphere B, mass $2m$ and at rest. Their line of centres is perpendicular to a wall, distance d from the impact. B hits the wall and rebounds to have a second impact with A. Find where the second impact occurs and determine wherther or not B hits the wall a second time. Take $e = \frac{2}{3}$.

5   A particle moves under the action of a single force F. The x, v equation of its motion is $cv^2 + xv = xw$ where c and w are constants.

Show that $F = \dfrac{m(w - v)^2}{c(2w - v)}$

and that the time taken to increase the speed from

0 to $\dfrac{w}{4}$ is $c\left(\dfrac{1}{3} + \ln\dfrac{4}{3}\right)$

6   The acceleration of particle of mass 5 units is $\begin{pmatrix} 1 \\ 0 \\ 0 \end{pmatrix}$

(a) Find the velocity, given the initial velocity is $\begin{pmatrix} 0 \\ 2 \\ -1 \end{pmatrix}$

(b) Find the force, **F**, acting on the particle.

(c) Find the kinetic energy, K, of the particle in terms of t.

(d) Find the power, P, of the force **F**.

(e) Show that the rate of change of K is equal to P.

(f) Find the position vector **r** given that the initial position is $\begin{pmatrix} 0 \\ 1 \\ 3 \end{pmatrix}$.

7   A rectangular plate ACDE, with AC = 8 and AE = 6, has point B at the middle of AC. The triangle BCD is removed to leave a trapezium ABDE. The trapezium is suspended from the point D. Find the inclination of DE to the vertical.

8 A particle P, mass m, is moving along a fixed straight line AB, between A and B, subject to forces of $mk^2 \overline{PA}$ and $4 mk^2 \overline{PB}$. AB $= 10a$. Find the equilibrium position, E.

P is displaced from E and released. Show that it performs SHM and find the period.

If the maximum acceleration is at B find the maximum velocity.

9 One end of a light rod of length r is fixed and the other end carries a mass m which is moving in a vertical circle. At the highest point the mass has velocity $3u$ and at the lowest point the velocity is $5u$. Express r in terms of u and g.

Find the stress in the rod when $\theta = \cos^{-1} \frac{2}{3}$, where θ is the angle made with the upward vertical through the centre of the circle, in terms of m, r and g.

10 Two particles A and B are fired simultaneously from the same point with equal horizontal components of velocity. The initial vertical component of B is twice that of A, which has horizontal and vertical components u and v respectively. If y is the vertical difference in heights between A and B at any time, and x is the horizontal distance travelled, show that $vx = uy$.

► An easier one to finish with!

Solutions to Worksheet 16

1

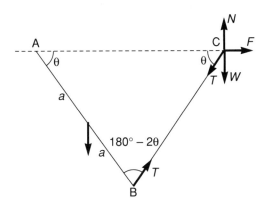

► Moments
► Resolution

Taking moments about A for AB:

$T\sin(180° - 2\theta) \times 2a = W \times a\cos\theta$

$\Rightarrow \quad T \times 2\sin\theta\cos\theta \times 2 = W \times \cos\theta$

$T = \dfrac{W}{4} \sin\theta$

Resolving horizontally for the ring: $\quad T\cos\theta = F$

$$\therefore \quad F = \frac{W\cos\theta}{4\sin\theta}$$

Resolving vertically for the ring:

$$N = T\sin\theta + W = \frac{W}{4} + W = \frac{5W}{4}$$

For equilibrium $\mu \geqslant \dfrac{F}{N} = \dfrac{W\cos\theta}{4\sin\theta} \times \dfrac{4}{5W} = \dfrac{1}{5}\cot\theta$

i.e. $5\mu \geqslant \cot\theta$

► NL2
► Resolution

2

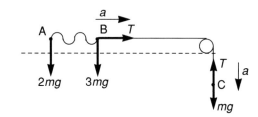

While AB is slack:

Applying NL2 for C: $\quad mg - T = ma$

Applying NL2 for B: $\quad T = 3ma$

$$\therefore \quad a = \frac{g}{4}$$

AB becomes taut when B has travelled 2 m.

Using the v, s equation: $\quad v^2 = u^2 + 2as \quad \Rightarrow \quad v^2 = 2 \times \frac{g}{4} \times 2 = g$

$$\therefore \quad v = \sqrt{g}$$

Applying COM when A is jerked into motion:

$$4m \times \sqrt{g} = 6m \times w \quad \Rightarrow \quad w = \tfrac{2}{3}\sqrt{g}$$

i.e. A starts to move with velocity $\frac{2}{3}\sqrt{g}$

and impulse on A, $J = 2m \times \frac{2}{3}\sqrt{g}$

$$\therefore \quad J = \tfrac{4}{3}m\sqrt{g}$$

► Circular motion – horizontal

3

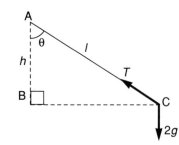

Applying NL2 along CB for C: $\quad T\sin\theta = 2 \times 1\sin\theta \times \omega^2$

$$\omega = 2\pi \times 3 = 6\pi$$

$$\therefore \quad T = 2 \times (6\pi)^2$$

Resolving vertically for C: $T\cos\theta = 2g$

$$\therefore \quad \cos\theta = \frac{2g}{2 \times (6\pi)^2} = 0.0276$$

$$h = 1\cos\theta = 0.028 \text{ m} = 2.8 \text{ cm}$$

4

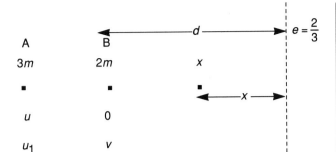

▶ Impacts

At the impact:

COM: $3u = 3u_1 + 2v$

NEL: $\frac{2}{3}u = v - u$

$v = u,\ u_1 = \frac{1}{3}u$

Second impact is at X, the point to where both A and B take the same time.

For B: $t = \dfrac{d}{u} + \dfrac{x}{eu}$

$\qquad = \dfrac{d}{u} + \dfrac{3x}{2u}$

For A: $t = \dfrac{d-x}{u/3} = \dfrac{3(d-x)}{u}$

$\therefore \quad \dfrac{3(d-x)}{u} = \dfrac{d}{u} + \dfrac{3x}{2u} \quad \Rightarrow \quad x = \dfrac{4}{9}d$

▶ Velocity on rebound
= e × velocity on approach

At the second impact:

A	**B**	
$3m$	$2m$	COM: $3 \times \dfrac{u}{3} - 2 \times \dfrac{2u}{3} = 3u_2 + 2v_2$
$\dfrac{u}{3}$	$-\dfrac{2u}{3}$	NEL: $-\dfrac{2}{3}\left(-\dfrac{2u}{3} - \dfrac{u}{3}\right) = v_2 - u_2$
u_2	v_2	i.e. $-\dfrac{u}{3} = 3u_2 + 2v_2$
		and $\dfrac{2u}{3} = v_2 - u_2$
		$\Rightarrow \quad v_2 = \dfrac{1}{3}u$

Therefore B hits the wall again because it has positive velocity after the second impact.

► Variable acceleration

5

$$cv^2 + xv = xw \tag{1}$$

Applying NL2: $F = ma = m\dfrac{dv}{dt}$

Hence differentiating **(1)**:

$$2cv\frac{dv}{dt} + \frac{dx}{dt} \times v + x \times \frac{dv}{dt} = w\frac{dx}{dt}$$

$$\frac{dx}{dt} = v \quad \Rightarrow \quad \frac{dv}{dt} = \frac{wv - v^2}{2cv + x}$$

The required result does not have x therefore substitute for x from **(1)**:

$$\frac{dv}{dt} = \frac{v(w-v)}{2cv + \frac{cv^2}{w-v}} = \frac{(w-v)^2}{2cw - cv} = \frac{(w-v)^2}{c(2w-v)}$$

$$\therefore \quad F = \frac{m(w-v)^2}{c(2w-v)}$$

We are interested in v, t so use $\dfrac{dv}{dt} = \dfrac{(w-v)^2}{c(2w-v)}$

Separating variables: $\displaystyle\int_0^{\frac{1}{4}w} \frac{c(2w-v)}{(w-v)^2}\, dv = \int_0^t dt$

The simplest way of integrating here is to let $u = w - v$.

Then we have $c \displaystyle\int_w^{\frac{3}{4}w} -\frac{w+u}{u^2}\, du = t$

$$\Rightarrow \quad -c\left[-\frac{w}{u} + \ln u\right]_w^{\frac{3}{4}w} = t$$

$$\therefore \quad t = -c\left\{-\frac{4}{3} + \ln\frac{3w}{4} + 1 - \ln w\right\}$$

$$\therefore \quad t = c\left(\frac{1}{3} + \ln\frac{4}{3}\right)$$

► Vectors
• acceleration
• force
• dot product
• position

6

$$\mathbf{a} = \begin{pmatrix} 1 \\ 0 \\ 0 \end{pmatrix}$$

(a) $\mathbf{v} = \displaystyle\int \mathbf{a}\, dt = \begin{pmatrix} t + A \\ B \\ C \end{pmatrix} = \begin{pmatrix} t \\ 2 \\ -1 \end{pmatrix}$

► Energy

(b) $\mathbf{F} = m\mathbf{a} = 5\begin{pmatrix} 1 \\ 0 \\ 0 \end{pmatrix}$

(c) $K = \frac{1}{2}mv^2 = \frac{5}{2}(t^2 + 4 + 1) = \frac{5}{2}(t^2 + 5)$

(d) $P = \mathbf{F} \cdot \mathbf{v} = 5\begin{pmatrix} 1 \\ 0 \\ 0 \end{pmatrix} \cdot \begin{pmatrix} t \\ 2 \\ -1 \end{pmatrix} = 5t$

(e) Rate of change of $K = \dfrac{\mathrm{d}K}{\mathrm{d}t} = 5t$.

  Hence $P = \dfrac{\mathrm{d}K}{\mathrm{d}t}$

(f) $\mathbf{r} = \displaystyle\int \mathbf{v}\,\mathrm{d}t = \begin{pmatrix} \frac{1}{2}t^2 + D \\ 2t + E \\ -t + F \end{pmatrix} \quad \therefore \quad r = \begin{pmatrix} \frac{1}{2}t^2 \\ 2t + 1 \\ 3 - t \end{pmatrix}$

7

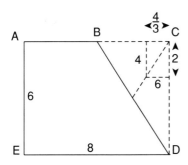

Taking moments about AE:

$48 \times 4 = 12 \times 6\frac{2}{3} + 36 \times \overline{x}$
$\qquad\quad\uparrow \qquad\quad \uparrow \qquad \uparrow$
$\qquad$ whole $\quad$ BCD $\;$ ABDE

► Centre of gravity

$\Rightarrow \quad \overline{x} = \dfrac{28}{9}$

Taking moments about ED:

$48 \times 3 = 12 \times 4 + 36 \times \overline{y}$

$\Rightarrow \quad \overline{y} = \dfrac{8}{3}$

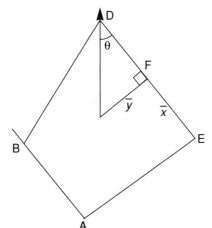

$\tan\theta = \dfrac{\overline{y}}{8 - \overline{x}}$

$= \dfrac{8/3}{44/9} = \dfrac{6}{11}$

i.e. $\theta = \tan^{-1}\dfrac{6}{11} = 28.6°$

► SHM

8

In equilibrium $\Rightarrow$ $F_1 = F_2$

$\therefore$ $mk^2\overline{PA} = 4mk^2\overline{PB}$

$\therefore$ $PA = 4(10a - PA)$

$PA = 8a$

Hence

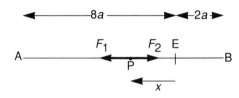

Applying NL2 for P: $F_1 - F_2 = m\ddot{x}$

$mk^2(8a - x) - 4mk^2(2a + x) = m\ddot{x}$

$\Rightarrow$ $-5k^2x = \ddot{x}$

i.e. SHM

Maximum acceleration occurs at B $\Rightarrow$ EB is the amplitude.

$\therefore$ amplitude $= 2a$

$v_{max} = 2ak\sqrt{5}$

► Circular motion – vertical

► Strut

► Tie

9

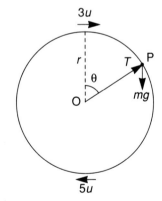

OP is a light rod therefore has no weight.

It can push outwards – a strut.

It can pull inwards – a tie.

COE: $\frac{1}{2}m \times 9u^2 + mg \times 2r = \frac{1}{2}m \times 25u^2$

$\Rightarrow$ $r = \dfrac{4u^2}{g}$

Applying NL2 along PO: $mg\cos\theta - T = \dfrac{mv^2}{r}$

COE: $\frac{1}{2}mv^2 - \frac{1}{2}m \times 9u^2 = mgr(1 - \cos\theta)$

Eliminating v^2: $T = mg(3\cos\theta - 2) - 9mu^2$

When $\theta = \cos^{-1}\frac{2}{3}$ $T = -9mu^2$

i.e. acts in the opposite direction from that shown on the diagram.

Substituting for u^2: $T = \dfrac{9mrg}{4}$ towards O.

10   ► Projectiles

For A and B: $x = ut$ **(1)**

For A: $y_A = vt - \frac{1}{2g}t^2$

For B: $y_B = 2vt - \frac{1}{2g}t^2$

$y = y_B - y_A = vt$ **(2)**

Eliminating t from **(1)** and **(2)**:

$\dfrac{x}{u} = \dfrac{y}{v}$

$\therefore \quad vx = uy$

Index